Electrical and
Electronic
Principles 2

Electrical and Electronic Principles 2

Second Edition

S. A. Knight

Lately Senior Lecturer in Mathematics & Electronic Engineering,
Bedford College of Higher Education

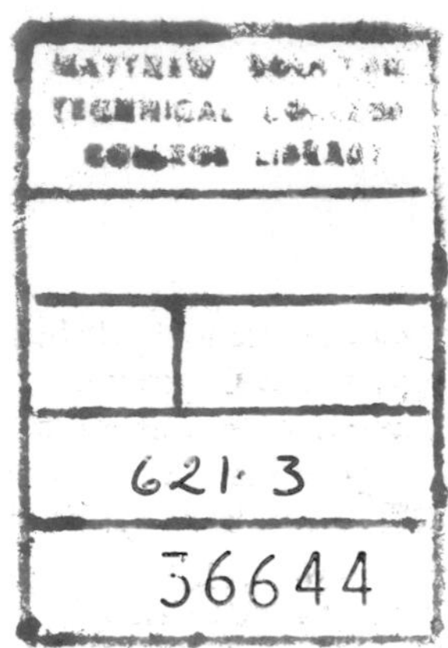

Newnes
An imprint of Butterworth-Heinemann Ltd
Linacre House, Jordan Hill, Oxford OX2 8DP

PART OF REED INTERNATIONAL BOOKS

OXFORD LONDON BOSTON
MUNICH NEW DELHI SINGAPORE SYDNEY
TOKYO TORONTO WELLINGTON

First published as *Electrical Principles for Technicians* 1978
Reprinted 1982, 1986
Second edition 1987
Reprinted 1989, 1990, 1991, 1992

British Library Cataloguing in Publication Data
Knight, Stephen Alfred
Electrical and electronic principles.
2. (Technician Series)
1. Electric engineering
I. Title II. Series
621.3 TK145 77-30611

ISBN 0 7506 0204 X

Printed by Hartnolls Limited, Bodmin, Cornwall

Preface

This book has been revised and updated to cover the essential syllabus requirements of BTEC Unit U86/329 for Electrical and Electronic Principles 2. The guide syllabus has been followed as closely as space will allow, and as a consequence much of the original material has been retained, though some rearrangement has helped in combining parts of the syllabus which were originally disjointed.

Two completely new chapters have been added to the existing material; these cover Principles of Control Systems and the Elements of Data Transmission which are new additions to the syllabus. An index has also been provided.

With the emphasis, as before, on worked and self-assessment examples throughout the text, it is hoped that this book will be of value to all those taking the BTEC programmes in the areas of Electrical and Electronic Engineering.

S.A.K

Contents

Read this introduction before going any further

There are two groups of problem examples included in the text of each Unit section throughout this book. One group comprises examples, worked out for you, which illustrate method and procedure; these are prefixed by the heading 'Example ( )'.

The second group are self-assessment problems which are for you to work out before proceeding to the next part of the text; these problems are simply given a number in parentheses: ( ). They are intended to illustrate those parts of the text which immediately precede them, though occasionally they refer to earlier work as well. All examples of either group are numbered through in order, so that the solutions can be found without difficulty. Solutions and comments are provided at the end of the book.

At the end of each Unit section also there are a number of exercises divided into two groups:

Group 1: these comprise relatively simple problems illustrating the basic principles covered in the section.

Group 2: these comprise slightly harder examples, in general covering a wider range of the basic principles and foregoing work.

There is one other point concerning the working of problems: do not get yourself tangled up in long decimal numbers. If you use a calculator (a device which will provide you with wrong answers as quickly as right ones!) don't go and write down the whole string of numbers such a machine generally provides. For nearly every problem in this book, two decimal places is quite sufficient accuracy, and very few of the worked solutions are given to anything better than this.

1 Units and definitions

Aims: At the end of this Unit section you should be able to:
State the units of basic electrical quantities.
Use multiples and sub-multiples of SI units in simple problems.
Recognise basic electrical symbols and conventions.

SYSTEM OF UNITS

The units used throughout this course will be those of the rationalised m.k.s. or SI system which, in engineering in general and electrical engineering in particular, has now replaced the three separate systems based on the c.g.s. (centimetre-gram-second) units of classical physics.

Whatever the system of units employed in any branch of science, the magnitudes (quantities) of some physical dimensions, like length or mass, must be arbitrarily selected and declared to have unit value. A man who buys a kilogram of potatoes in Birmingham, for example, expects to get the same quantity of potatoes if he buys a kilogram in London. Once selected, therefore, such magnitudes as the kilogram then form a set of standards which are called *fundamental units.* Any consistent system of units derived from or related to the fundamental units by definitions is then called an *absolute system*, and both the fundamental units and those expressible in terms of them are known as *absolute units.* The rationalised m.k.s. (metre-kilogram-second) system of units is such an absolute system.

FUNDAMENTAL DIMENSIONS

The fundamental dimensions are those of *length, mass* and *time*, and the standard units for each of these dimensions are respectively the *metre*, the *kilogram* and the *second.* To these three is added a fourth unit which links the mechanical units to the electromagnetic units: this is the *ampere*, the unit of electrical current.

Each of these four fundamental units can be expressed in multiples and sub-multiples of the standard unit, and a conversion factor is necessary. In the metric system the conversion factors are all conveniently powers of 10. *Table 1.1* deals with the standard units and the appropriate conversion factors associated with them.

Table 1.1

Dimension	*Standard unit*	*Multiple*	*Sub-multiple*
Length	metre (m)	kilometre (km) = 10^3 m	centimetre (cm) = 10^{-2} m millimetre (mm) = 10^{-3} m
Mass	kilogram (kg)	tonne = 10^3 kg	gram = 10^{-3} kg
Time	second (s)		millisecond (ms) = 10^{-3} s microsecond (μs) = 10^{-6} s
Current	ampere (A)		milliampere (mA) = 10^{-3} A microampere (μA) = 10^{-6} A

DERIVED UNITS

From the fundamental units in *Table 1.1*, a great number of derived units can now be obtained.

All the important derived units necessary for this part of the course will be given in this section. It is necessary to become completely familiar with these units and definitions, though not at this stage to attempt to learn them by rote. Familiarity will come with usage.

Velocity

The average velocity between any two positions is the ratio of the change in position to the time taken:

$$v_{av} = \frac{\text{Change in position}}{\text{Time taken}} = \frac{\text{Distance}}{\text{Time}}$$

The unit of velocity is the *metre per second* (m/s).

Acceleration

The average acceleration between any two positions is the ratio of the change in velocity to the time taken:

$$a_{av} = \frac{\text{Change in velocity}}{\text{Time taken}}$$

The unit of acceleration is the *metre per second, per second* (m/s^2)

Force

This is defined as *mass* × *acceleration*. Thus unit force will produce unit acceleration (1 m/s) in unit mass (1 kg). The unit of force defined in this way is the newton (N), hence 1 N of force will produce an acceleration of 1 m/s in a mass of 1 kg.

The force due to gravity on a mass of 1 kg is the weight of the mass, called the *kilogram-force* (kgf). On the earth's surface a mass of 1 kg experiences a force equal to (mass × gravitational acceleration, g), and since $g = 9.81\ m/s^2$

$$1\ kgf = 1\ kg \times 9.81\ m/s^2 = 9.81\ N$$

Hold a 1 kg bag of sugar in your hand. What you experience is a downwards force of 9.81 N.

Make certain you appreciate the difference between mass and weight. Mass concerns the *amount* of material in a body and this remains constant wherever the mass happens to be, on the earth or way out in space. Weight is a manifestation of the gravitational attraction of the earth (or the moon or the sun) on a mass, so weight is not constant, but depends whereabouts the mass happens to be. In space objects may be weightless, but they are never 'massless'.

Now try the first of your self-assessment problems:

(1) What force is required to give a mass of 10 kg an acceleration of 50 m/s^2?

(2) A car weighing 8000 kgf increases its speed with a constant acceleration of 5 m/s^2. What is the accelerating force?

Work and energy

The action of a force may result in the expenditure of energy and in work being done. Work or energy can therefore be expressed in terms of force and distance. Unit work is done when a uniform force of 1 N acts through a distance of 1 m in the direction of the force. Unit energy is the *newton-metre* or *joule* (J):

Work done = Force × Distance moved = joules

Power

Power (P) is the rate of doing work or energy expended per second:

$$P = \frac{\text{Work performed}}{\text{Time taken}} = \frac{\text{joules}}{\text{seconds}}$$

The unit of power is a rate of working equal to *1 joule per second* (J/s) and 1 J/s is equal to *1 watt* (W). A multiple unit is the kilowatt (kW) = 10^3W. Although not an SI unit it is useful to remember, especially if you intend working through past examination papers for revision, that a rate of working of 746 J/s = 746 W is 1 horsepower.

> (3) A load of 2000 kgf is raised through a height of 10 m in 25 s. What is the work done and the horsepower required?
>
> (4) An electromagnet exerts a force of 20 N and moves an iron armature through a distance of 1 cm in 0.05 s. What is the power consumed?

Torque

When a force produces rotation of a body without motion of translation (motion in any particular direction), there must be a second force acting upon the body equal and opposite to the first. In *Figure 1.1 (a)* the spanner has a force F applied to one end as shown; this sets up a force at the nut which is equal and opposite, and acting parallel to, force F, i.e. force F_1. If this were not so the spanner would move in the direction of F. A force F acting at right-angles to a radius R produces torque:

$$\text{Torque } (T) = \text{Magnitude of force} \times \text{Arm of torque}$$

$$= F \times R \text{ newton-metres (N m)}$$

Acting on a wheel or pulley (see *Figure 1.1(b)*) the force will move a distance equal to the circumference, $2\pi R$, in one revolution, hence

$$\text{Work done per revolution} = 2\pi FR = 2\pi T \text{ joules}$$

> (5) An electric motor having a speed of 20 rev/s does 2000 J of work per second. Calculate the torque developed.

(a)

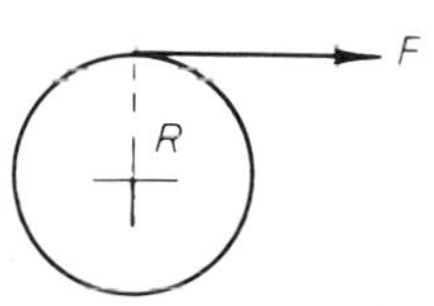

(b) Torque = Force x Radius

Figure 1.1

ELECTRICAL UNITS

A simple electrical circuit is shown in *Figure 1.2*. We shall refer to this circuit as we work through the electrical units in this section.

Current flows in a circuit when an electromotive force, provided by the battery in this case, is connected into the circuit. The current, which is a flow of free electrons, passes through the lamps (the circuit load)

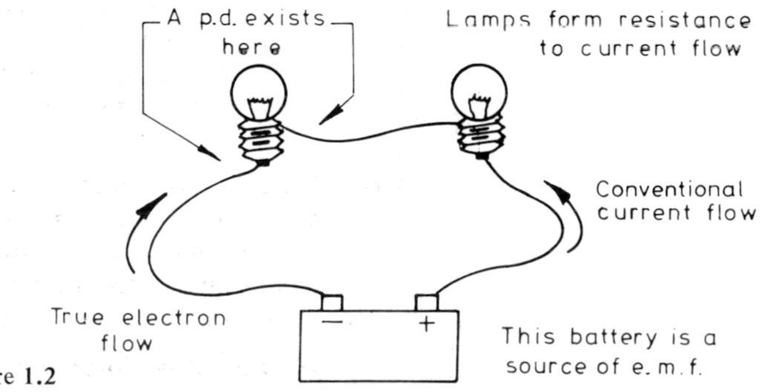

Figure 1.2

and these provide light and some heat, so work is being done by the current. Each electron carries a definite negative charge, and if unit current (1 A) flows for unit time (1 s) the number of electrons which pass is 6.24×10^{18}

There is a sign convention which we must keep in mind at all times. The early experimenters into electrical science assumed that electricity flowed naturally from a terminal at high electrical potential to a terminal at low electrical potential, that is, from the positive (+) terminal of a battery or generator to the negative (–) terminal, and all electrical rules were based on this convention. We know today that the flow of electrons which forms the current, being negatively charged particles, is away from the negative terminal and towards the positive terminal. This is the *true electronic flow* of current.

To avoid having to turn all electrical rules on their heads, as it were, the *conventional flow* is retained for all ordinary electrical calculations, and the true electronic flow is only brought into matters when electronic devices like valves and transistors are being investigated. Until such time as we come to those parts of the syllabus, we take the flow of current to be conventional, that is, from the positive to the negative terminals of the supply.

Current

The unit of current (I) is the *ampere* (A). We do not use C for current as this would cause confusion with the coulomb. Current is defined in terms of the force acting between two parallel conductors when each of the conductors is carrying unit current (1 A), and this definition will be fully explained in Unit Section 6. We note here:

1 ampere = 6.24×10^{18} electrons per second

Charge

Unit charge (Q) is the *coulomb* (C). The coulomb is a measure of the quantity of electricity, and one coulomb is the quantity of electricity carried by 6.24×10^{18} electrons. This is the number of electrons in a current of 1 A which flows for 1 s, hence

Q coulombs = Current × Time

or

$$Q = I.t \text{ coulombs}$$

From this we can state that the ampere is the rate of flow of quantity and 1 A is equal to a rate of 1 coulomb per second (C/s).

Potential difference

Electrons flow around a circuit as the result of an electromotive force (e.m.f.) being applied to the circuit. Such a force is provided by a battery or dynamo, for example. It is very difficult to measure the actual e.m.f. acting in a circuit, but it is easier to measure the effect of the force which results when current flows through a particular part of the circuit. A potential difference (p.d.) then exists across that part of the circuit.

The unit of potential difference (and of e.m.f.) is the volt (V). Unit potential difference exists between two points in a circuit which carries a constant current of 1 A, when the power dissipated between the two points is equal to 1 W. From this it follows that

Watts = Current × Voltage = $I.V$

But the work done is

Watts × Time = IVt = QV joules

So as an alternative definition of the volt we may say that unit potential difference exists between two points in a circuit if 1 J of work is done in transferring 1 C from one point to the other.

Resistance

The current encounters electrical 'friction' or resistance to its passage as it travels around the circuit. The unit of resistance (R) is the ohm (Ω), and is that resistance between two points in a circuit when a constant potential difference of 1 V applied between the two points produces in the circuit a current of 1 A. Hence

Resistance = volts per ampere

Now try these self-assessment problems:

(6) What quantity of electricity is carried by 6.24×10^{20} electrons?
(7) In what time would a current of 20 A transfer 100 C?
(8) How much power will a current of 5 A and an e.m.f. of 100 V product?

RADIAN MEASURE

It is conventional to measure rotation either in degrees or radians and generally in an anticlockwise sense from a horizontal reference line. In terms of degrees, one complete revolution is 360° and it is usual to divide a circle into four quadrants, each of 90°, as shown in *Figure 1.3(a)*.

It is then possible to define the angular velocity of a rotating arm OA as shown in *Figure 1.3(b)* as being so many degrees per second. Such a definition, however, is not a convenient one in problems associated with alternating currents which we shall encounter later on in the course. Instead, the angular velocity is measured in *radians per second*, where the radian is defined as the angle subtended at the centre of the circle by an arc on the circumference equal in length to the radius. As the circumference of a circle is 2π times the radius, there are 2π radians in a complete revolution. From this it follows that:

$$2\pi \text{ radians} = 360°$$

or $$1 \text{ radian} = 57.3°$$

The angular velocity, in rad/s, is then simply 2π times the number of revolutions made in one second. The symbol for angular velocity is ω (omega), so

$$\omega = 2\pi \times \text{Number of revolutions per second}$$

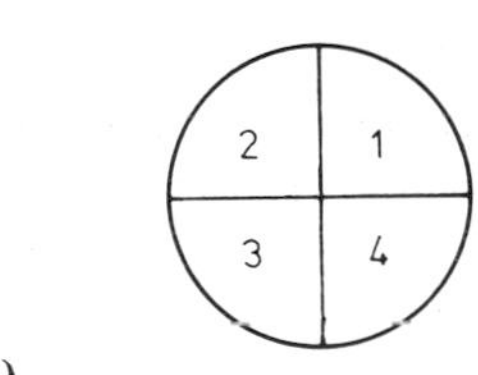

(a)

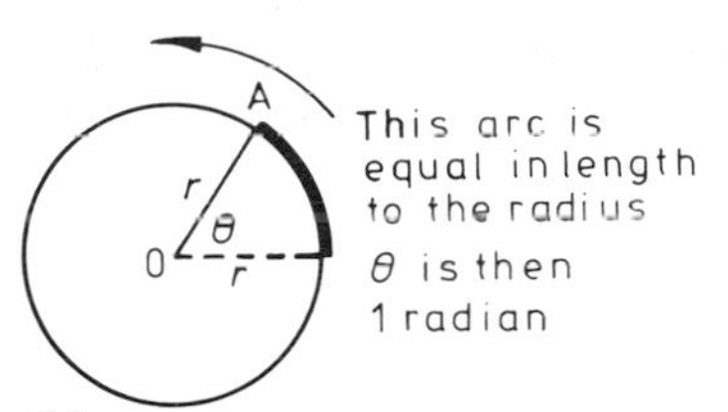

(b)

Figure 1.3

(9) A wheel rotates at 10 rev/s. What is its angular velocity?
(10) A pulley has an angular velocity of 20 rad/s. How many revolutions does it make in 1 min?

SYMBOLS

A number of basic symbols and conventions for electrical science are shown in *Figure 1.4*, and most of these are used at one place or another throughout this part of the course. If you are not familiar with them all, don't spend a lot of time trying to memorise them at this stage. Each one will be explained as it turns up in the text, and you will find most of them self-explanatory in any event.

There now follows your first selection of test problems relating to everything we have covered in the Unit section. You should work these, and all others in the book, in accordance with the instructions given in the introductory note at the front of the book.

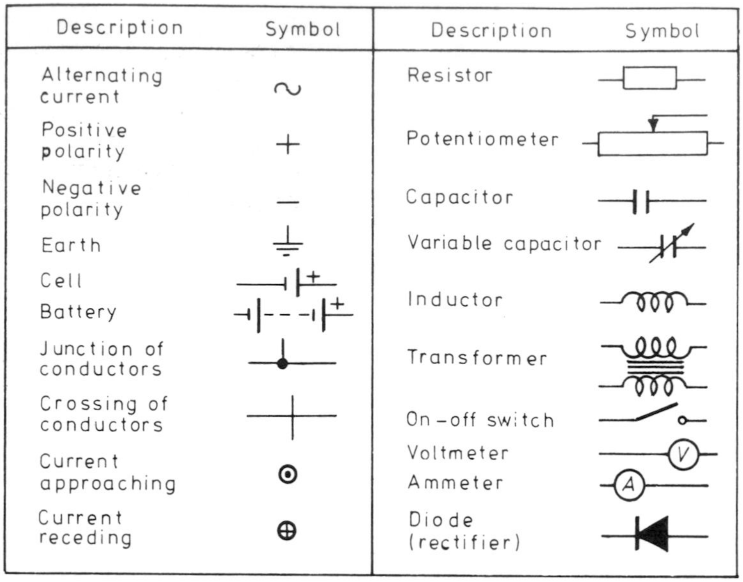

Description	Symbol	Description	Symbol
Alternating current	∼	Resistor	—▭—
Positive polarity	+	Potentiometer	—▭— (with slider arrow)
Negative polarity	—	Capacitor	—‖—
Earth	⏚	Variable capacitor	—‖— (with arrow)
Cell	—|├+	Inductor	coil
Battery	—|├- - -|├+	Transformer	two coils with core
Junction of conductors	—●—	On–off switch	—/ o—
Crossing of conductors	—┼—	Voltmeter	—(V)—
Current approaching	⊙	Ammeter	—(A)—
Current receding	⊕	Diode (rectifier)	—▶|—

Figure 1.4

PROBLEMS FOR SECTION 1

Group 1

(11) State the units of (a) force, (b) work, (c) power, (d) velocity, (e) acceleration.

(12) State the units of (a) current, (b) p.d., (c) resistance, (d) e.m.f., (e) quantity.

(13) What force is required to give a mass of 20 kg an acceleration of 20 m/s^2?

(14) Calculate the acceleration acquired by a mass of 8 kg under the action of a force of 50 N.

(15) Calculate the mass of an iron core which is drawn towards a magnet with an acceleration of 15 m/s^2 under a force of 3 N.

(16) A car increases its speed uniformly from 25 m/s to 45 m/s in 5 s. What is its acceleration?

(17) A force of 30 N accelerates a mass uniformly from rest to 10 m/s in 5 s. What is the mass?

(18) Convert (a) 50 rev/min to rad/s, (b) 10 rad/s to rev/min.

(19) The wheels of a bicycle are 0.7 m diameter. If the cycle is travelling at 15 km/h, what is the angular velocity of the wheels?

(20) A current of 100 A flows for 5 s. How many electrons pass in that time?

(21) 500 C of electricity is transferred between two points in a time of 10 s. What current is flowing?

(22) How much work is done when 1000 C is transferred between two points having a potential difference of 10 V?

(23) A car developing a power of 35 kW is accelerated for 25 s. Calculate the energy used.

Group 2

(24) A pump raises 500 litre of water from a depth of 20 m in 2 min. Calculate the work done and the power developed.

(25) The resistance to motion of a car is 100 kgf. What horsepower is required to keep the car moving at 40 km/h?

(26) A pulley 0.15 m diameter rotates at 10 rev/s. Calculate (a) its angular velocity, (b) the linear speed of its driving belt.

(27) The cutting resistance of a lathe tool is 1.5 kN and the average diameter of the work piece is 10 cm. If it is revolving at 3 rev/s, calculate (a) the torque, (b) the work done per min, (c) the power used.

2 Series and parallel circuits

Aims: at the end of this Unit section you should be able to:
Understand series and parallel connections.
Use Ohm's law to solve simple series and parallel circuit problems.
Understand the theory of voltage and current division.
Deal with problems of electrical power.

OHM'S LAW

The current I flowing in an electrical circuit depends on the applied voltage V and the circuit resistance R. These are related by *Ohm's law* which is usually expressed as follows:

The current flowing in a circuit is directly proportional to the applied voltage and inversely proportional to the resistance.

By the proper choice of units, therefore

$$I = V/R$$

Ohm's law is one of the fundamental laws of electrical and electronic engineering.

You have already learned that the unit of current is the ampere (A); the unit of potential difference is the volt (V), and the unit of resistance is the ohm (Ω). In many calculations it is necessary to work in subunits or in multiples of the basic units. Most electronic work, for example, deals in very small voltages and currents, while electrical power engineering deals in very large voltages and currents.

Although the subunits and multiple units can always be expressed in decimal or fractional form, you will generally find it much neater and less liable to error if you work in index form.

Example (1). Express the following quantities in decimal and index form:

(a) 38 mA, (b) 655 mA, (c) 86.5 μV, (d) 2630 mV.

(a) 38 mA can be expressed as 0.038 A or 38×10^{-3} A.
(b) 655 mA can be expressed as 0.655 A or 655×10^{-3} A.
(c) 86.5 μV can be expressed as 0.0000865 V or 86.5×10^{-6} V.
(d) 2360 mV can be expressed as 2.630 V or 2360×10^{-3} V

You should already have had some experience in using Ohm's law to work out simple circuit problems, but to refresh your memory try working through the following examples. The first two have been worked for your guidance.

Example (2). An electromagnet has a coil with a resistance of 50 Ω. What current will flow through the coil when it is connected to a supply of 175 V?

Here we are given the voltage V and the resistance R, and require the current I.

Using $I = V/R$ we have $I = 175/50 = 3.5$ A

Example (3). What is the resistance of a relay coil which draws a current of 25 mA when the voltage applied to it is 10 V?

Here we use the relationship $R = V/I$, but note that we must first express the current in amperes for the solution to be in ohms. Then

$$25 \text{ mA} = 25 \times 10^{-3} \text{ A (or, if you wish} = 0.025 \text{ A)}$$

and so

$$R = \frac{V}{I} = \frac{10}{25 \times 10^{-3}} = \frac{10^4}{25}$$

$$= 400\ \Omega$$

(4) An electric kettle has a resistance of 40 Ω. What current will flow when it is connected to a 240 V supply?

(5) Calculate the resistance of a relay coil which draws a current of 75 mA from a 50 V supply.

(6) What voltage is required to produce a current of 1.5 A through a coil whose resistance is 5.5 Ω?

(7) The cold resistance of a certain tungsten lamp is 30 Ω and its hot resistance at the operating voltage of 240 V is 600 Ω. Find (a) the current at the instant the lamp is switched on, (b) the normal working current.

ARRANGEMENTS OF RESISTORS

A *resistor* is a component part which is specially designed and made to introduce a known value of resistance into a circuit. It usually takes the form of coils of special high resistance wire (wire wound resistors) or carbon compound rods (carbon resistors). Wire wound resistors are, in general, used where large currents are concerned and a lot of heat may be generated, and their values lie between a fraction of an ohm and about 100 kΩ. Carbon resistors cover a much greater range of values, with an upper limit in general use of about 25 MΩ.

Series connection

If two or more resistors are joined in series, that is, so that the current flows through each in turn, their total resistance is simply the sum of the separate resistances. So, from *Figure 2.1*

$$R = R_1 + R_2 + R_3 + \ldots$$

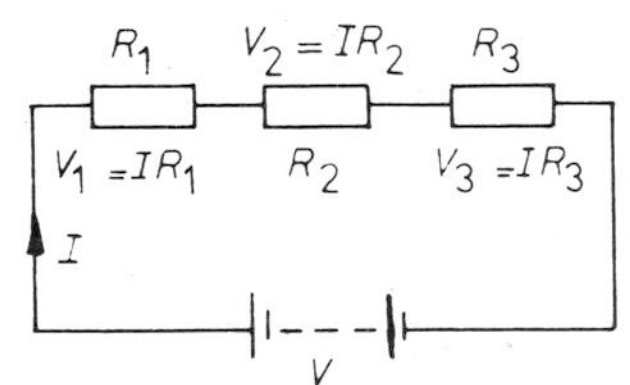

Figure 2.1

Although this result is really just an application of common sense, it is very easy to prove. For suppose the three resistors shown have an equivalent single resistance of R_E. We notice that the *same* current I flows in turn through each resistor, so that the voltages across each resistor will be (by Ohm's law) IR_1, IR_2 and IR_3 respectively. But clearly the sum total of these three voltages must equal the applied voltage V, which in terms of a single equivalent resistor would be IR_E. Hence

$$IR_E = IR_1 + IR_2 + IR_3$$

or

$$R_E = R_1 + R_2 + R_3$$

And so on for any number of series-connected resistors.

Now work through the next worked example and then try the following assignments on your own.

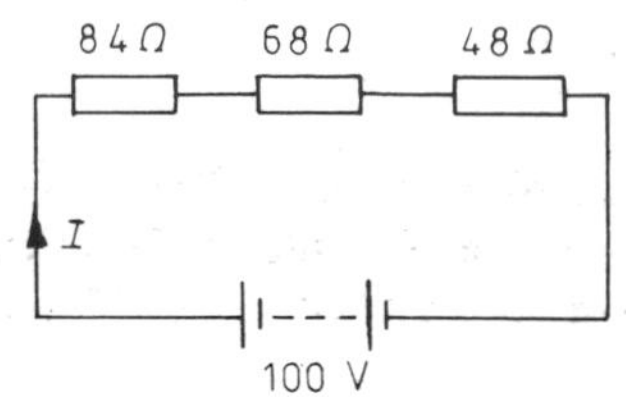

Figure 2.2

Example (8). A circuit, illustrated in *Figure 2.2*, consists of three resistors of value 84 Ω, 68 Ω and 48 Ω respectively, connected in series across a battery of terminal voltage 100 V. Find (a) the equivalent resistance, (b) the current flowing, (c) the voltage across each resistor.

(a) In series $R_E = 84 + 68 + 48 = 200\ \Omega$

(b) $I = \dfrac{V}{R_E} = \dfrac{100}{200} = 0.5\text{ A (or 500 mA)}$

(c) $V_1 = IR_1 = 0.5 \times 84 = 42\text{ V}$
$V_2 = IR_2 = 0.5 \times 68 = 34\text{ V}$
$V_3 = IR_3 = 0.5 \times 48 = 24\text{ V}$

Check total 100 V

The totalling of the individual voltages is a quick check on the accuracy of your working.

(9) A 5 Ω resistor is connected in series with a 10 Ω resistor across a 30 V supply. Find the voltage across each resistor.

(10) A battery of terminal voltage 1.5 V is connected to a circuit made up of three resistors in series of values 0.5 Ω, 1.0 Ω and 1.5 Ω. Find (a) the total circuit resistance, (b) the current, (c) the voltage across each resistor.

(11) Two resistors are connected in series to a supply of 120 V. If the circuit current is 75 mA and one of the resistors is 600 Ω, find the value of the other resistor.

(12) An electromagnet takes 10 A at 220 V. It is desired to reduce the current to 7 A. Find the value of the resistor which must be connected in series with the electromagnet to achieve this.

Division of voltage

We can use the idea of resistors in series to devise a simple method of obtaining a lower voltage from a fixed voltage supply.

Consider two resistors R_1 and R_2 in series, *Figure 2.3,* and let our lower output be taken from across resistor R_1. Then

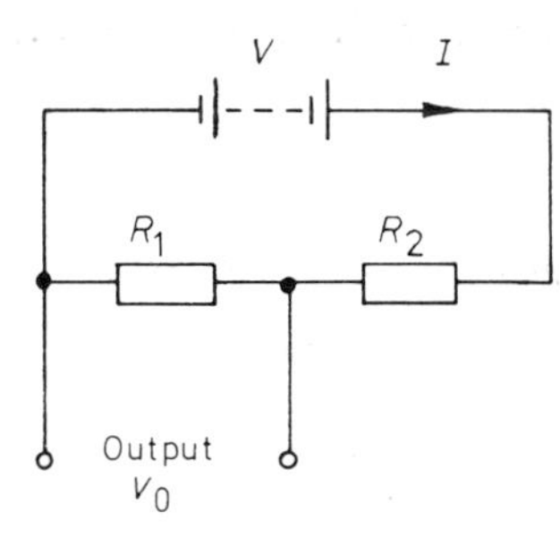

Figure 2.3

Output voltage across $R_1 = V_o = IR_1$

But

$$\text{Current flowing } I = \frac{V}{R} = \frac{V}{R_1 + R_2}$$

Hence, by substitution for I,

$$V_o = V \cdot \frac{R_1}{R_1 + R_2}$$

and we have the desired fraction of V as output voltage.

You should notice that this fraction is true *only* if the current drawn from the output terminals is negligible compared with I, otherwise the resistors will be carrying unequal currents, and our assumption has been that they have carried equal currents.

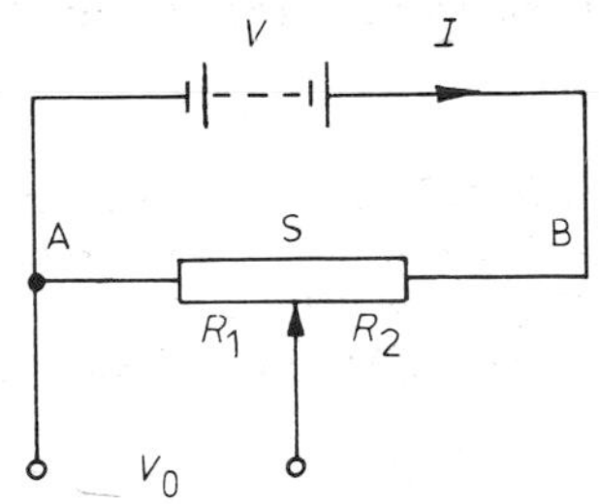

Figure 2.4

It is often necessary to obtain a continuously variable voltage from a fixed supply, and in this case a resistor with a sliding contact is used. Such a device is known as a *potentiometer*. Looking at *Figure 2.4*, the position of the slider S clearly determines the ratio of the resistances R_1 and R_2 and hence the output voltage V_o.

Example (13). A potentiometer has a total resistance between A and B of 30 Ω, and is connected across a 20 V supply. What will be the resistance between A and S when voltages of 5 V, 12 V and 16 V are obtained at the output?

As we see from the above expression of ratios, $V_o/V = R_1/R_E$. Hence:

for 5 V output $5/20 = R_1/30$

$$R_1 = 7.5\ \Omega$$

for 12 V output $12/20 = R_1/30$

$$R_1 = 18\ \Omega$$

for 16 V output $16/20 = R_1/30$

$$R_1 = 24\ \Omega$$

Obviously, any voltage between 0 and 20 V can be tapped off between terminal A and the slider S as S moves from left to right along the potentiometer track.

Parallel connection

If two or more resistors are arranged so that each forms a separate path for a part of the total current, they are connected in parallel. This time the *voltage* across each resistor is the same and equal to V, as *Figure 2.5* shows. What the equivalent single resistor R_E is which can replace the parallel grouping is not quite so easy to visualise as it was in the case of series resistors, but it is not too difficult to find it out.

From *Figure 2.5* the total current I must be the sum of the separate branch currents, that is

$$I = I_1 + I_2 + I_3$$

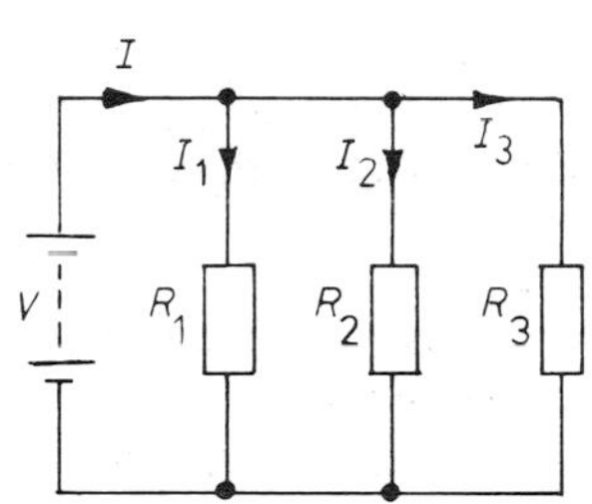

Figure 2.5

Now since each resistor has V volts across it, the branch currents are

$$I_1 = \frac{V}{R_1},\quad I_2 = \frac{V}{R_2},\quad I_3 = \frac{V}{R_3}$$

So, if R_E is the equivalent resistance, then $I = V/R_E$ and then

$$\frac{V}{R_E} = \frac{V}{R_1} + \frac{V}{R_2} + \frac{V}{R_3}$$

Hence

$$\frac{1}{R_E} = \frac{1}{R_1} + \frac{1}{R_2} + \frac{1}{R_3}$$

and so on, for any number of resistors in parallel.

Consequently, to find the equivalent of a number of resistors in parallel, we must add up the *reciprocals* of the component resistors and then invert the answer. You should make a note, by the way, that the reciprocal of resistance is called *conductance*, symbol G. The SI unit is the Siemen, symbol S.

There is a particularly neat way of finding the equivalent of *two* resistors connected in parallel, and you should get used to using it. Since

$$\frac{1}{R_E} = \frac{1}{R_1} + \frac{1}{R_2} = \frac{R_1 + R_2}{R_1 \times R_2}$$

$$\therefore R_E = \frac{R_1 \times R_2}{R_1 + R_2} = \frac{\text{Product of the resistors}}{\text{Sum of the resistors}}$$

Bear in mind that this only works for *two* resistors in parallel.

Example (14). Two resistors of 3.5 Ω and 5.4 Ω are connected in parallel. Find their equivalent resistance.

$$R_E = \frac{\text{Product}}{\text{Sum}} = \frac{3.5 \times 5.4}{3.5 + 5.4} = \frac{18.9}{8.9}$$

$$= 2.12\,\Omega$$

You should have no difficulty with the next few problems.

(15) What single resistor will replace three resistors of 5, 10 and 20 Ω connected in parallel?

(16) What resistance must be connected in parallel with one of 12 Ω to give the equivalent of 3 Ω?

(17) How many 100 Ω resistors must be connected in parallel to give the equivalent of 20 Ω? Can you reach some definite conclusion about the equivalent resistance of any number of *equal* resistors wired in parallel?

Division of current

In a series circuit we noticed that the applied *voltage* was divided up into as many parts as there were resistors. In a parallel circuit, the *current* divides up into as many parts as there are resistors. It is necessary for you to understand how the current in a circuit divides up when it encounters parallel resistors.

Obviously we shall expect the *smallest* resistance to take the *greatest* share of the current, and the *largest* resistance to take the *least* current. This is what is called an inverse relationship. Other resistors will take intermediate currents. Think about a 3 Ω resistor in parallel with an 8 Ω resistor connected to a 24 V supply.

$$\text{Current in the } 3\,\Omega \text{ resistor} = \frac{24}{3} = 8\text{ A}$$

and

$$\text{Current in the } 8\,\Omega \text{ resistor} = \frac{24}{8} = 3\text{ A}$$

So, when the resistance ratio is 3 : 8, the current ratio is 8 : 3.

Follow through the next worked example.

Example (18). Three resistors of 3, 9 and 12 Ω are connected in parallel and the total circuit current is measured as 38 A. Find the current in each resistor.

First of all, find the equivalent resistance:

$$\frac{1}{R_E} = \frac{1}{3} + \frac{1}{9} + \frac{1}{12} = \frac{12 + 4 + 3}{36} = \frac{19}{36}$$

$$\therefore \quad R_E = \frac{36}{19}\ \Omega$$

The applied voltage which will cause a current of 38 A to flow through this resistance is

$$V = IR_E = 38 \times \frac{36}{19} = 72\ \text{V}$$

Applying Ohm's law to each branch, we get

$$\text{Current in } 3\ \Omega \text{ resistor} = \frac{72}{3} = 24\ \text{A}$$

$$\text{Current in } 9\ \Omega \text{ resistor} = \frac{72}{9} = 8\ \text{A}$$

$$\text{Current in } 12\ \Omega \text{ resistor} = \frac{72}{12} = 6\ \text{A}$$

Check that the sum total of these currents is 38 A, the total current flowing.

(19) Three resistors of 6, 12 and 24 Ω are connected in parallel across a 20 V supply. Calculate the current flowing in each resistor and the total current taken from the supply.

(20) A d.c. milliammeter has a resistance of 10 Ω and gives a full-scale deflection (f.s.d.) for a current of 50 mA. Find the value of the parallel resistor (shunt resistor) required to adapt this meter for use as an ammeter having an f.s.d. of 2 A?

You should now be in a position to work out problems involving circuits made up of both series and parallel groupings.

Series-parallel circuits

There is nothing new to learn. Circuits made up of both series and parallel arrangements can be dealt with by first replacing all the parallel groups by their equivalent resistances. The circuit can then be reduced either to a simple series case or a simple parallel case which in turn will reduce to the required equivalent R_E.

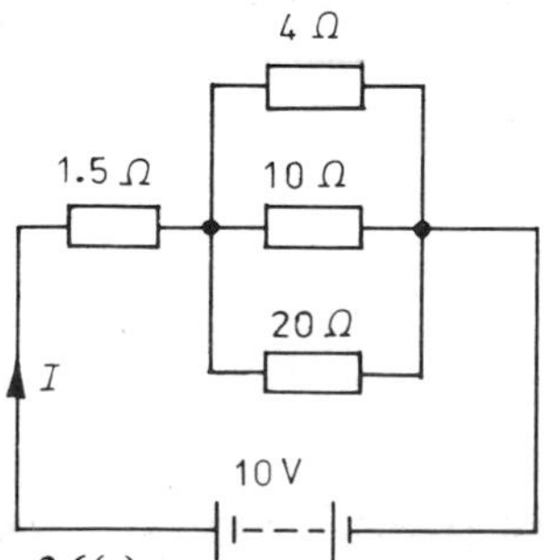

Figure 2.6(a)

Example (21). Find the equivalent resistance of the circuit shown in *Figure 2.6(a)*. Find also the currents in each of the resistors.

For the parallel group

$$\therefore \quad \frac{1}{R_E} = \frac{1}{4} + \frac{1}{10} + \frac{1}{20} = \frac{5 + 2 + 1}{20} = \frac{8}{20}$$

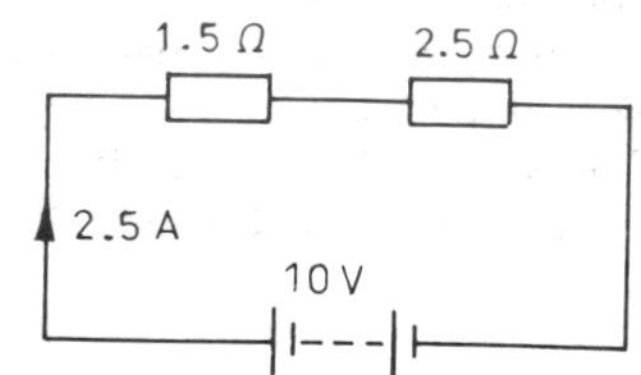

Figure 2.6(b)

$\therefore \quad R_E = 2.5\,\Omega$

The circuit then reduces to 2.5 Ω in series with 1.5 Ω as shown in *Figure 2.6 (b)*,

∴ Total circuit resistance = 4 Ω

and

$$\text{Total circuit current} = \frac{10}{4} = 2.5\text{ A}$$

Hence, from *Figure 2.6 (b)*, voltage across 1.5 Ω = 1.5 × 2.5 = 3.75 V

∴ Voltage across parallel group = 10 − 3.75 = 6.25 V

$$\therefore \text{Current through } 4\,\Omega \text{ resistor} = \frac{6.25}{4} = 1.5625\text{ A}$$

$$\text{Current through } 10\,\Omega \text{ resistor} = \frac{6.25}{10} = 0.625\text{ A}$$

$$\text{Current through } 20\,\Omega \text{ resistor} = \frac{6.25}{20} = 0.3125\text{ A}$$

Check total = 2.5 A

The current through the 1.5 Ω is, of course, the circuit current 2.5 A.

(22) *Figure 2.7 (a), (b)* and *(c)* shows three series-parallel circuits. Find for each of these circuits the equivalent resistance.

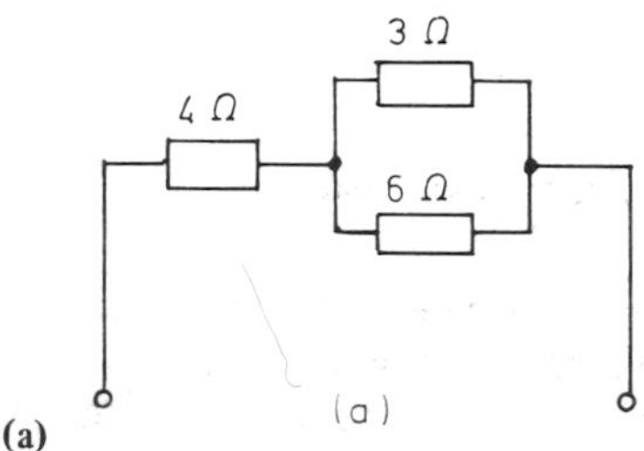

(a)

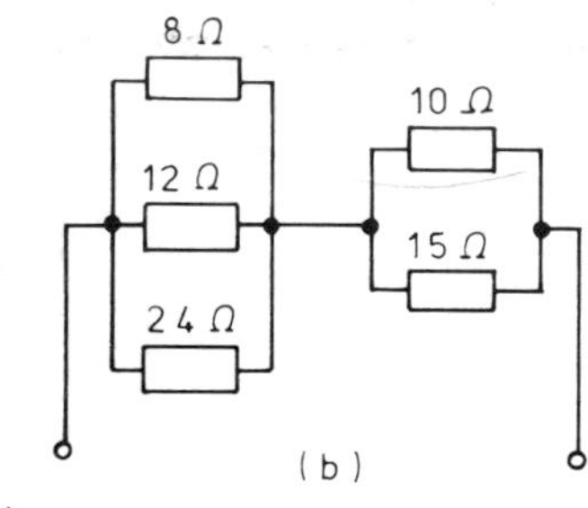

(b)

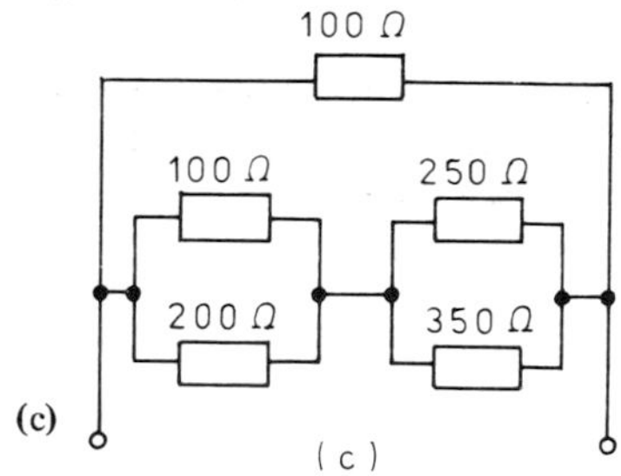

(c)

Figure 2.7

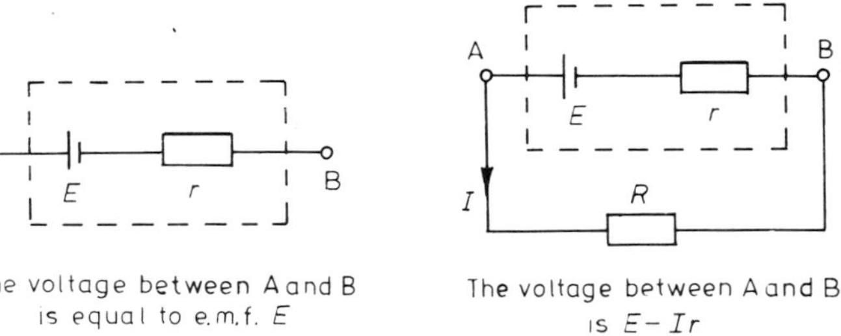

Figure 2.8

INTERNAL RESISTANCE

So far we have shown batteries or other sources of supply as giving a certain voltage at their *terminals.* Strictly, what we measure at the terminals of a battery is *not* equal to the electromotive force of the battery, but rather the terminal potential difference. Both are measured in volts. Any cell, battery or generator has an *internal resistance* whose magnitude depends upon the particular form of construction of the cell or generator. This internal resistance can be represented as a small resistor connected in series with the true source of e.m.f. as shown in *Figure 2.8.* If the cell there depicted is on open circuit, then the voltage present between terminals A and B is equal to e.m.f. E, since there is no voltage drop across r, the current through r being zero.

If now a resistor of relatively low value is connected across A and B the measured terminal voltage will be *less* than the e.m.f. E for the cell is now delivering an appreciable current and there is an internal voltage drop across r. We are now measuring the terminal p.d.

Let E be the e.m.f. of the cell and V the terminal p.d. Then if a current I is flowing round the circuit through an external resistor R,

$$V = E - Ir$$

and the voltage 'lost' in the cell is $E - V$.

Clearly we can express the current I in three ways:

$$I = \frac{E}{r + R} = \frac{V}{R} = \frac{E - V}{r}$$

Make certain you understand how these three expressions are derived.

(23) A battery delivers a current of 2 A when a 1 Ω resistor is wired across its terminals. When a 3 Ω resistor is used, the current falls to 0.71 A. What is the e.m.f. and the internal resistance of the battery?

(24) A battery has an e.m.f. of 15 V and an internal resistance of 0.35 Ω. What will be its terminal voltage when a load resistor of 20 Ω is connected across the battery?

POWER IN A CIRCUIT

Power is the rate of doing work, that is

$$\text{Power} = \frac{\text{Work done}}{\text{Time taken}} = \frac{\text{joules}}{\text{s}}$$

in the appropriate units.

The electrical unit of power is the *watt*, which is equivalent to work being done at the rate of 1 joule per second. Hence another name for the joule is the watt-second.

We have noted in Section 1 that if a current I amps flows through a resistance R for a time t seconds, then the work done $= VQ$ joules where $V = IR$ is the voltage acting across the circuit.

But

$$Q = It \text{ coulombs}$$

$$\therefore \text{ Energy expended} = VIt \text{ joules}$$

$$= I^2Rt \text{ joules}$$

Hence

$$\text{Power} = \frac{I^2Rt}{t} = I^2R \text{ watts}$$

This is the usual form in which electrical power is stated. However, from Ohm's law $I = V/R$ or $R = V/I$, so substituting each of these in turn into the above expression we obtain two alternative forms of power equation:

$$\text{Power} = \frac{V^2}{R} \text{ or } V \times I \text{ watts}$$

You must make certain that you are familiar with all three forms.

Example (25). Two resistors of 20 Ω and 30 Ω are connected in series to a 150 V supply. Find the power dissipated in each resistor.

The circuit resistance is 50 Ω, therefore the current flowing $I = 150/50 = 3$ A. Using the power formula $P = I^2 R$ we have

Power in the 20 Ω resistor = 3 × 3 × 20 = 180 W

Power in the 30 Ω resistor = 3 × 3 × 30 = 270 W

The total power used in the circuit is, of course, 180 + 270 = 450 W.

Example (26). Two coils connected in parallel take a total current of 3 A from a 100 V supply. The power dissipated in one of the coils is 120 W. Find the power dissipated in the other coil and the resistance of each coil.

As 3 A is flowing at 100 V, the total power dissipated in the circuit is $V \times I = 300$ W.

But one coil dissipates 120 W, hence the second coil dissipates

300 − 120 = 180 W

Knowing the power dissipated by each coil and the voltage across them, i.e. 100 V, we require to find the resistance of each coil, hence we must use the power equation

$$P = \frac{V^2}{R} \quad \text{or} \quad R = \frac{V^2}{P}$$

So for the dissipation of 120 W

$R = 100^2/120 = 83.3$ Ω

and for the dissipation of 180 W

$R = 100^2/180 = 55.6$ Ω

Your practice examples now follow.

PROBLEMS FOR SECTION 2

Group 1

(27) The hot resistance of a 240 V metal filament lamp is 1200 Ω. What current is taken by this lamp?

(28) Calculate the resistance of a relay coil which takes 75 mA from a 75 V supply.

(29) What voltage must be applied to a 2000 Ω resistor in order that a current of 20 mA may flow?

(30) Find the equivalent resistance in each of the following cases:

(a) 6 Ω, 8 Ω and 10 Ω connected in series
(b) 6 Ω, 8 Ω and 10 Ω connected in parallel
(c) 1.3 Ω, 1.2 Ω and 0.8 Ω connected in parallel.

(31) What resistance must be connected in parallel with one of 5 Ω to give the equivalent of 2 Ω?

(32) A resistance of 5.6 Ω is connected in series with another of 6.8 Ω. What resistance must be connected in parallel with the 5.6 Ω so that the total resistance will be 7.2 Ω?

(33) An electric motor takes 100 mA at 6 V. If it is to be operated from a 9 V supply, what value of resistor would you connect in series with it?

(34) A p.d. of 20 V is applied to a resistor of 4.5 Ω. Calculate the current flowing and the power dissipated.

(35) A d.c. generator supplies 100 A at 250 V. What is its power output in kW? What is this expressed in horsepower?

(36) Find the hot resistance of a 150 W lamp which is rated at 240 V. How many such lamps can be run for the expenditure of power equivalent to 2 horsepower?

Group 2

(37) Three resistors of 32, 48 and 64 Ω are connected in parallel and a total current of 24 A is passed through the circuit. Find the current in each resistor and the voltage across the parallel combination.

(38) Three resistors of 2, 5 and X Ω are joined in series across a 100 V supply. If a current of 5 A flows, find the value of X, the voltage across each resistor, and the power dissipated in each resistor.

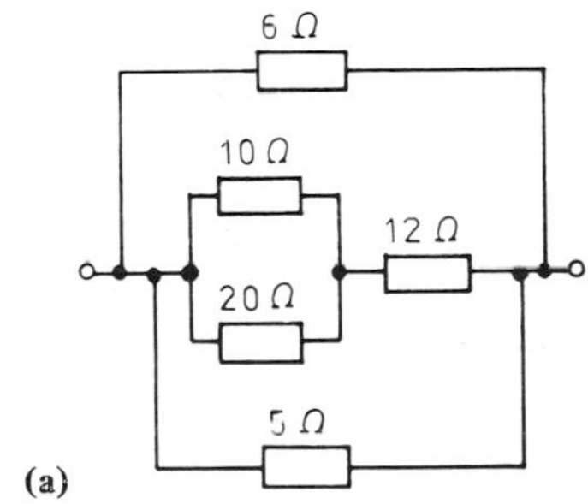

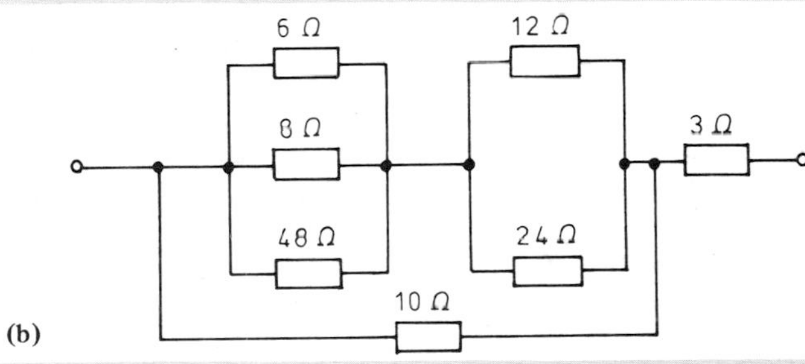

Figure 2.9

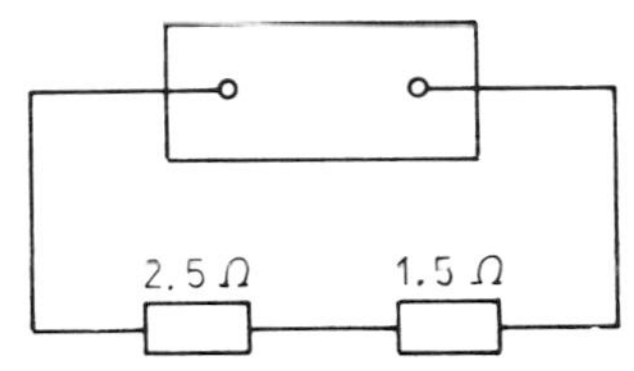

Figure 2.10

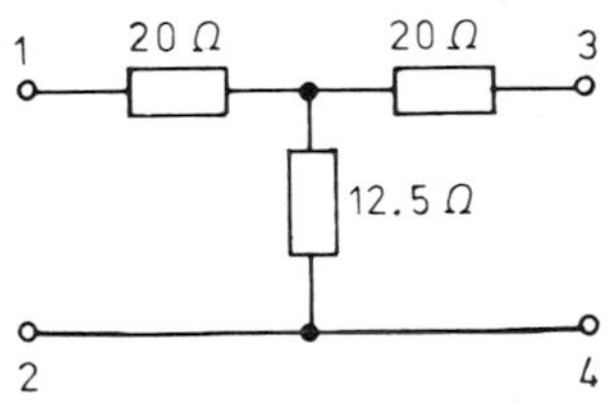

Figure 2.11

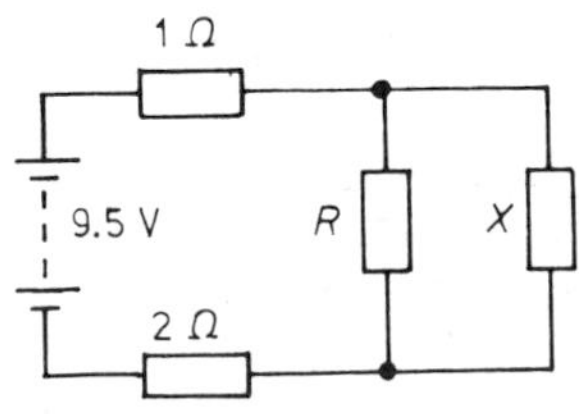

Figure 2.12

(39) Two 100 Ω resistors are connected in series across a 150 V supply. What resistance must be connected in parallel with one of the 100 Ω resistors for the voltage across it to be 65 V?

(40) The equivalent resistance of four resistors joined in parallel is 5 Ω, and the currents flowing through them are 200 mA, 500 mA, 800 mA and 2.5 A. Find the values of the resistors.

(41) Find the equivalent resistance of each of the circuits shown in *Figure 2.9*.

(42) In the circuit of *Figure 2.10*, the voltage across the 1.5 Ω resistor was 0.375 V but this rose to 0.943 V when the 2.5 Ω resistor was short-circuited. What is the e.m.f. and internal resistance of the cell?

(43) A circuit is made up of three resistors as shown in *Figure 2.11*; this kind of circuit is called a T-section. What resistance X would you connect across terminals 3 and 4 in order that the resistance measured between terminals 1 and 2 would also be X?

(44) Three heating elements are connected in parallel across 240 V mains supply. One heater dissipates 1 kW and the second 1.5 kW. The total energy used by the whole circuit in 5 min is 1290 kJ. Find the resistance of the third element and the current in each element.

(45) In the circuit of *Figure 2.12*, the current in resistor X is 2 A when R is 4 Ω. What will the current in X be when R is reduced to 2 Ω?

(46) A battery of e.m.f. 12.4 V is connected to a resistor R Ω. The current flowing is 10 A and the terminal p.d. is 11.8 V. Find (a) the value of R, (b) the internal resistance of the battery.

3 Electrical networks

Aims: At the end of this Unit section you should be able to:
State the Superposition Theorem.
Apply the Superposition Theorem to the solution of networks containing up to two sources of e.m.f.
State Kirchhoff's laws.
Apply Kirchhoff's laws to the solution of networks involving up to two unknown currents.

The problems we have solved so far by means of Ohm's law have all been based on relatively simple series and parallel circuits associated with a single source of e.m.f. Although such methods of solution can be applied to more complicated circuits, the resulting calculations tend to become tedious and so mistakes are more easily made. There are two alternative methods of solution, and although they may not at first appear to be anything like Ohm's law, they are in fact simple adaptations of it.

These new methods go under the names of

(a) the Superposition Theorem, and
(b) Kirchhoff's laws.

To use these methods we shall, of course, require to keep constantly in mind and use where necessary all the elementary theory we have learned in the previous section.

THE SUPERPOSITION THEOREM

This is a theorem which enables us to split a more complicated circuit up into easier pieces, as it were, and deal with each of these pieces in turn, using nothing more than the Ohm's law methods we have already learned. Put into more formal terms, the theorem may be expressed as follows: in any network made up of linear resistances, the current flowing in any branch is the algebraic sum of the currents that would flow in that branch if each generator (or battery) was considered separately, all other generators being replaced at that time by resistances equal to their internal resistance.

Don't worry at the moment about the words 'linear resistances'. This term simply refers to resistances in which the current and voltage obey Ohm's law. There is another term 'algebraic sum' that you may not be familiar with. This means that the addition must take note of the signs attached to the relevant terms; the algebraic sum of 5, −3, 2 and −1 is, for example, $5 + (-3) + 2 + (-1) = 3$, even though part of the operation involves subtraction.

You will perhaps best understand the Superposition Theorem by following through a worked example. Master each step before you go on to the next.

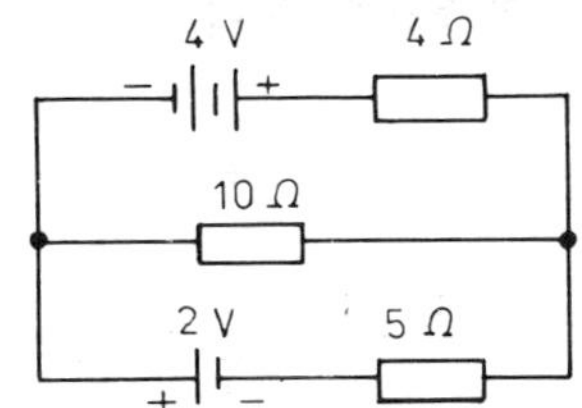

Figure 3.1

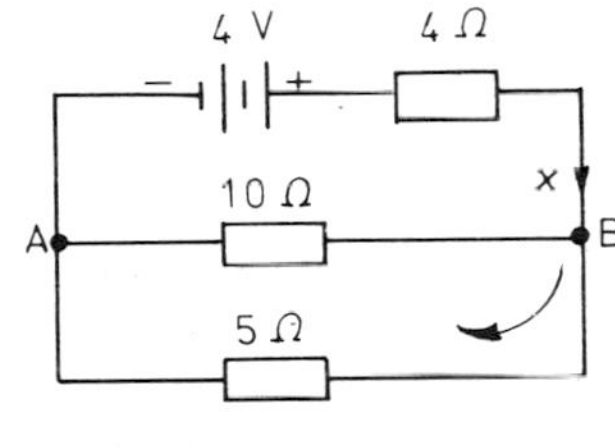

(a)

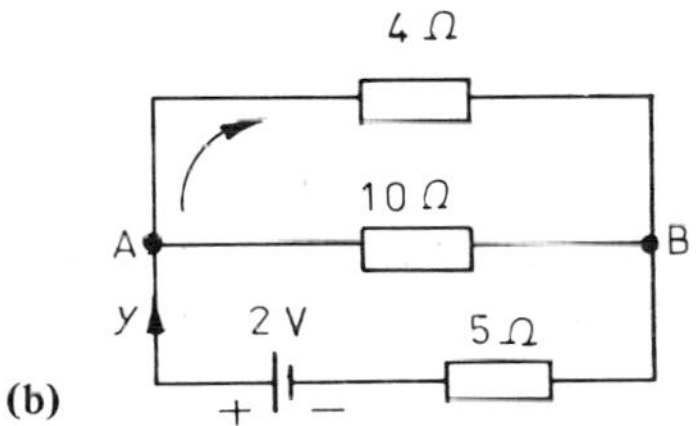

(b)

Figure 3.2

Example (1). In *Figure 3.1* a circuit is shown containing two sources of e.m.f., each with a series resistor representing its internal resistance. We require to find the current flowing in the 10 Ω resistor.

You might try applying Ohm's law directly to the circuit. If you do (and it is instructive to do so) you may find that things get a little confusing. This doesn't mean that it cannot be solved that way, but by using the Superposition Theorem, difficulties are greatly eased.

The theorem tells us that we can divide the given circuit up into two sub-circuits, each containing only one battery, the other battery at that time being simply replaced by its internal resistance. Doing this we obtain the two circuits shown in *Figure 3.2*.

Let the current due to the 4 V battery *acting alone* be x, and let the current due to the 2 V battery *acting alone* be y. Then from *Figure 3.2 (a)*, by a direct application of Ohm's law

$$\text{Total circuit resistance} = 4 + \frac{5 \times 10}{5 + 10} = 7.33\ \Omega$$

$$\therefore \text{Current } x = \frac{4}{7.33} = 0.545\text{ A}$$

Of this current, a proportion equal to 5/(5 + 10) = 1/3 flows through the 10 Ω branch.

∴ Current in the 10 Ω branch due to the 4 V battery alone

$$= 0.545 \times \frac{1}{3} = 0.182\text{ A}$$

Note that this current flows in the direction B to A.

For the 2 V battery alone, we use the circuit of *Figure 3.2 (b)*.

$$\text{Total circuit resistance} = 5 + \frac{4 \times 10}{4 + 10} = 7.86\ \Omega$$

$$\therefore \text{Current } y = \frac{2}{7.86} = 0.254\text{ A}$$

Of this current, a proportion equal to 4/(10 + 4) = 2/7 flows through the 10 Ω branch,

∴ Current in the 10 Ω branch due to the 2 V battery alone

$$= 0.254 \times \frac{2}{7} = 0.073\text{ A}$$

Note that this current flows in the direction A to B.

The two currents, 0.182 A and 0.073 A, therefore flow through the 10 Ω resistor *in opposite directions*. The resultant current is therefore 0.182 – 0.073 = 0.109 A.

This is the required current in the 10 Ω. It clearly flows from B to A.

You should now be able to proceed on your own, but in easy steps to begin with.

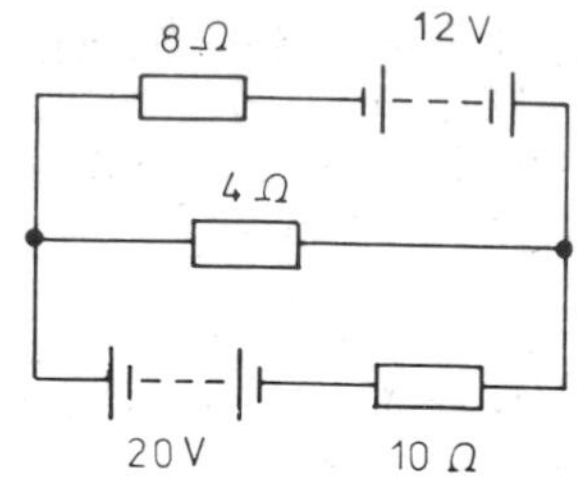

(a)

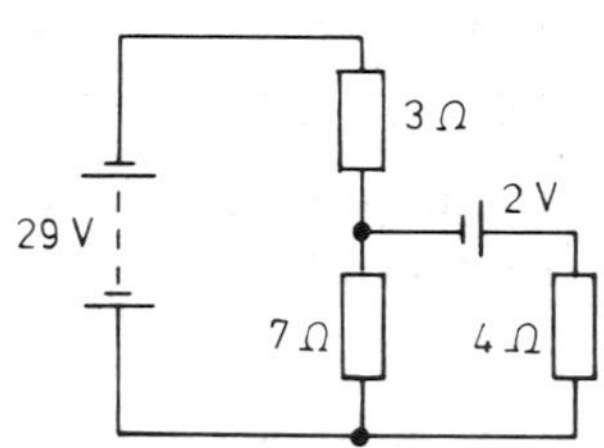

(b)

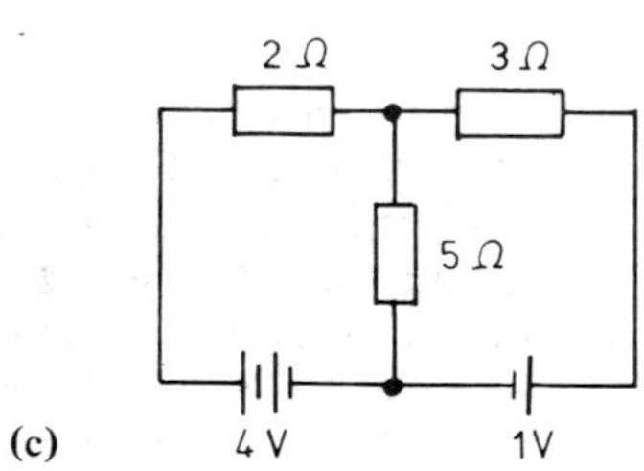

(c)

Figure 3.3

(2) Three circuit arrangements are shown in *Figure 3.3*. Draw suitable circuit arrangements (after the method shown in *Figure 3.2*) which split up these circuits into single-battery forms preliminary to the application of the Superposition Theorem, and check your solutions.

The choice of current direction depends upon battery polarity, conventionally flowing, that is, from the positive terminal of the battery around the circuit and back to the negative terminal.

By now you should have completed and checked your answers to Problem (2). Now use your simplified circuits to find the solutions to the next three problems.

(3) Calculate the current in the 4 Ω resistor of circuit (a) (*Figure 3.3*).

(4) What current is drawn from the 29 V battery of circuit (b).

(5) Find the current in all three branches of circuit (c).

We can now recapitulate on the method of solution using the Superposition Theorem:

1. Split the circuit into sub-circuits, each containing only one source of e.m.f., and replacing all other batteries by their respective internal resistances.
2. Letter the current flowing from the battery and mark with an arrow or arrows the current directions in the various parts of the circuit.
3. Calculate, using only Ohm's law, the currents flowing in the various parts of the circuit, with particular attention to those parts which will be concerned in the solution asked for.
4. Repeat these headings for all sub-circuits involved.
5. Find the algebraic sums of the currents flowing in those parts of the circuit for which solutions are required.

KIRCHHOFF'S LAWS

There are two of these laws: the *current law* and the *voltage law*. The current law tells us:

> At any junction in an electric circuit the total current flowing to that junction is equal to the total current flowing from the junction.

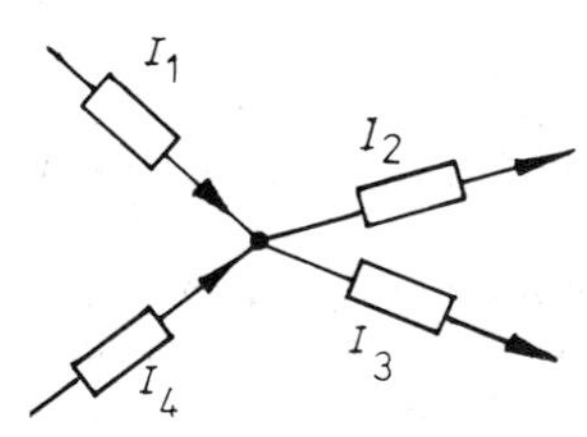

Figure 3.4

Figure 3.4 explains what this means. Here we see four currents acting at a junction; I_1 and I_4 are flowing towards the junction and I_2 and I_3 are flowing away from it. So, by Kirchhoff's current law, $I_1 + I_4$ must equal $I_2 + I_3$, or what comes to the same thing

$$I_1 + I_4 - I_2 - I_3 = 0$$

That is, by assigning positive signs for currents entering the junction and negative signs to those leaving it, we can say that the law tells us that the *algebraic sum* of all currents meeting at a point is zero. The actual signs we attach to the currents are quite arbitrary. Reversing the sign order still leaves the end result as a zero summation.

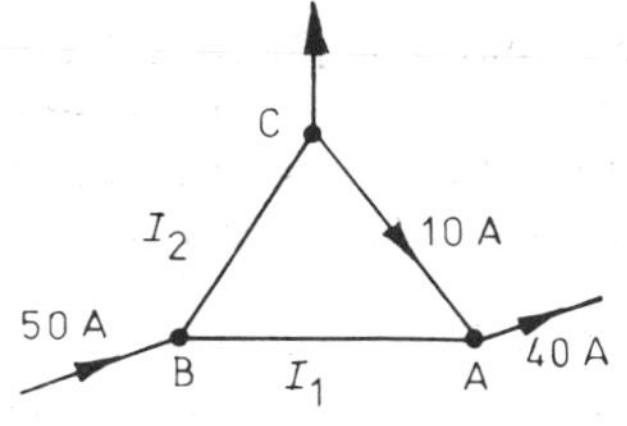

(a)

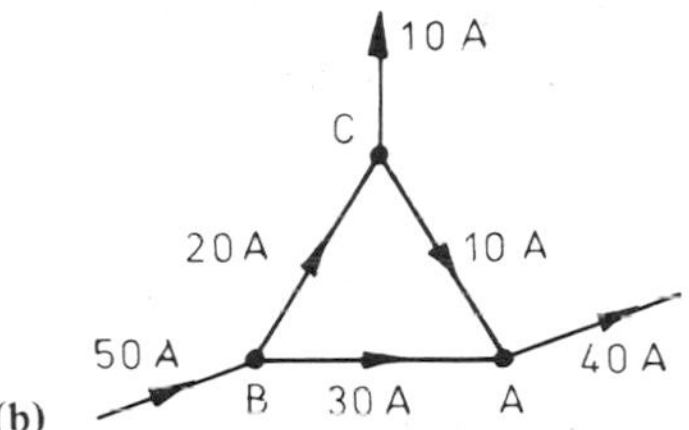

(b)

Figure 3.5

Example (6). Use Kirchhoff's current law to find the currents I_1, I_2 and I_3 flowing in the network of *Figure 3.5 (a)*.

Starting at junction A, we notice that 10 A is entering it along wire CA and 40 A is leaving it. Hence current I_1 must be 40 – 10 = 30 A flowing along the wire BA.

Turning to junction B, we notice that 50 A is entering it, and I_1 = 30 A is leaving it along wire BA. Hence the difference, 20 A, must be flowing along the wire BC towards C, call it I_2.

Finally, at junction C, 20 A is entering it along BC and 10 A is leaving it along CA. The difference, 10 A, must therefore be flowing out of the network from C. The full current distribution is shown in *Figure 3.5(b)*. Notice, as a check on the solution, that the total current entering the network at B, i.e. 50 A, is equal to the total current leaving it at A and C, i.e. 10 + 40 = 50 A.

(7) Find all the currents, I_1, I_2, etc., flowing in the various branches of the networks shown in *Figure 3.6*.

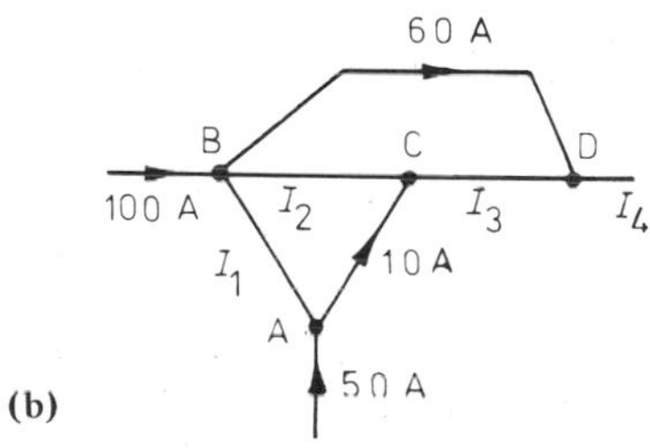

(b)

Figure 3.6

We turn now to Kirchhoff's voltage law, which tells us:

> In any closed loop in a network, the algebraic sum of the voltage drops taken around the loop is equal to the e.m.f. acting in that loop.

A closed loop (or mesh as it is sometimes called) means exactly what it says: in *Figure 3.7*, both routes ABDA and BCDB are closed loops. Route ABCEFA is also a closed loop. You can identify one or two more if you look carefully. The first two of the loops mentioned do not include the battery, so that the e.m.f. acting in either of them is *zero*. The third loop does include the battery, so the e.m.f. acting in that loop is E volts. Kirchhoff's voltage law simply tells us something which is intuitively obvious: that if we select any one of these loops and add up the IR voltage drops as we proceed around it, we can equate the resulting sum to the e.m.f. acting in the loop.

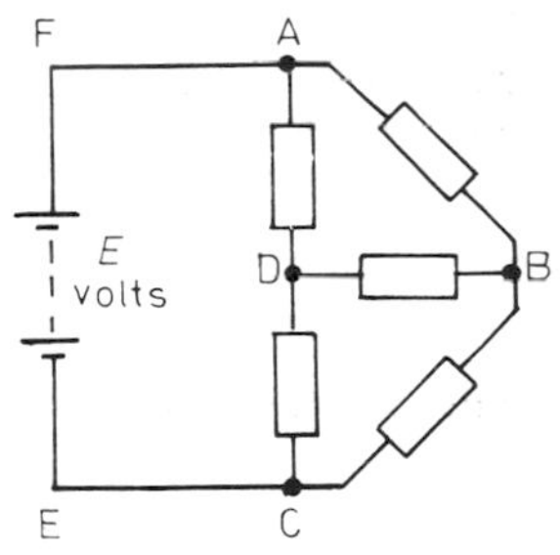

Figure 3.7

The direction in which we proceed around the loop is quite arbitrary. It is only necessary to proceed wholly in one direction and to reckon (as a general rule) the IR products and any e.m.f.s as positive when acting with the assumed direction of the current and negative when acting against it. The algebra will then take care of everything else.

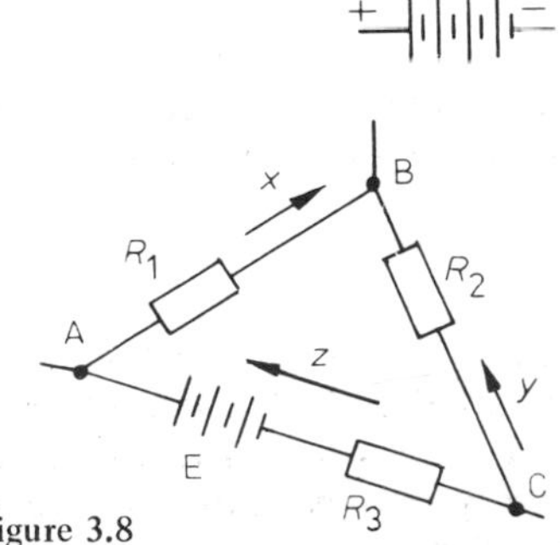

Figure 3.8

Example (8). In the loop sketch in *Figure 3.8*, (which can be considered as part of a more complicated network), the currents x, y and z have been assigned the *arbitrary* directions shown. Write down an expression illustrating Kirchhoff's voltage law by working round the loop from any one of the junction points A, B or C.

Let us proceed in a clockwise direction from point A. Proceeding along the R_1 branch from A towards B we notice that we are going along with the assumed direction of current x; hence we can assign a *positive* sign to the voltage drop xR_1 which exists between A and B. From point B we proceed along the R_2 branch from B towards C. This time we notice that we are going in *opposition* to the current y; hence we assign a *negative* sign to the voltage drop yR_2, i.e. we write $-yR_2$. At point C we proceed along the last branch back to our starting point A. In this branch we notice that not only is there a resistor but also a source of e.m.f.

Now in resistor R_3 our direction is the same as current z, so the zR_3 voltage drop will be given a positive sign. What about the source of e.m.f. E volts which we now encounter? Well, ask yourself in which direction is this e.m.f. acting ?—in the conventional sense, that is. Recall that we take the conventional flow of current to be from the positive terminal of a battery, around the circuit and back to the negative terminal. So for any source of e.m.f. which has positive and negative terminals as shown at the side of *Figure 3.8*, the direction in which the e.m.f. acts is as indicated by the arrow: from the *negative* terminal to the *positive, through* the battery.

Finally, then, we can attach a *positive* sign to the e.m.f. E as it is clearly acting in the same direction as current z. Hence by Kirchhoff's voltage law we can write down the expression which tells us that the algebraic sum of the IR voltage drops around the loop is equal to the e.m.f. acting in the loop, that is

$$xR_1 - yR_2 + zR_3 = E$$

(9) Suppose there had been no battery in the loop, what would the Kirchhoff expression have been?

(10) Starting at point B, go round the loop in an *anticlockwise* direction. Write down the voltage law expression, and hence verify that algebraically it is exactly the same as that derived in worked Example 8.

You should now be able to apply Kirchhoff's laws to various circuit problems. For your guidance, two worked examples follow.

Example (11). Find the currents in each branch of the circuit shown in *Figure 3.9(a)*.

This is a simple parallel resistance circuit which could be solved very easily by Ohm's law. However, we will solve it by using Kirchhoff's laws.

Now, for junction A, let the current flowing through the 6 Ω resistor be x amps and the current flowing through the 10 Ω resistor be y amps. In an example like this, with only one source of e.m.f. the current directions are easily deduced. By the current law of Kirchhoff, the current flowing in the battery branch is clearly $(x + y)$ A. We have, therefore all *three* circuit currents marked out using *only two* unknown quantities, x and y.

Now we require loops to apply the voltage law. Using the upper part of the circuit, as at *Figure 3.9(b)*, we can derive an equation; starting at A and proceeding anticlockwise we equate the volt drops to the circuit e.m.f.

Then

$$6x + 2(x + y) = 12$$

or

$$8x + 2y = 12$$

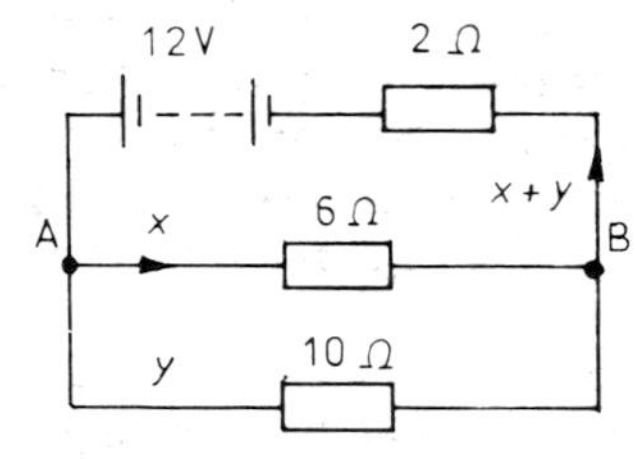

(a)

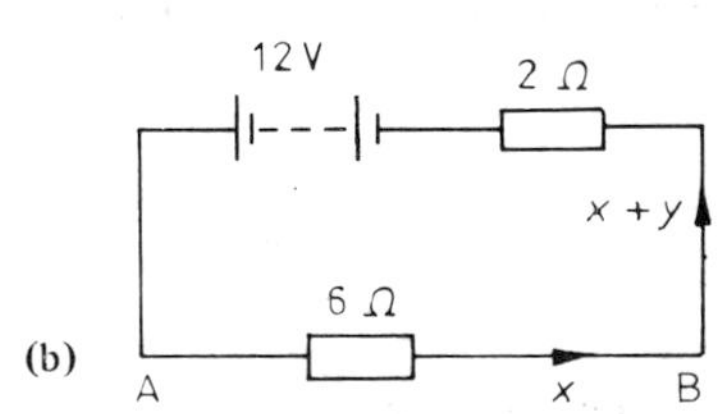

(b)

Figure 3.9

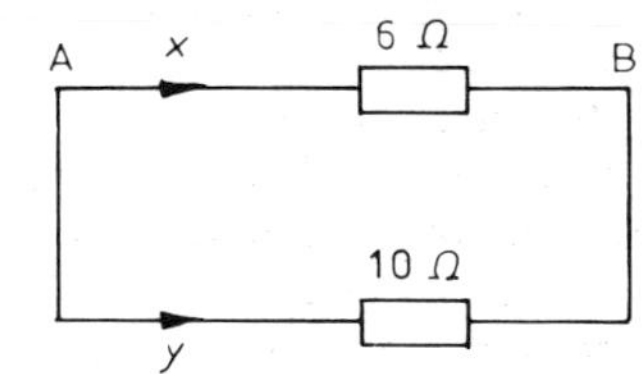

Figure 3.9(c)

This gives us one equation relating the currents x and y, so to find the values of x and y we require a second equation.

Let us use the lower part of the circuit (*Figure 3.9(c)*). This time the e.m.f. acting in the circuit is zero. Starting again from A and going anticlockwise, we have

$$10y - 6x = 0$$

Note that current x is in opposition to our chosen direction and so is given a negative sign. We now have two equations which we can solve simultaneously. Doing this we find

$$x = 1.3 \text{ A} \qquad y = 0.78 \text{ A}$$

From this

$$x + y = 2.08 \text{ A}$$

The currents in the branches are therefore:

0.78 A flows in the 10 Ω resistor
1.3 A flows in the 6 Ω resistor
2.08 A flows in the battery branch

Although it was clear from the circuit which way the currents would actually flow, in many circuits, in fact, it is not possible to say which way certain currents may be flowing. If you happen to choose the wrong direction, the answer you will get for the current value will simply carry a negative sign and this will indicate that the current actually flows in a direction opposite to your choice.

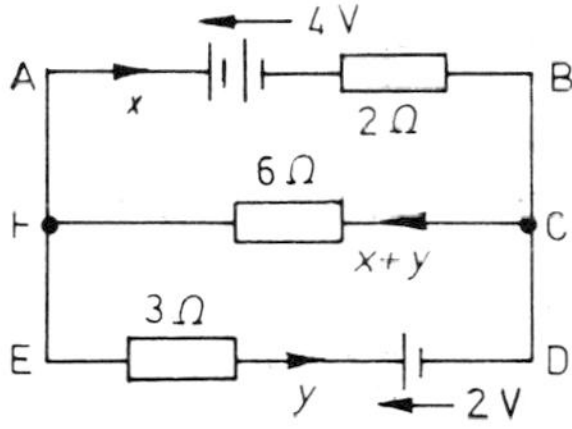

Figure 3.10

Example (12). In the circuit of *Figure 3.10*, calculate the currents flowing in each branch, and determine their proper directions.

It is a good plan to mark in first of all the directions in which the e.m.f.s are acting. After this, use capital letters clearly to mark out the various branches of the network. These things have been done in the figure. Now apply the current law: suppose that current x flows from A to B, and that current y flows from E to D. Then the sum of these, $(x + y)$, must flow along the centre branch from C to F. Keep in mind that Kirchhoff's current law must be obeyed at any junction.

Now we have two unknown currents x and y to find, so we shall need two independent equations. We obtain these by applying Kirchhoff's voltage law to any two different loops. There are three loops to choose from, and we shall use loop FCDE and loop ABCF.

Using loop ABCF and starting at A in a clockwise direction, we get

$$2x + 6(x + y) = -4$$

or

$$8x + 6y = -4$$

Notice the -4, as we moved *against* the battery e.m.f.

Using loop FCDE and starting at E in a clockwise direction, we get

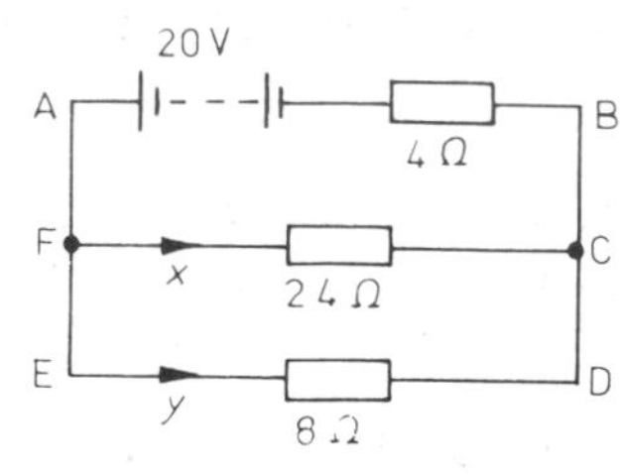

(a)

$$-6(x + y) - 3y = 2$$

or

$$-6x - 9y = 2$$

Notice again the reason for the particular sign pattern. Solving the two equations simultaneously we find

$$x = -\frac{2}{3}\text{ A}; \qquad y = \frac{2}{9}\text{ A}; \qquad (x + y) = -\frac{2}{3} + \frac{2}{9} = -\frac{4}{9}\text{ A}$$

We have negative signs attached to both current x and current $(x + y)$. This tells us that the directions we assigned to these currents were 'wrong'; x actually flows from B to A, and $(x + y)$ flows from F to C. The values $x = 2/3$ A and $(x + y) = 4/9$ A are, of course, perfectly correct.

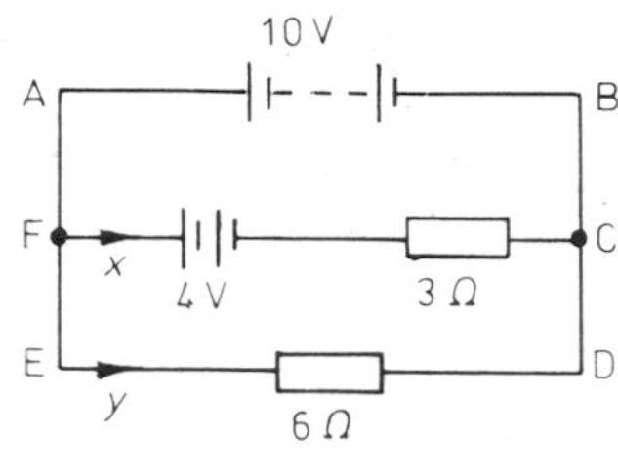

(b)

So as not to throw you in at the deep end straightaway, your next assignments consist of practice in setting up loop equations. When you have tackled these, you can apply your equations to the solution of the network problems which will follow.

(13) *Figure 3.11* shows three networks. For each of these obtain the equations (but do not solve them yet) for every possible closed loop. Check your answer in the usual way when you have done your best with the problems. Trace any errors back and find out where (and why) you made them.

(14) Referring to *Figure 3.11*, find, using the equations you have already derived as necessary:

(a) The current in the 4 Ω resistor in circuit (a).
(b) The current in the 3 Ω resistor in circuit (b).
(c) The currents in all branches of circuit (c).

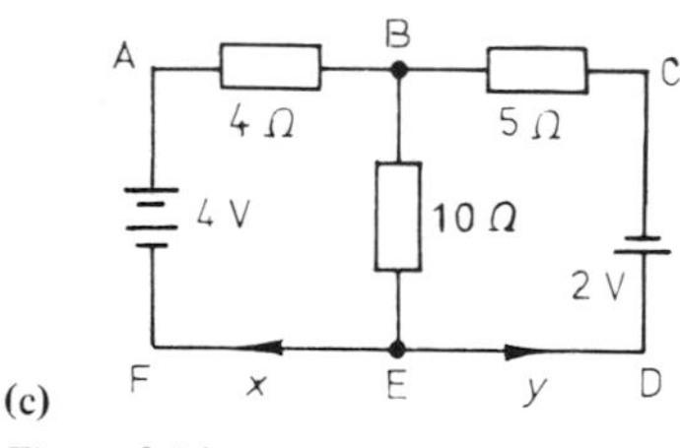

(c)

Figure 3.11

POTENTIAL DIVIDERS

You will recall that when a potential divider or potentiometer was being discussed in Section 2, we noted that the output fraction of the voltage applied across the potentiometer would only be equal to the ratio $R_1/(R_1 + R_2)$ if the current drawn from the output terminals was negligible. Look at *Figure 3.12*, and assume that the slider S is set at the centre of the potentiometer track, that is, assume that $R_1 = R_2$. The voltage V_0 will be equal to $\frac{1}{2}V$ *provided* that no current is drawn by whatever we have connected to terminals V_0. If current is drawn, and it is extremely unlikely in practice that it would not, the resistance sections R_1 and R_2 will be carrying unequal currents and the voltage drops across them will also be unequal. Consequently, although R_1 may equal R_2, the voltage V_0 will not longer be $\frac{1}{2}V$, and the slider S will have to be shifted in order to restore the required output of $\frac{1}{2}V$. This argument clearly applies to any slider position giving us a desired output fraction of the input. The next assignment question will enable you to think this problem out for yourself.

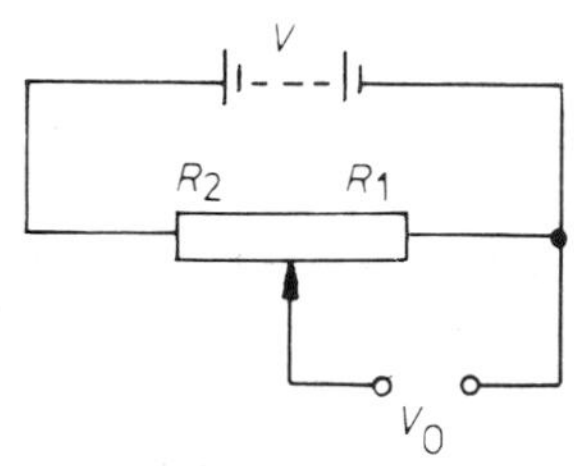

Figure 3.12

(15) Which way would the slider S have to be shifted, and why, in order for V_0 to be equal to $\frac{1}{2}V$ again, assuming that the V_0 terminals draw an appreciable current.

Problems involving voltage division are best dealt with by using Kirchhoff's current law. The next example will illustrate this for you.

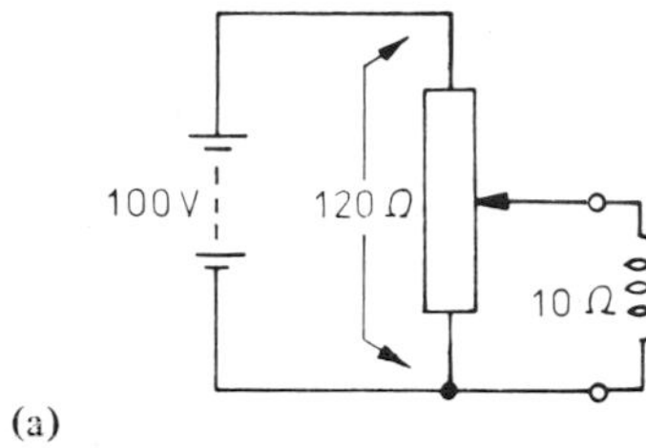

(a)

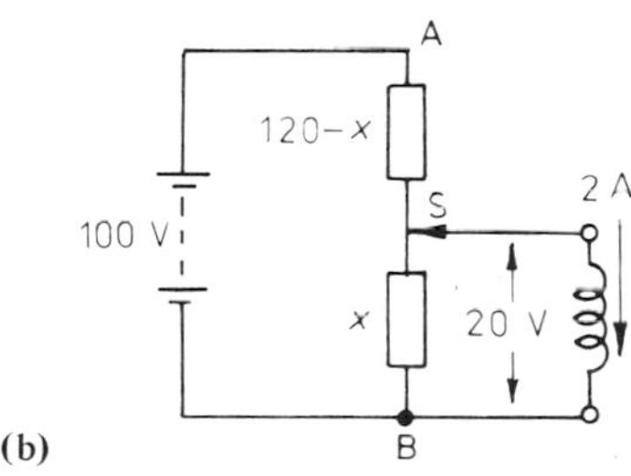

(b)

Figure 3.13

Example (16). The potentiometer in the circuit of *Figure 3.13(a)* has a total resistance of 120 Ω and is connected across a 100 V supply. Find the position of the slider S so that a current of 2 A will flow through the 10 Ω coil.

The first step is to redraw the circuit and fill in all the given information, together with the unknown quantities. This has been done in *Figure 3.13(b)*. A current of 2 A flows through the 10 Ω coil, so the voltage drop across the coil will be 20 V. This must also be the voltage across the points S-B of the potentiometer, hence the voltage across the points A-S must be 100 − 20 = 80 V. As we are asked to find the position of the slider, we call the lower portion of the potentiometer x Ω and the remaining upper portion is then $(120 - x)$ Ω. Now applying Kirchhoff's current law to the slider junction point, we have

(i) Current entering the junction $= \dfrac{80}{120 - x}$ A

(ii) Current leaving the junction $= \dfrac{20}{x} + 2$ A

These currents must be equal, so

$$\frac{80}{120 - x} = \frac{20 + 2x}{x}$$

Cross-multiplying:

$$80x = (120 - x)(20 + 2x)$$
$$= 2400 + 220x - 2x^2$$

Dividing by 2 and rearranging, we get

$$x^2 - 70x - 1200 = 0$$

and solving this gives

$x = 84.24$ Ω (taking the positive root)

Hence, the slider position has to be 84.24 Ω along the track from the lower end.

In most questions you will not be given a circuit diagram, so it is necessary to give yourself plenty of practice in interpreting the words of a problem into a clearly labelled diagram.

(17) A potentiometer of total resistance 24 Ω is connected across a 50 V supply. What will be the current through a 10 Ω coil when the sliding contact is exactly half-way along the potentiometer track?

(18) A potentiometer of total resistance 1000 Ω is connected across a 25 V supply. It is required to supply a current of 10 mA to a 500 Ω load. Calculate the resistance between the position of the slider and the end to which the load is connected.

PROBLEMS FOR SECTION 3

Group 1

(19) Without looking back in the text, write down Kirchhoff's current and voltage laws.

(20) Using Kirchhoff's current law, calculate the currents represented by I_1, I_2, etc., in each of the branches of the circuits shown in *Figure 3.14*.

(21) Use (a) the Superposition theorem, (b) Kirchhoff's laws, to find

(i) the current in the 5 Ω resistor of *Figure 3.15*;
(ii) the current in the battery and the p.d. between points A and B in the circuit of *Figure 3.16*;
(iii) the current in all three branches and the p.d. across the 4 Ω resistor in the circuit of *Figure 3.17*.

(22) Two batteries A and B are connected in parallel (like terminals together) across a 10 Ω resistor. Battery A has e.m.f. = 6 V and internal resistance 2 Ω; battery B has e.m.f. = 2 V and internal resistance 1.5 Ω. Calculate

(a) the current flowing in each battery;
(b) the terminal p.d. of each battery;
(c) the power dissipated in the 10 Ω resistor.

(23) Two batteries, each with internal resistances of 1 Ω, are connected as shown in *Figure 3.18*, the e.m.f.s being as given. Find the current flowing in each battery and in the 2 Ω resistor.

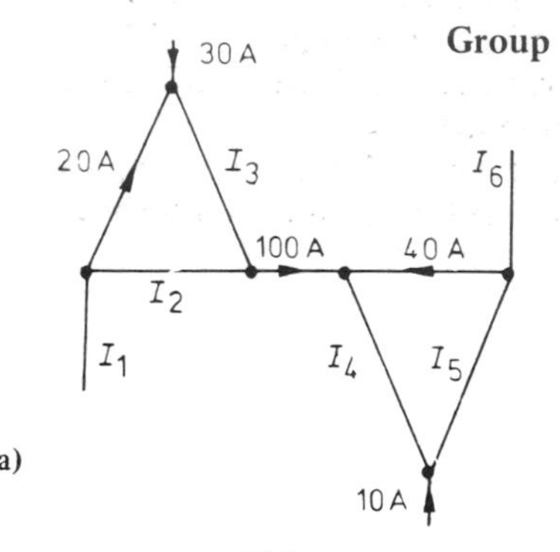

(a)

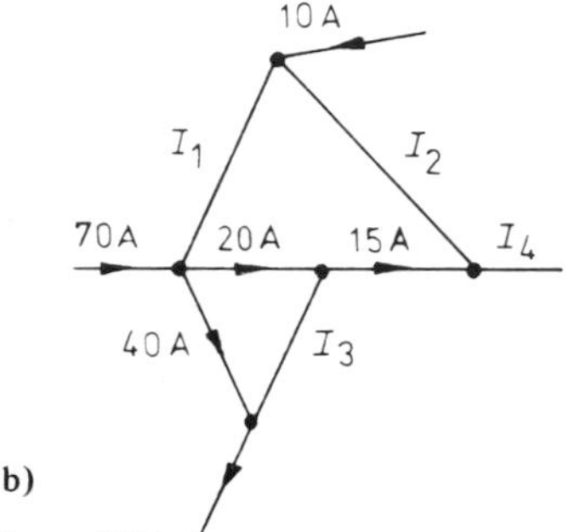

(b)

Figure 3.14

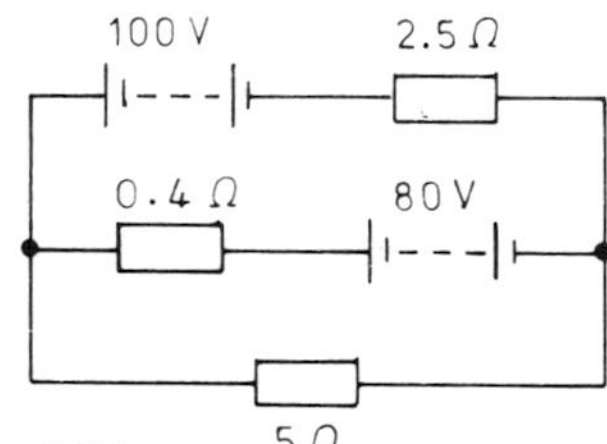

Figure 3.15

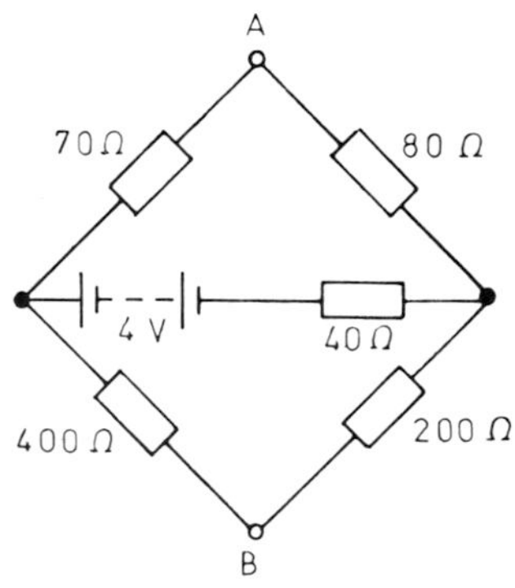

Figure 3.16

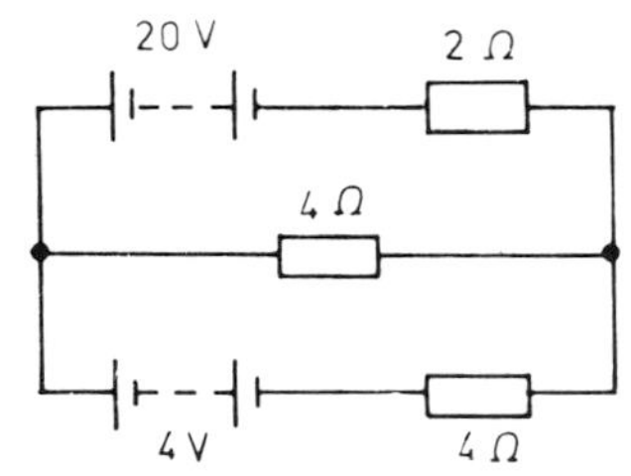

Figure 3.17

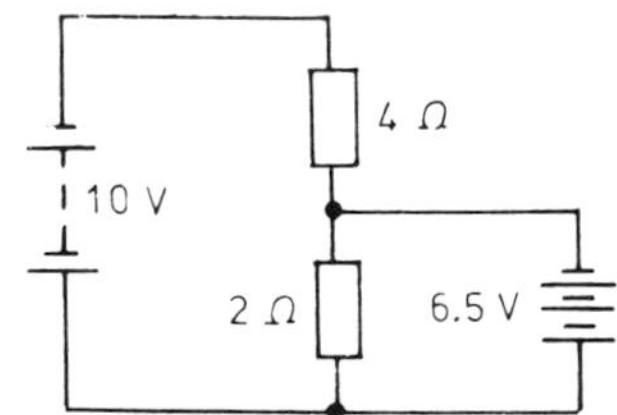

Figure 3.18

Group 2

(24) In *Figure 3.19*, find the value of the load resistor R.

(25) The potential divider shown in *Figure 3.20* has a total resistance of 24 Ω, and is connected across a supply of 110 V. What will be the current in the coil when the sliding contact S is set at a point equivalent to 6 Ω from the end B?

(26) In *Figure 3.21* the p.d. between points A and D is 24 V and between C and B is 20 V. Find the e.m.f.s of the batteries E_1 and E_2.

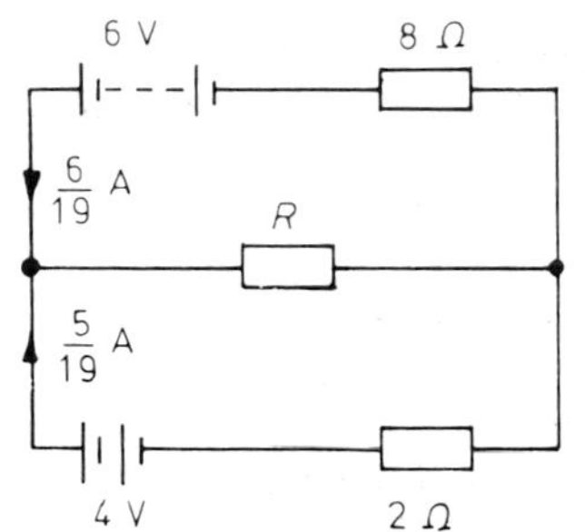

Figure 3.19

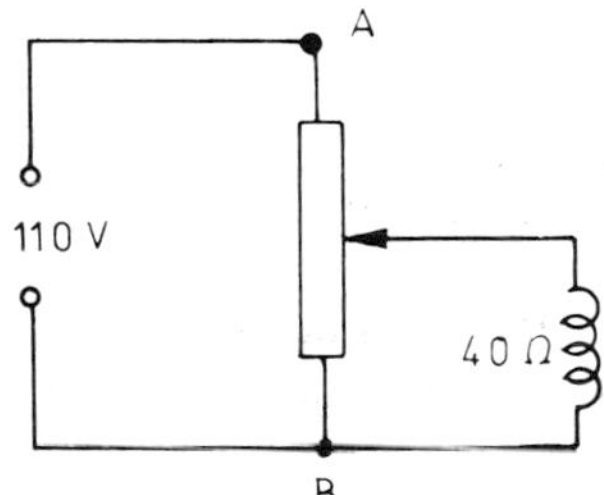

Figure 3.20

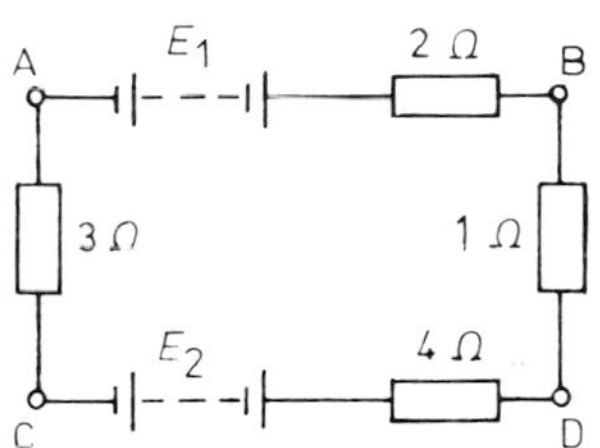

Figure 3.21

4 Capacitors and capacitance

Aims: At the end of this Unit section you should be able to:
Visualise the nature of an electric field.
Define electric flux density and electric field strength.
State that charge is proportional to applied voltage.
Understand the meaning of permittivity.
Define capacitance and state the unit of capacitance.
Define a capacitor as a device capable of storing electric charge.
Perform calculation relating to capacitors.

It is possible to add electrons to a conductor so as to give the conductor an excess of free electrons; the conductor is then said to be *negatively charged*. Also, electrons may be removed from a conductor, giving it a deficit of negative charges; the conductor is then said to be *positively charged*. An uncharged or neutral conductor has neither an excess nor a deficit of electrons.

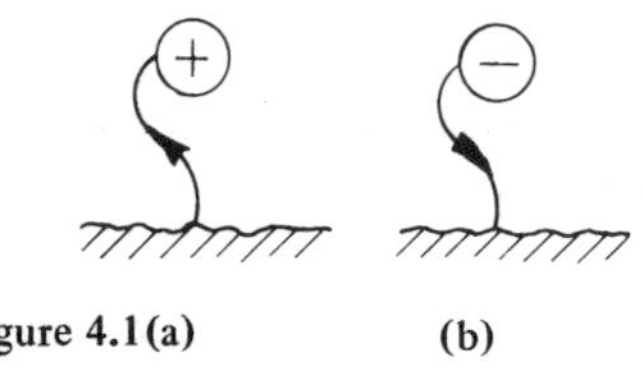
Figure 4.1 (a) (b)

If a positively charged conductor is connected to earth, as shown in *Figure 4.1(a)*, electrons flow from the earth to the body to make up the deficit and render the body neutral. If a negatively charged conductor is connected to earth, as in *Figure 4.1(b)*, electrons flow from the body to earth to clear the excess and again render the body neutral. So we may consider the general mass of the earth to be permanently neutral and conductors may carry charges in the form of an excess or a deficit of electrons with respect to the earth.

Frictional forces between two non-conducting materials of different kinds always result in a displacement of electrons. A plastics-cased pen rubbed on the sleeve will afterwards be found to attract small scraps of paper to itself. One of the materials, the plastics case, will acquire extra electrons from the sleeve and become negatively charged. The affected area of the sleeve, now being short of these electrons, has become positively charged.

If a charged body is freely suspended on a fine dry thread it will demonstrate that there is a force acting when another body is brought close to it. Similar charges will repel, while unlike charges will attract. There will also be attraction between a charged body and a neutral body, as the pen case experiment will show you. Since there is no contact between the bodies, the attractive or repulsive force acting between them must be a manifestation of a field of influence surrounding each of the bodies. This field is called an *electric field*. This field can be visualised by drawing lines between the bodies to represent the direction of action of the force, and the distribution of the lines in the sense of their relative density (or closeness together) can be used as an indication of field strength. *Figure 4.2* shows a few typical fields mapped out in this way. You should notice that lines of electric force are considered to start from *positive* electric charges and terminate on equal and opposite *negative* charges. The direction of the field is thus defined as that of the force acting upon a positive charge placed in the field. Bear in mind that lines of force have no existence in reality and in a real electric field we would not find forces acting along such discrete lines.

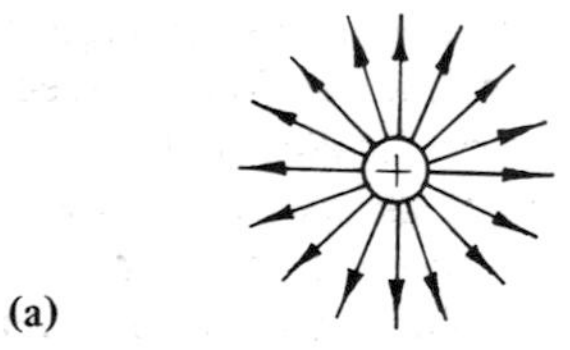
(a)

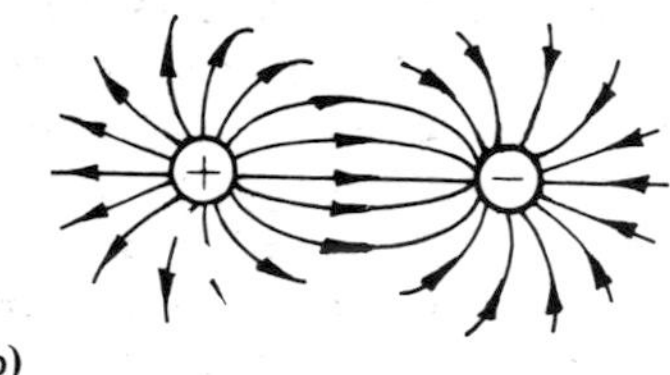
(b)

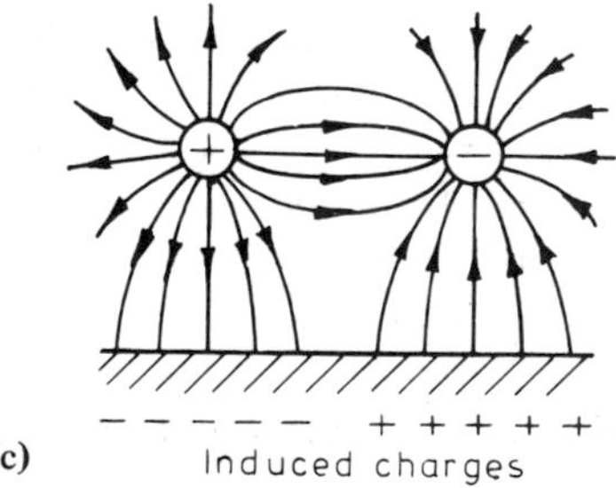

(c)

Figure 4.2

Example (1). Can you say why the charged plastics case will attract pieces of uncharged (neutral) paper?

When a charged body is brought into proximity to an uncharged body an *induced* charge of opposite sign appears on the uncharged body because the lines of force from the charged body terminate on its surface.

FLUX DENSITY

Unit *flux* is defined as emanating from a positive charge of one coulomb, so that electric flux, denoted by the symbol ψ (psi), is measured in coulombs and for a charge of Q coulombs the flux $\psi = Q$ coulombs. The *electric flux density* is measured in terms of the total flux passing through unit area situated at right-angles to the direction of the field. Hence, flux density, denoted by D, is measured in coulombs per square metre.

$$\text{Flux density } D = \frac{\text{Flux}}{\text{Area}} = \frac{\psi}{A} \text{ coulomb/m}^2$$

Clearly the greater the charge Q, the greater will be the flux density at a particular location in the vicinity of the charge.

ELECTRIC FORCE

Suppose we have two insulated parallel metal plates as shown in *Figure 4.3.* The mechanical force acting upon a charge of one coulomb placed between the plates is a measure of the *electric force* or *electric field strength*, denoted by the symbol E. The force is measured in the direction of the field and its magnitude depends upon the potential difference acting between the plates and also upon their distance apart. In moving from one plate to the other along a line of force we move from, say -50 V to $+50$ V. The potential difference between the plates is therefore 100 V and this potential changes linearly as we move from one plate to the other. We move, therefore, along a *voltage gradient* which changes by equal amounts for each unit of distance moved. Lines may now be drawn connecting all points in the field having equal potentials, and in *Figure 4.4* such *equipotential lines* have been traced in for -25, 0 and $+25$ V. You should notice that the zero equipotential line represents earth potential, and that the charges on the plates are in this case respectively above and below earth potential.

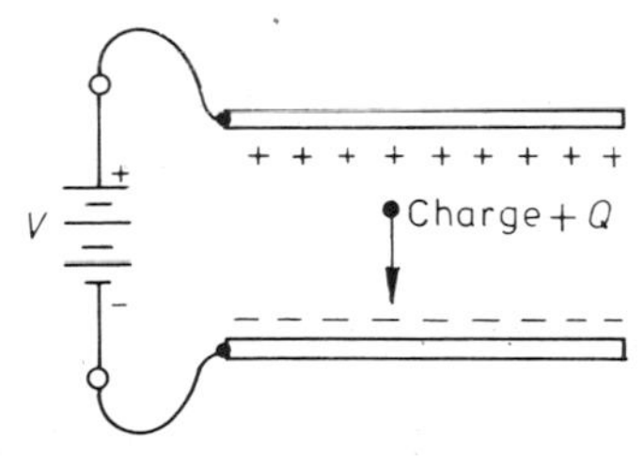

Figure 4.3

Now the electric force producing the field is determined by the voltage acting across the field and the distance across which it acts. By choosing two points in the field where the potential difference between equipotential lines is V volts and their distance apart is d metres, then the electric force is measured as the volts per unit spacing:

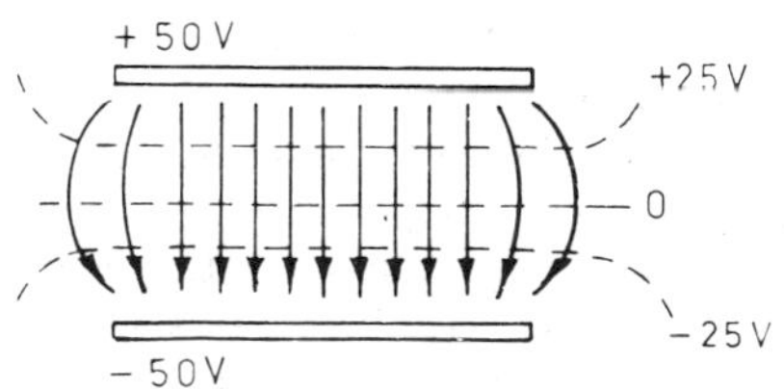

Figure 4.4

$$\text{Electric force } E = \frac{\text{Potential difference}}{\text{Distance}} = \frac{V}{d} \text{ V/m}$$

But the ratio V/d is also a measure of the voltage gradient in the field, hence

Electric force = Potential gradient

Example (2). Find the electric flux density between two parallel rectangular metal plates measuring 300 x 400 mm carrying an electric charge of 0.5 μC. If the plates are spaced 10 mm apart and the potential between them is 100 V, calculate the electric field strength.

Take particular care that you always express everything in the proper units of coulombs, metres and square metres. Then

$$\text{Flux density} = \frac{\psi}{A} = \frac{0.5 \times 10^{-6}}{300 \times 400 \times 10^{-6}}$$

$$= 4.16\,\mu\text{C/m}^2$$

$$\text{Electric field strength} = \frac{V}{d} = \frac{100}{10^{-2}}$$

$$= 10^4 \text{ V/m}$$

Now try the next problem yourself.

(3) The flux density between two circular plates, each of radius 200 mm, is 10μCm. What is the charge on the plates.

PERMITTIVITY

At any point in an electric field the electric force E maintains the electric flux ψ and so produces a particular value of flux density D at that point. It is found experimentally that if the electric force E changes for any reason, the flux density D changes proportionally. For an electric field established in a vacuum, therefore

$$\frac{D}{E} = \text{a constant } \epsilon_0 \text{ (epsilon)}$$

and this constant is called the *permittivity of free space* or the free space constant. Its value can be shown to be 8.85×10^{-12} SI units.

If the space occupied by the field is filled with air or some other medium, the air or the medium is known as the *dielectric*, and the flux is found to increase above the value it had in vacuum. The *relative permittivity* of the dielectric is defined as the ratio representing the proportional flux increase and is symbolised ϵ_r. Hence

$$\epsilon_r = \frac{\text{Flux density of the field in the dielectric}}{\text{Flux density of the field in vacuum}}$$

So, with a dielectric other than vacuum

$$\frac{D}{E} = \epsilon_0 \epsilon_r = \epsilon$$

where ϵ is the *absolute permittivity*.

Relative permittivity is a dimensionless number. It is unity strictly in a vacuum, but the slight difference when air is involved (1.0006) is usually ignored in calculations. Other values are $\epsilon_r = 2 - 3$ for waxed paper, 3-7 for mica, and 5-10 in glass and certain plastics.

(4) A metal sphere, suitably insulated from earth, carries a charge of 0.25 μC. The radius of the sphere is 150 mm. What is the field strength at the surface of the sphere? (The surface area of a sphere is $4\,\pi R^2$.)

You have possibly been introduced to several new terms and definitions in this Unit section. You should try to fix them clearly in your memory by filling in the blank spaces in the following statements.

(5) (a) The region around any . . . . . constitutes an electric field.

(b) Electric flux is measured in . . . . .

(c) Electrical force is identical with . . . . .

(d) In vacuum, ϵ_0 represents the ratio . . . . . which has the value . . . . .

(e) Absolute permittivity ϵ = ...

(f) For all practical purposes the permittivity of air is equal to the permittivity of . . . . .

THE CAPACITOR

By adding a charge Q to a conductor the potential of that conductor is altered. The charge Q is measured in coulombs and is, for any conductor, proportional to the potential V volts. Thus quantity of charge varies as potential or

$$Q = CV$$

where C is a constant. This constant is called the *capacity* of the conductor. The unit of capacitance is the farad, and this is the capacity of a conductor when the addition of 1 C of charge raises its potential by 1 V. The farad (F) is a very large unit for practical purposes, and the sub-units are the microfarad (μF = 10^{-6} F), the nanofarad (nF = 10^{-9} F) and the picofarad (pF = 10^{-12} F).

The parallel plate capacitor

Let parallel plates A and B be connected into a circuit as shown in *Figure 4.5*. Start with the plates in an uncharged condition and then let the switch S be placed in position 1. Plates A and B must finally have a p.d. between them of V volts, and a current must flow around the circuit so that B becomes positively charged and A becomes negatively charged. This requires a movement of electrons round the circuit. The current which flows while the plates are being charged is called a *displacement current*. Suppose Q coulombs is the charge stored on each plate. Then

$$\text{Capacity of conductors A and B} = \frac{Q}{V} \text{ farad}$$

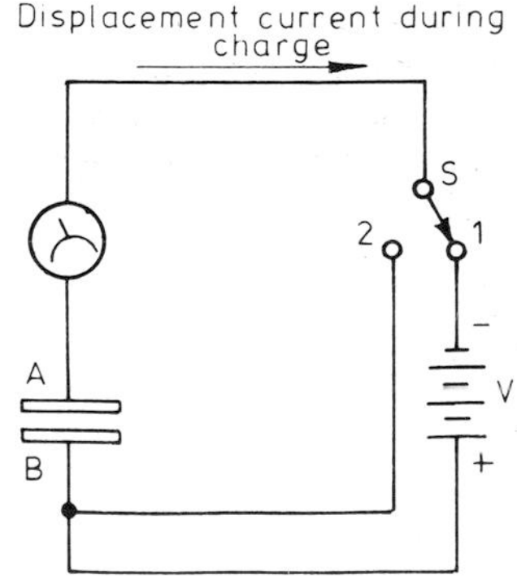

Figure 4.5

The arrangement of two plates as illustrated is called a parallel-plate capacitor.

If the switch is now placed in position 2, the capacitor will discharge, a momentary displacement current flowing in the circuit until the plates both have the same (neutral) potential.

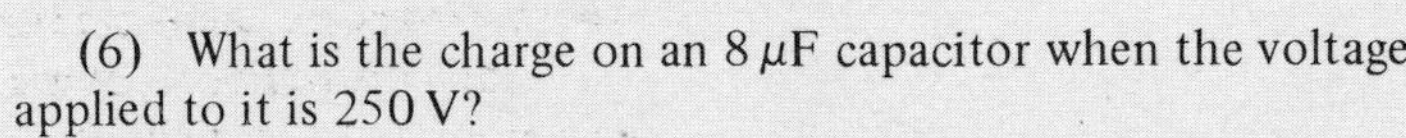

(6) What is the charge on an 8 μF capacitor when the voltage applied to it is 250 V?

(7) A capacitor carries a charge of 100 μC when the applied voltage is 100 V. What is its capacitance?

Capacitance of a parallel plate capacitor

We may reasonably expect the capacitance of a parallel plate arrangement to depend upon (a) the area of the plates, (b) the spacing between them, and (c) the dielectric material filling the space between them. Let the plates shown in *Figure 4.5* be charged and let the charge be uniformly distributed over each plate so that the field between them is uniform. The flux density $D = Q/A$ C/m² and the potential gradient or electric field strength is V/d V/m. So

$$D = \frac{Q}{A} \qquad \text{and} \qquad E = \frac{V}{d}$$

But $$\frac{D}{E} = \epsilon_0 . \epsilon_r$$

$$\therefore \quad \frac{Q}{A} \times \frac{d}{V} = \epsilon_0 . \epsilon_r$$

$$\therefore \quad C = \frac{Q}{V} = \epsilon_0 . \epsilon_r \frac{A}{d} \text{ farad}$$

From this expression we see that capacitance is

(a) directly proportional to plate area A,
(b) inversely proportional to plate spacing d,
(c) directly proportional to the dielectric permittivity ϵ_r.

To obtain a large capacitance you will notice that a large plate area is required with a very small spacing between the plates.

Example (8). A mica dielectric capacitor has an effective plate area of 5 cm² separated by 0.05 mm mica of relative permittivity 6.3. Calculate the capacitance in picofarads (pF). If the capacitor is given a charge of 0.5 μC, what will be the voltage between the plates?

You must first express all the given quantities in unit form:

$$A = 5 \text{ cm}^2 = 5 \times 10^{-4} \text{ m}^2$$

$$d = 0.05 \text{ mm} = 5 \times 10^{-5} \text{ m}$$

$$\epsilon_0 = 8.85 \times 10^{-12} \qquad \epsilon_r = 6.3$$

$$Q = 0.5\ \mu\text{C} = 0.5 \times 10^{-6} \text{ C}$$

Then

$$C = \epsilon_0 . \epsilon_r \frac{A}{d} \text{ F}$$

or

$$\epsilon_0 . \epsilon_r \frac{A}{d} \times 10^{12} \text{ pF}$$

as the answer is required in picofarads.

$$\therefore \; C = 8.85 \times 10^{-12} \times 6.3 \times \frac{5 \times 10^{-4}}{5 \times 10^{-5}} \times 10^{12} \text{ pF}$$

$$= 8.85 \times 6.3 \times 10 = 557.5 \text{ pF}$$

To find the voltage, we require the relationship $V = Q/C$.

Again using the basic units

$$V = \frac{0.5 \times 10^{-6}}{557.5} \times 10^{12}$$

$$= 896 \text{ V}$$

There is one point about capacitance calculations like Example (8) which you should bear in mind. The plate area A is only counted as the area of *one* of the plates.

You should not experience much difficulty in working out the next two problems for yourself.

(9) A paper dielectric capacitor has an effective plate area of 2.0 m^2 separated by waxed paper of thickness 0.1 mm and relative permittivity 2.5. Calculate the capacitance in μF. What voltage must be applied to the capacitor to charge it with 10 μC?

(10) Find the area of the plates required to construct a 1000 pF capacitor if the dielectric is mica of permittivity 6.0 and thickness 0.15 mm.

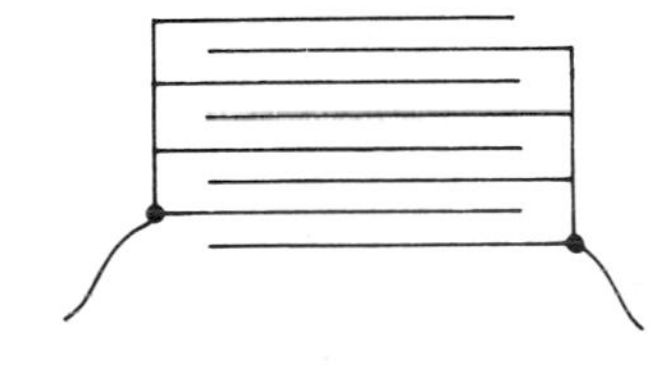

Figure 4.6

If we consider the above examples, it is clearly not practicable to make capacitors with a single pair of parallel plates if a large capacitance is called for, since the area needed becomes prohibitively large. To increase the capacitance of this kind of capacitor, therefore, a number of plates are interleaved as shown in *Figure 4.6*. This sketch shows eight plates, four of each being alternately brought out to opposite terminals. The best way actually to see capacitors of this sort is to look at the variable capacitors used for tuning purposes in radio receivers, where the dielectric between the plates is nearly always air. In fixed capacitors, paper or mica insulation can be used between the plates.

Let the total number of plates be N, then there are $(N - 1)$ *active* plates in the stack, since there are two 'unused' surfaces on the outsides of the stack and these represent the equivalent of one plate; there are also $(N - 1)$ layers of dielectric. Hence the total capacitance is $(N - 1)$ times the capacitance between one pair of plates, and so our formula becomes

$$C = \epsilon_0 . \epsilon_r \frac{A(N - 1)}{d} \text{ F}$$

Example (11). A capacitor is made up of eight metal plates arranged as in *Figure 4.6*. Each plate is separated by a layer of polyester film of thickness 0.1 mm, having a permittivity of 2.5. The effective area of overlap of each plate is 6 cm². Find the capacitance.

Here $A = 6 \times 10^{-4} \text{ m}^2$ $\qquad d = 0.1 \times 10^{-3} \text{ m}$

$\epsilon_r = 2.5$ $\qquad N = 8$

$$\therefore \quad C = \epsilon_0 . \epsilon_r \frac{A(N - 1)}{d} \text{ F}$$

$$= \frac{8.85 \times 10^{-12} \times 2.5 \times 6 \times 10^{-4} \times (8 - 1)}{0.1 \times 10^{-3}} \text{ F}$$

If we cancel out the 10^{-12} we shall have the answer in pF.

$$\therefore \quad C = 8.85 \times 2.5 \times 6 \times 7 = 930 \text{ pF}$$

The following general exercises on the contents of this Unit section are arranged, as before, in order of difficulty.

PROBLEMS FOR SECTION 4

Group 1

(12) What is the charge, in coulombs, carried by a single electron?

(13) An electric field of 10 μC is set up between two identical rectangular plates each measuring 50 x 30 cm, spaced 1 mm apart in air. Find the flux density between the plates.

(14) How many electrons have been displaced to produce the flux in the previous problem?

(15) A metal sphere, suitably insulated from earth, carries a charge of 0.5 μC. The diameter of the sphere is 0.2 m. What is the field strength at the surface of the sphere?

(16) Two parallel plates having a potential difference of 100 V between them are spaced 0.5 mm apart. What is the electric field strength and the flux density in the case of (a) air dielectric between the plates, (b) a dielectric with $\epsilon_r = 2.7$ between the plates?

(17) The flux density between two plates, separated by a mica dielectric of relative permittivity 6.3, is 3 $\mu C/m^2$. What is the voltage gradient between the plates?

(18) Two parallel plates, each of area 0.25 m^2, are spaced 0.3 mm apart by a dielectric whose ϵ_r value is 2.5. A p.d. of 250 V is maintained across the plates. What is the flux between the plates?

(19) Find the charge on a 10 μF capacitor when the voltage across it is 500 V.

(20) The charge on a capacitor is 150 μC and the applied voltage is 250 V. What is the value of the capacitance, in μF?

(21) A p.d. of 200 V is maintained across a capacitor of 0.05 μF. The effective area of each plate of the capacitor is 0.05 m^2 and the absolute permittivity of the dielectric is 2×10^{-11}. Calculate (a) the electric flux density, (b) the electric force in the dielectric.

Group 2

(22) Two insulated metal plates form a capacitor. When the distance between the plates is 1 mm, the capacitance is 50 pF. What will the capacitance be if the spacing is increased to 3 mm? If under this condition a sheet of glass, relative permittivity 5.0, is introduced to fill the space between the plates, what will the capacitance be?

(23) A 1 μF capacitor is made up from two plates separated by a paper dielectric having a thickness of 0.1 mm and an absolute permittivity of 2.213×10^{-11}. What is the effective area of the plates?

(24) Two plates each of area 150 cm^2 are spaced 1 mm apart in air, and a p.d. of 100 V is applied across them. Find (a) the capacitance, (b) the charge stored, (c) the potential gradient between the plates.

(25) A capacitor used in a transmitter consists of 11 interleaved plates each of area 60 cm^2. The plates are spaced 2 mm apart in air. What is the capacitance?

5 Capacitors in circuit

Aims: At the end of this Unit section you should be able to:
Perform calculations for series and parallel capacitor connections.
Calculate the energy stored in a charged capacitor.
Discuss the constructional problems of practical capacitors.
Have a general acquaintance with types of practical capacitor.

We must acquaint ourselves with the effects of series and parallel connections of capacitors, using the fundamental relationship $Q = CV$ already derived.

CAPACITORS IN SERIES

Consider three capacitors connected in series as shown in *Figure 5.1*. We must note first of all that the charge residing in each capacitor when they are connected to a source of voltage V is the same, irrespective of the values of the individual capacitors. This may be a little difficult to grasp at first, but remember that charge involves a certain number of electrons. The charge of electrons on one plate of capacitor C_1 involves the movement of an identical number of electrons from its second plate to the connected plate of C_2. And similarly, from the second plate of C_2 an identical number will move on to the connected plate of C_3, and so back through the supply to the first plate of C_1 again. So in a series circuit the charge Q is constant round the circuit, analogous to a series resistive circuit where the *current* is the same in all parts of the circuit. Now, from our basic relationship $V = Q/C$

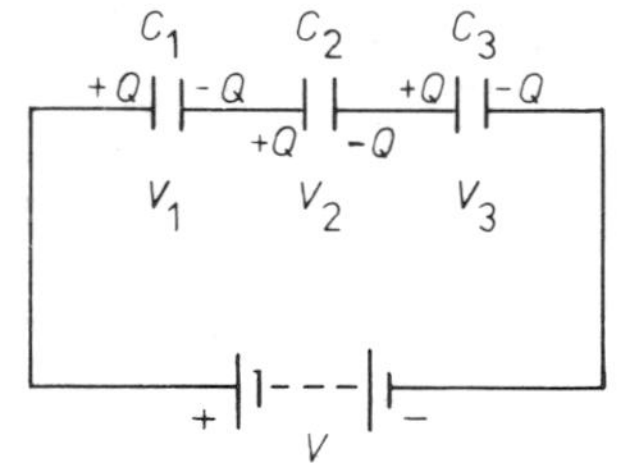

Figure 5.1

$$\text{Voltage across } C_1 = V_1 = \frac{Q}{C_1}$$

$$\text{Voltage across } C_2 = V_2 = \frac{Q}{C_2}$$

$$\text{Voltage across } C_3 = V_3 = \frac{Q}{C_3}$$

But

$$V = V_1 + V_2 + V_3 = \frac{Q}{C_E}$$

where C_E is the *equivalent single capacitance* representing C_1, C_2 and C_3 in series.

$$\therefore \frac{Q}{C_E} = \frac{Q}{C_1} + \frac{Q}{C_2} + \frac{Q}{C_3}$$

$$\therefore \frac{1}{C_E} = \frac{1}{C_1} + \frac{1}{C_2} + \frac{1}{C_3}$$

Notice that this is a reciprocal formula similar to the one we use to find the combined value of resistance in parallel.

Keep in mind, recalling resistors in parallel, that if *two* capacitors are connected in series, the equivalent capacitance can be found as

$$C_E = \frac{\text{Product}}{\text{Sum}} = \frac{C_1 C_2}{C_1 + C_2}$$

Example (1). Calculate the equivalent capacitance of two capacitors of 8 μF and 12 μF wired in series.

$$C_E = \frac{C_1 C_2}{C_1 + C_2} = \frac{8 \times 12}{8 + 12}\ \mu\text{F}$$

$$= 4.8\ \mu\text{F}$$

Example (2). Three capacitors of values 4 μF, 5 μF and 8 μF are connected in series across a 20 V supply. Calculate the equivalent capacitance of the chain and find the voltage across each capacitor.

For series capacitors

$$\frac{1}{C_E} = \frac{1}{C_1} + \frac{1}{C_2} + \frac{1}{C_3}$$

$$\therefore \frac{1}{C_E} = \frac{1}{4} + \frac{1}{5} + \frac{1}{8} = \frac{10 + 8 + 5}{40} = \frac{23}{40}$$

$$\therefore C_E = \frac{40}{23} = 1.74\ \mu\text{F}$$

The circuit charge Q is the same as the charge on any of the capacitors, hence

$$Q = C_E V = 1.74 \times 20 = 34.8\ \mu\text{C}$$

$$V_1 = \frac{Q}{C_1} = \frac{34.8}{4} = 8.70\ \text{V}$$

$$V_2 = \frac{Q}{C_2} = \frac{34.8}{5} = 6.96\ \text{V}$$

$$V_3 = \frac{Q}{C_3} = \frac{34.8}{8} = 4.35\ \text{V}$$

We check that the sum of the individual voltages total to the supply voltage (20 V), and notice that the *greatest* voltage is developed across the *smallest* capacity, and vice versa.

(3) Two capacitors having capacitances of 10 μF and 15 μF are connected in series. Calculate the value of a third capacitor which, when connected in series with the other two, will give a resultant capacitance of 3 μF.

(4) Three capacitors of 5 μF, 10 μF and 15 μF are connected in series across a 100 V supply. Find the equivalent capacity, the charge on each capacitor, and the voltage across each capacitor.

CAPACITORS IN PARALLEL

When capacitors are wired in parallel, the full circuit voltage V is present across each capacitor, but this time the charges on each capacitor will depend upon the individual capacitances, since $Q = CV$. In *Figure 5.2* three capacitors are wired in parallel across a source of voltage V volts.

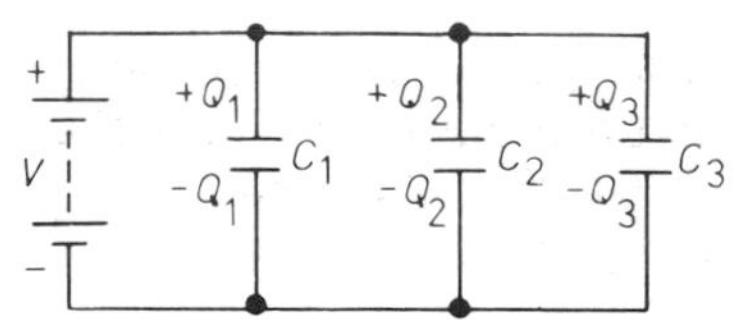

Figure 5.2

Now

$$Q = Q_1 + Q_2 + Q_3$$

$$\therefore\ Q = C_1V + C_2V + C_3V = C_EV$$

where C_E is the equivalent single capacitance representing C_1, C_2 and C_3 in parallel.

$$\therefore\ C_EV = V(C_1 + C_2 + C_3)$$

$$C_E = C_1 + C_2 + C_3$$

This is a straightforward summation, similar to the condition for resistors wired in series.

Example (5). Three capacitors of 16 μF, 20 μF and 48 μF are wired in parallel across a 100 V supply. Find the equivalent capacitance and the charge on each capacitor.

For parallel capacitors $C_E = C_1 + C_2 + C_3$.

$$\therefore\ C_E = 16 + 20 + 48 = 84\ \mu F$$

The charge on each capacitor is found from $Q = CV$, hence

$$Q_1 = C_1V = 16 \times 100 = 1600\ \mu C$$

$$Q_2 = C_2V = 20 \times 100 = 2000\ \mu C$$

$$Q_3 = C_3V = 48 \times 100 = 4800\ \mu C$$

The total charge stored is, of course, the sum of these charges, i.e. 8400 μC, which would be the equivalent charge on a 84 μF capacitor connected across a 100 V supply.

You have probably noticed by now that we have worked the examples throughout in μF, without the introduction of the 10^{-6} at each stage. The charges then come out directly in μC. Try to work out capacitor problems this way.

The next example shows you how to deal with mixed series and parallel connnections.

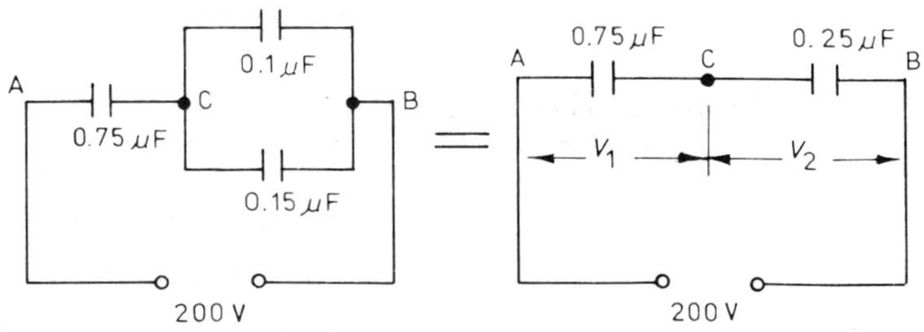

Figure 5.3

Example (6). Three capacitors are connected as shown in *Figure 5.3* and a 200 V supply is connected across terminals A–B. Calculate (a) the equivalent capacitance of the arrangement, (b) the voltage across the points A–C.

We replace the two parallel capacitors with a single equivalent of 0.1 + 0.15 = 0.25 μF. The circuit is then equivalent to a 0.25 μF capacitor in series with a 0.75 μF capacitor, as the figure shows. The total equivalent capacitance is then

$$\text{(a) } C_E = \frac{\text{Product}}{\text{Sum}} = \frac{0.25 \times 0.75}{0.25 + 0.75} = 0.1875\ \mu\text{F}$$

(b) Referring to the simple series equivalent, the charge on C_1 and C_2 will be the same, hence

$$Q = V_1C_1 = C_2V_2$$

$$\therefore\ 0.75V_1 = 0.25V_2$$

$$\therefore\ V_2 = 3V_1$$

$$\text{But}\ V_1 + V_2 = 200\ \text{V}$$

$$\therefore\ 4V_1 = 200$$

$$V_1 = 50\ \text{V}$$

This is the voltage present across the points A–C.

(7) A circuit has a capacitance of 30 μF which is to be reduced to 10 μF. What additional value of capacitor is required and how would you connect it?

(8) Three capacitors of 10 μF, 15 μF and 25 μF are connected in parallel across a 120 V supply. Calculate the equivalent capacitance and the charge of each capacitor.

(9) The charges present on three capacitors connected in parallel across a 50 V supply are 80 μC, 500 μC and 1400 μC respectively. Calculate the value of each capacitor and the equivalent capacitance of the combination.

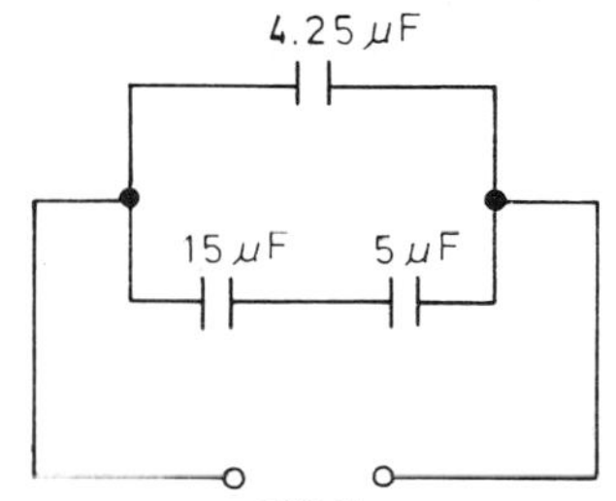

Figure 5.4

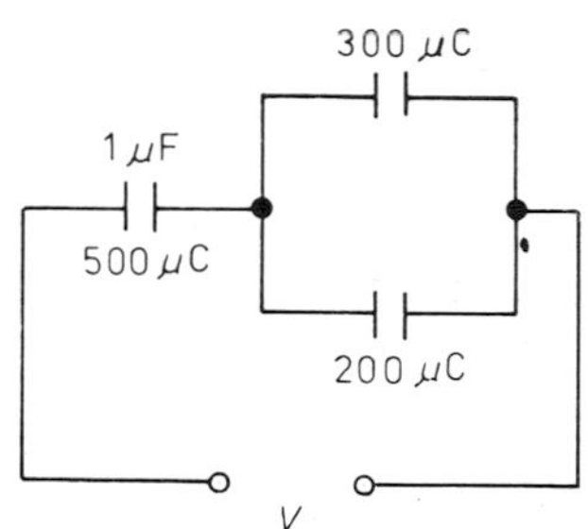

Figure 5.5

There should have been no difficulty in solving these problems. The next two deal with mixed series and parallel arrangements.

(10) In the combination shown in *Figure 5.4*, find the voltage across each capacitor and the equivalent capacitance.

(11) Three capacitors are connected as shown in *Figure 5.5*. The charges on the capacitors are as given, and the voltage across the 1 μF capacitor is 500 V. Find the applied voltage V and the value of each of the unmarked capacitors.

ENERGY IN A CHARGED CAPACITOR

Suppose a capacitor to be charged slowly by the successive addition of small equal charges, each of q coulomb. As the voltage v on the capacitor at any time will be proportional to charge, the voltage will increase linearly with time, as shown in *Figure 5.6*. At any instant

$$q = Cv = It \text{ coulomb}$$

where I is the charging current, also proportional to time. Now the amount of work necessary to add each increment of charge q is $vIt = vq$.

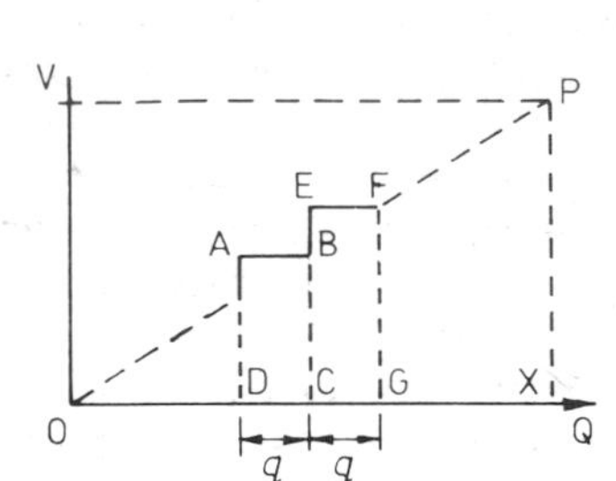

Figure 5.6

This is represented in the figure by the area of the rectangle ABCD. This increase in charge raises the voltage by the amount BE, and in an exactly similar manner, the next addition of charge q will raise the voltage the further amount FG and will add energy represented by the rectangle EFGC. The total energy of the charged capacitor is given by the addition of all the small rectangles representing the incremental energies, that is, it is given by the area of the triangle OPX. Hence

$$\text{Energy stored} = \text{area OPX} = \tfrac{1}{2}V \times Q$$

where Q is the final charge at applied voltage V.

But $Q = CV$

$$\therefore \text{ Energy stored} = \tfrac{1}{2}CV^2 \text{ J}$$

This energy is stored in the electric field between the plates, i.e. it is stored *in the dielectric*.

(12) What is the energy stored in a 2 μF capacitor when charged to 500 V?

(13) An 8 μF capacitor is required to store 5 J of energy. Determine the voltage to which the capacitor must be charged.

PRACTICAL CAPACITOR CONSTRUCTION

There is a variety of problems associated with the construction of capacitors for practical circuit use. These can usually be roughly divided into electrical problems and mechanical problems. We mention a couple of electrical problems first.

When an electric field is established in a dielectric, there is a distortion of the electron orbits around the atoms making up the dielectric material. This effect produces a mechanical stress in the dielectric which in turn produces heat. Because the production of heat represents a dissipation of power, practical dielectrics always introduce a power loss, generally very small, but particularly important when the capacitors are used in high frequency circuits where there is a continual and rapid change of plate polarities.

If the potential difference between the plates of a capacitor is increased beyond a certain amount, a point is reached where the dielectric insulation is unable to withstand the electric stress set up across it and there is a spark discharge which penetrates the material and destroys its insulating properties in the region of the breakdown. The potential gradient necessary to cause such a breakdown is a measure of the ability of a material to resist breakdown, and is usually expressed in volts or kilovolts per millimetre. Such figures are useful for relative comparisons of various dielectric materials and are naturally a very important factor in the design of capacitors. Dielectric strength is not proportional to thickness, so simply doubling the thickness of a dielectric does not double the voltage at which breakdown may occur. All practical capacitors have a safe *working* voltage stated on them, often noted at a particular maximum temperature.

The mechanical problems of capacitor design depend largely upon three factors: the capacity required, the maximum working voltage at which it can be used, and whether it is to be employed at d.c. and low frequencies or at high frequencies. As we have seen, capacitance is a function of plate area, plate separation and dielectric permittivity, so for a given capacitance in a given space a large plate area, small spacing and high permittivity are the order of the day. The requirement of small plate spacing conflicts with the provision of a high working voltage, and that of a particular dielectric material conflicts often with the necessity of maintaining low dielectric loss.

Air has unity permittivity and negligible loss at all frequencies, but because of the plate area problem, air-spaced capacitors are extremely bulky relative to the capacitance they can provide. They are found normally only in high power transmitting systems where a solid dielectric material would introduce prohibitive heat loss, and in receiver circuits where a *variation* of capacity is required for tuning purposes. Assembly problems limit the narrowness of the plate spacing. They are made in a range of capacitances from about 10 pF (trimmers) up to some 1000 pF.

Wax or oil impregnated paper is used fairly extensively as a dielectric material, though it being replaced on a large scale by polyester film. Polyester is chemically inert and unlike paper is non-hygroscopic; unlike paper, also, it is comparatively loss free and has a higher permittivity, so making for a more compact assembly for a given working voltage. Both paper and polyester types take the form of a rolled assembly, the metal foil used for the plates being brought out at each side of the roll. Capacities range from about 50 pF up to several microfarads.

Mica has a high permittivity compared with paper and is stable with temperature. It has low loss and high dielectric strength but it is much more expensive than paper or polyester. It consequently makes a capacitor with a much poorer size-to-capacitance ratio than a paper or polyester type since it cannot be rolled and has therefore to be made up in the form of a multiplate parallel assembly. Silvered-mica capacitors have films of silver deposited directly on to the mica sheets by an evaporation process. This makes for a capacitor of high stability, reproducible to close limits.

Certain ceramic (steatite) materials have extremely high permittivities, so making their use as dielectrics in capacitors very attractive. Tubular and disc type ceramic capacitors are in general use.

So called electrolytic capacitors depend upon oxide surfaces being formed upon aluminium or tantalum foils. The commonest type consists of two such foils, one of which has an oxide coating. The two foils are separated by an absorbent film saturated by a suitable electrolyte. The oxide film acts as the dielectric and is maintained by the applied voltage. This film is extremely thin (and self-healing) and so very large capacities can be obtained in a small volume. They have the disadvantage of a small but continual leakage and can only be used in circuits where the applied polarity does not reverse. The terminals of electrolytics are consequently marked + and – or appropriately coloured. Capacities range from about 1 μF up to many thousands of microfarads.

PROBLEMS FOR SECTION 5

Group 1

(14) Two capacitors having capacitances 5 μF and 15 μF respectively are connected in series, then in parallel. Find the equivalent capacitance in each case.

(15) What capacitance must be connected in series with a 10 μF capacitor for the equivalent capacitance to be 6 μF?

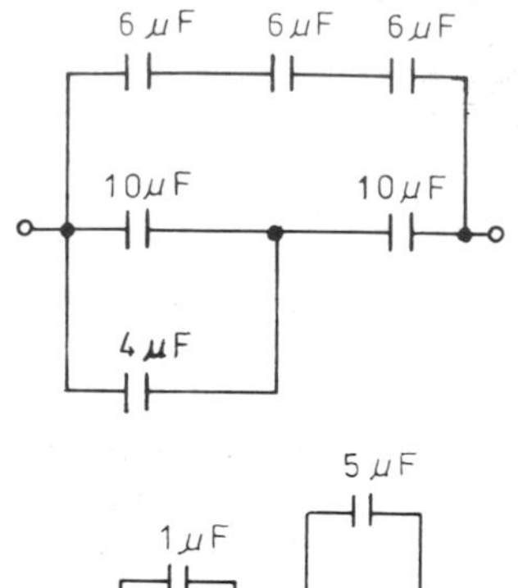

Figure 5.7

(16) Four 4 μF capacitors are wired in parallel and a 16 μF capacitor is connected in series with the combination. What is the total capacitance of the arrangement?

(17) Two capacitors, 3 μF and 7 μF, are wired in parallel. A third capacitor is connected in series with the arrangement and the total capacitance is 5 μF. Find the value of the third capacitor.

(18) Two capacitor networks are shown in *Figure 5.7.* Calculate the equivalent capacitance in each case.

(19) When a capacitor is connected across a 100 V supply, the charge is 2 μC. Find (a) the capacitance, (b) the energy stored.

(20) A 10 μF capacitor connected to a battery is charged with 0.0004 C. Calculate (a) the battery voltage, (b) the energy stored.

(21) Three capacitors are connected in series across a 200 V supply. If the capacitances are 5, 10 and 15 μF respectively, find (a) the equivalent capacitance, (b) the voltage across each capacitor, (c) the charge on each capacitor.

(22) Capacitances of 20 μF and 30 μF are connected first in series and then in parallel across a 120 V supply. Find the energy stored in each case.

(23) Two capacitors of 3 μF and 6 μF are wired in series across a d.c. supply. The charge on each capacitor is 0.0002 J. Find (a) the voltage across each capacitor, (b) the supply voltage.

Group 2

(24) A capacitor is charged with 10 mC. If the energy stored if 0.5 J, find (a) the voltage, (b) the capacitance.

(25) A 5 μF capacitor is connected to a 250 V supply and allowed fully to charge. In this state it is isolated and connected across an uncharged 7 μF capacitor. Find the voltage across the combination.

(26) Three capacitors of 2, 4 and 0.8 μF are joined in series across a 100 V supply and charged. Without any losses, they are now disconnected and then connected in parallel with plates of like polarity together. Find (a) the total charge on the combination, (b) the charge on each capacitor, (c) the voltage across the parallel combination.

(27) A capacitor is made up of two metal plates each of area 100 cm^2 spaced 0.1 mm apart in air. The capacitor is connected to a 100 V supply. Calculate (a) the energy stored, (b) the electric flux density, (c) the potential gradient.

(28) A multiplate capacitor has a total of 11 plates, each separated by waxed paper of thickness 0.5 mm and relative permittivity 2.12. The area of each plate is 400 cm^2. Find (a) the capacitance, (b) the charge stored if the capacitor is connected across a 1000 V supply.

(29) *Figure 5.8* shows an arrangement of capacitors. A, B and C are identical capacitors, and the total equivalent capacitance of the circuit is 1 μF. Find the value of A, B or C.

(30) A 100 V battery is connected across a series combination of a 2 μF and a 3 μF capacitor. Calculate the voltage across each capacitor and the total energy stored. The capacitors are disconnected from the battery and without any loss of charge, plates of like polarity are then joined to form a parallel arrangement. Calculate the new total energy and explain why it differs from the original total energy.

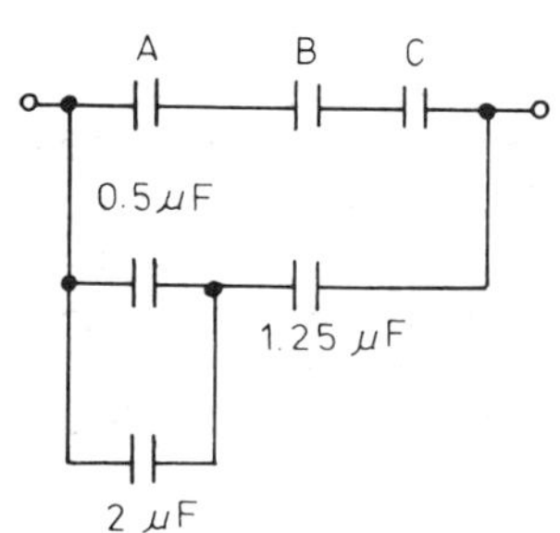

Figure 5.8

6 Magnetism and magnetisation

Aims: At the end of this Unit section you should be able to:
Define the terms flux, flux density, magnetomotive force and magnetising force.
Define permeability as the ratio of flux density to magnetising force.
Understand the effects of ferromagnetic materials on flux density.
Draw magnetisation curves for various ferromagnetic materials.
Understand the effect of magnetic hysteresis.

A piece of magnetic material, such as iron or steel, placed in the vicinity of a magnet will experience a mechanical force tending to move it towards one or other of the poles of the magnet. A freely suspended bar magnet will align itself to a position where one end points towards the earth's North magnetic pole. In the same way, a small compass needle will align itself in a definite direction when placed in the area of influence of a magnet.

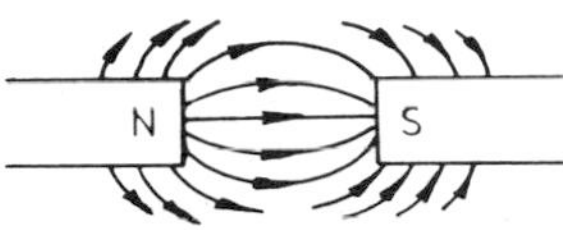

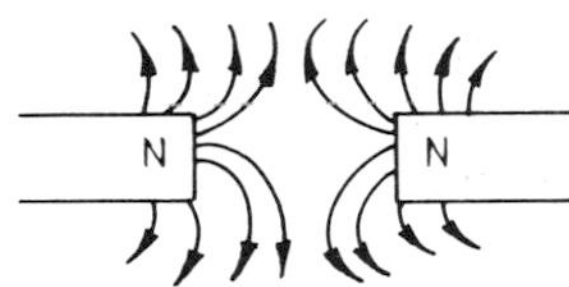

Figure 6.1

Since this aligning force is exerted on the magnetic material without physical contact taking place, there is clearly a field of influence around the magnet exactly as there is around an electrically charged body. Any region in which the magnetic influence can be detected in this way is called a *magnetic field* and the direction of the field is defined as being that of the direction of the force acting on an isolated *North* pole placed within the field. The field may be represented by drawing lines of magnetic force or magnetic flux lines, and *Figure 6.1* shows a few typical fields mapped out in this way. Magnetic fields, in theory at least, extend to infinity, but their influence falls off very quickly, so for most practical purposes the fields are of importance only in the vicinity of the poles.

Lines of magnetic force form closed loops, unlike lines of electric force which terminate in induced charges at the surface of conductors. The magnetic lines are assumed to leave the North pole, enter at the South pole, and form the remainder of their loops inside the magnet itself.

Magnetic flux, symbol Φ, can be regarded as the number of lines of force, or flux, and the *magnetic flux density*, symbol B, can be regarded as the number of flux lines passing through a unit area perpendicularly. As we shall see, flux is not measured in lines as such, but in terms of the electromagnetic effect the field will produce. For the time being, we shall note that the SI units of flux Φ and flux density B are respectively the *weber* (Wb) and the *tesla* (T); and that 1 T is 1 Wb/m^2. For a magnetic field of cross-sectional area A square metres, with flux Φ Wb threading that area

$$B = \frac{\Phi}{A} \quad \text{Wb/m}^2 \text{ or tesla}$$

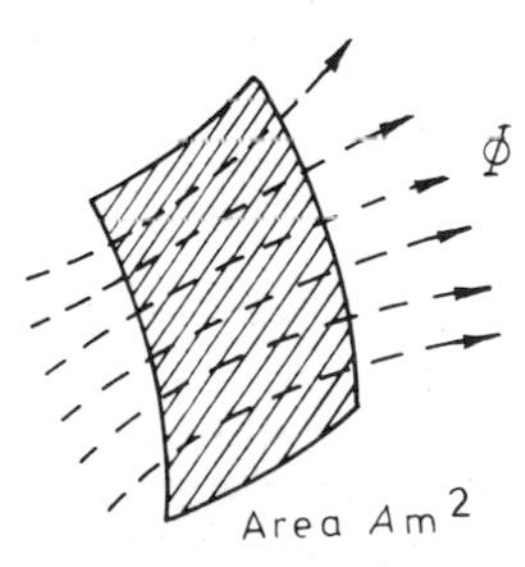

Figure 6.2

Figure 6.2 explains this point.

ELECTROMAGNETISM

When an electric current flows in a conductor, a magnetic field is established in the space surrounding the conductor. The field consists of circular lines of magnetic flux, concentric with the wire. The direction in which the lines of force are defined to act is given by *Maxwell's corkscrew rule*, which tells us that their direction is the same as the direction of rotation of a corkscrew that is travelling with its axis in the direction of the current. *Figure 6.3* should make this rule clear for you.

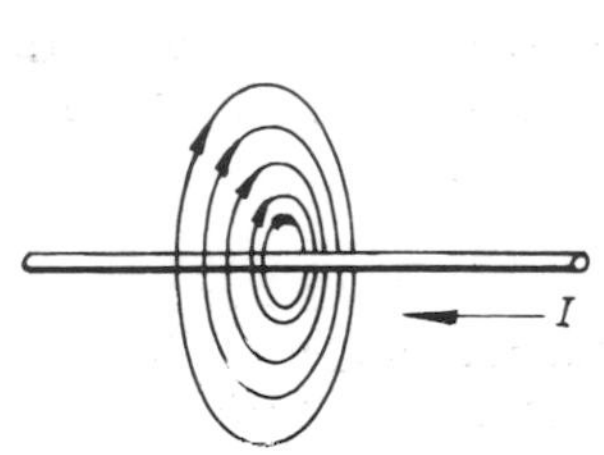

Figure 6.3

When there are two parallel wires, both carrying current, each will produce its individual field of concentric rings, but the resultant field will be the combined effect of these fields. The resultant fields for the two cases where (a) the currents flow in the same direction, and (b) the currents flow in opposite directions will be as shown in *Figure 6.4*. For currents in the same direction there is force of attraction between the wires tending to pull them together. When the currents are in opposite directions, the lines of flux do not interlink, but lie so that there is a force of repulsion between the conductors.

Attraction

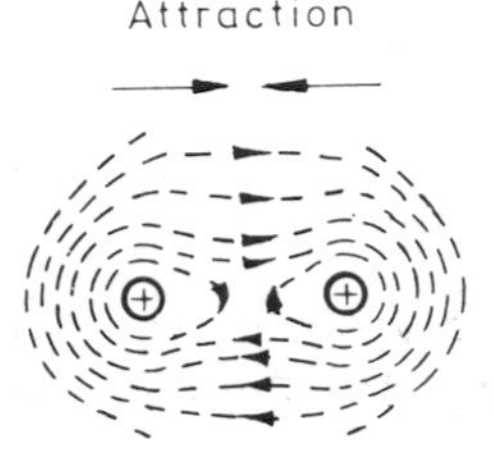

Both currents flowing into the plane of the paper

Repulsion

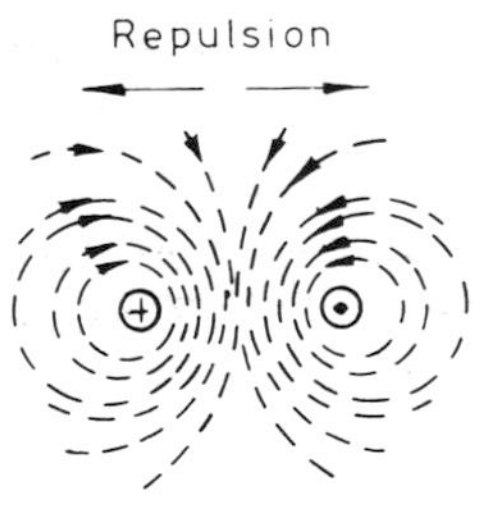

Currents flowing in opposite directions

Figure 6.4

If now instead of being spaced apart the conductors are placed closely side by side, and carry currents in opposite directions, the fields cancel and there is negligible resultant effect; if the currents flow in the same direction, the resultant magnetic effect is greater than that due to one conductor alone. It is easy to demonstrate that the magnetic effect produced is directly proportional to the current in the conductor.

For a given number of conductors, therefore, the *current* can be taken as a measure of the force which produces the magnetic field. This force is called the *magnetomotive force* (m.m.f.), and N conductors each carrying I amperes produce the same magnetic effect as a single conductor carrying NI amperes.

Now the available m.m.f. in a particular case is the same for *all* the circular flux paths set up around the conductor, so that as we go further from the conductor the lengths of the flux paths become greater and the less m.m.f. per unit length is available to maintain the flux in that path. The m.m.f. per unit length of flux path is called the *magnetising force* (or *magnetic field strength*), and is given the symbol H. It is measured in ampere turns per metre. For a single conductor therefore

$$H = \frac{I}{\ell} \text{ A/m}$$

and for N conductors

$$H = \frac{NI}{\ell} \text{ At/m}$$

where ℓ is the length of the flux path in metres. In our present case where the flux paths are circular, ℓ is, of course, equal to $2\pi r$, where r is the radius of any particular ring.

DEFINITION OF UNIT CURRENT

We may now relate the unit of current, the ampere, directly with the unit of force, the newton, if conditions are properly stated.

Let two parallel conductors each carry a current I amperes, and let their distance apart in a vacuum be d metres. Then it is found that the force per unit length acting on each of the conductors is given by

$$F = 2 \times 10^{-7} \times \frac{I^2}{d} \text{ N}$$

For unit current of 1 A in conductors spaced unit distance 1 m apart, the force acting between them is therefore

$F = 2 \times 10^{-7}$ N per metre length

This is an extremely small force, but it nevertheless enables us to relate current to mechanical force and so rationalise the electrical and mechanical units into one system of measurement.

Example (1). What is the flux density in a magnetic field of cross-sectional area 20 cm² having a flux of 2.5 mWb?

$$\text{Flux density } B = \frac{\text{Flux } \Phi}{\text{Area } A} \text{ Wb/m}^2 \text{ (tesla)}$$

$$= \frac{2.5 \times 10^{-3}}{20 \times 10^{-4}}$$

$$= 1.25 \text{ T}$$

Example (2). Two parallel conductors carry equal currents of 100 A. What is the force acting between them if they are spaced 5 cm apart in air?

We may take the above formula to be equally true for conductors spaced apart in air or a vacuum. Then

$$F = 2 \times 10^{-7} \times \frac{100^2}{5 \times 10^{-2}} \text{ N/m}$$

$$= 0.0004 \text{ N/m}$$

(3) Two conductors carry the same current of 2000 A. Calculate the least spacing of the conductors if the force between them is to be limited to 1 N per metre run.

THE SOLENOID

With circular lines of flux around a current-carrying conductor, you have probably noticed that no North or South pole is apparent. If however, we bend the conductor into a loop or join a number of loops together to form a coil, the concentric flux lines produced by each turn of wire become additive and the resultant magnetic field closely resembles that surrounding a bar magnet. *Figure 6.5* illustrates this effect. The direction of the field inside the coil, which is usually

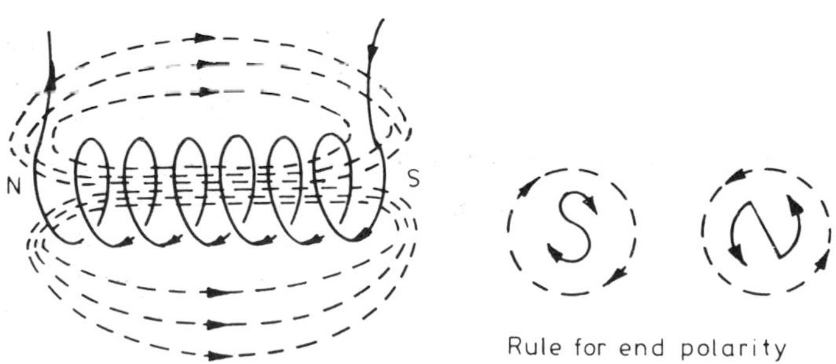

Figure 6.5

known as a *solenoid*, is best determined by using the so-called *end rule* which is sketched at the side of the figure and is self-explanatory.

For a long straight solenoid of length ℓ metres wound with N turns of wire carrying a current of I amperes, the m.m.f. is NI ampere-turns, and the magnetising force inside the solenoid is

$$H = \frac{NI}{\ell} \text{ At/m}$$

PERMEABILITY

At any point in a magnetic field the magnetising force H maintains the magnetic flux Φ and produces a particular value of flux density B at that point. Clearly, if H changes, B will change, and if the field is established in air or in any non-magnetic medium, the ratio of B to H is found to be constant:

$$\frac{B}{H} = \text{a constant } \mu_o$$

This constant, μ_o, is called the *permeability of free space* or the magnetic space constant and has the value $4\pi \times 10^{-7}$ SI units.

When iron or any other ferromagnetic material is used to provide the medium in which the magnetic flux is established, for example, an iron rod may be inserted into a solenoid, there is a very large increase in the flux density B for a given magnetising force H. Lines of flux find it much 'easier' to pass through a ferromagnetic material than they do through free space or air, and consequently they crowd together wherever such a magnetic material is provided. The factor by which the flux density increases from its value in air, for the same value of magnetising force, is called the *relative permeability* (μ_r) of the material. In the magnetic material, therefore

Flux density $B = \mu_r \times$ Flux density in air

But the flux density in air is $\mu_o H$, since $B/H = \mu_o$

$$\therefore B = \mu_o \mu_r H$$

in a material of relative permeability μ_r.

The product $\mu_o \mu_r$ is called the *absolute permeability* μ, and this has a definite value which is much greater than μ_o for all fields other than those established in air or non-magnetic materials.

(4) Find the flux density produced in an air-cored solenoid due to a uniform magnetising force of 10 000 At/m.

(5) A piece of iron of relative permeability μ_r 200 under the given conditions is inserted into the solenoid of Problem (4). What now is the flux density in the solenoid?

We noted above that the permeability of free space μ_o is a constant, and you may perhaps have drawn a conclusion that the relative permeability μ_r of various magnetic materials is, for a given material, also constant. This is not so, however. μ_r is not constant between different materials and even varies considerably for one particular material.

Example (6). A magnetising force of 350 At/m produces a flux density of 0.75 T in a sample of silicon iron. What is the relative permeability of the iron under this condition?

$$B = \mu_o \mu_r H \quad \text{so that} \quad \mu_r = \frac{B}{\mu_o H}$$

$$\therefore \mu_r = \frac{0.75}{4\pi \times 10^{-7} \times 350} = 1705$$

MAGNETISATION CURVES

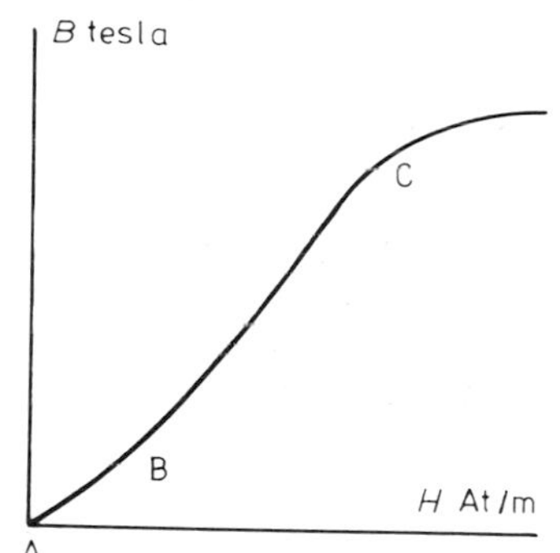

Figure 6.6

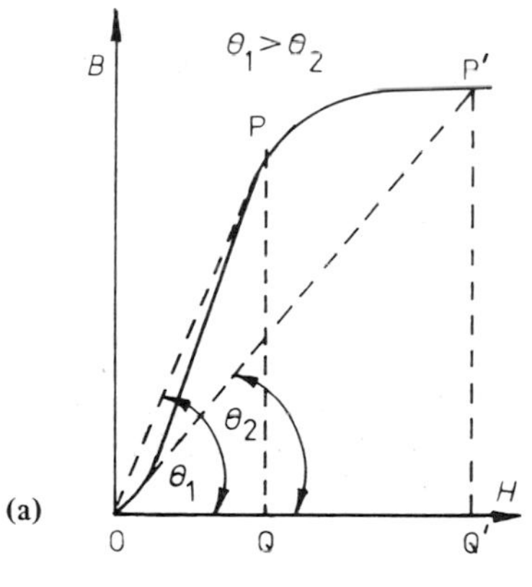

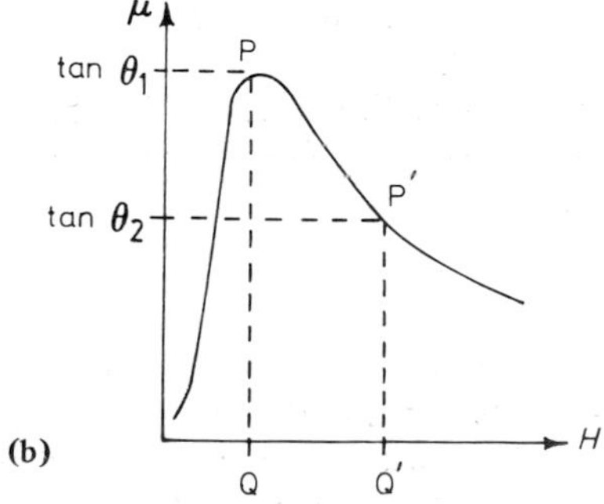

Figure 6.7

Magnetisation curves (or B–H curves) can be drawn for all magnetic materials by plotting measured values of flux density B against magnetising force H, and a typical curve of the B–H relationship is shown in *Figure 6.6.* The theory of the magnetisation process is very complex, but we can get a general picture of what is happening if we regard the ferrous material as made up of a great number of tiny magnets normally distributed in a completely haphazard way. Groups of these diminutive magnets which appear to be present in the core form themselves into clusters or *domains*, each domain having its constituent magnet axes all set in the same direction. When an external magnetising force is applied to the material, the domains gradually align themselves with the field direction and contribute to the flux already present. Hence there is a gradual increase in the flux density as the magnetising force increases.

When a magnetising force is initially applied, those domains having their magnetic axes close to the direction of the field flux align themselves relatively easily and there is a small initial magnetisation of the ferrous core. This preliminary alignment shows up on the B–H curve as a region close to the origin of axes marked A–B in the diagram, though it is here drawn to a greatly exaggerated scale for the sake of illustration. As H is increased more of the domains align themselves with the field and there is a closely linear region on the graph, marked B–C, when this is taking place. Over this region B is proportional to H and so μ_r is sensibly constant. At higher values of H, rotation of the remaining domains occurs, often rather abruptly, so that when this has taken place there is no further increase of B. The material is then said to be *saturated* and the point C which approximates to the turn of the curve is the *saturation point* of the material under test.

If the magnetic field is removed the domains do not entirely revert to their original disorder and so some alignment and hence magnetic flux is retained. This retained magnetism is known as *residual magnetism* and the amount depends upon the material concerned. Soft iron, for example, retains very little magnetism by comparison with hard steel.

At any point P on a magnetisation curve the ratio of B to H is given by the ratio PQ/QO, that is, by tan θ as shown in *Figure 6.7.* If you imagine the point P moving along the magnetisation curve from the origin to the saturation region, the angle θ will at first increase, but will later decrease. This variation represents the change occurring in μ_r as H increases. The curve shown in *Figure 6.7(b)* is derived from the curve in *Figure 6.7(a)* by plotting μ, i.e. tan θ against H. It shows a maximum value for μ which coincides with the steepest part of the magnetisation curve, after which there is a fall in the value of μ which finally becomes very small when the material is fully saturated. Since the ratio B/H =

$\mu_o \mu_r = \mu$, the curve represents the variation in μ_r when drawn to the appropriate axes.

In calculations where flux density is required, the value of μ_r for a particular value of H must be known, and reference is usually made directly to magnetisation curves drawn up for a range of materials in common use. As it is necessary for you to have practice in the plotting of such curves, the following worked example should be carefully followed through.

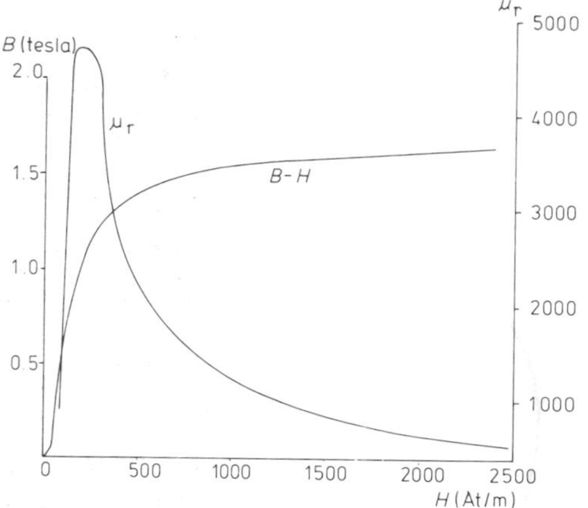

Figure 6.8

Example (7). The following table gives related values of B and H for a specimen of pure iron. Plot the magnetisation curve for this material, and from this curve derive the curve of μ_r against H.

H (At/m)	50	100	200	400	600	800
B (T)	0.05	0.6	1.08	1.34	1.45	1.52

H (At/m)	1000	1200	1400	1600	2000	2400
B (T)	1.54	1.56	1.58	1.59	1.60	1.63

The magnetisation curve of B against H is shown plotted in *Figure 6.8.* The usual rules for plotting graphs must be followed; a large piece of graph paper is necessary, though whether this is in inch squares or metric is not particularly important. What is important is that the scaling of the axes can be fitted conveniently to the divisions of the paper without unnecessary compression along either axis. The full extent of the paper should be used to obtain the greatest clarity and accuracy. Fiddling little sketches are a waste of time.

To derive the curve of μ_r we make use of the expression $\mu_r = B/\mu_o H$. As we have a table of related B and H values we can use this to evaluate the ratio B/H and hence μ_r, knowing that $\mu_o = 4\pi \times 10^{-7}$. If only a magnetisation curve was available to us, we should have to form a table of related B and H values taken from selected points along the curve.

Our new table will be as follows:

B/H	0.001	0.006	0.0054	0.003 35	0.0024	0.0019
$\frac{B}{\mu_0 H}$	796	4775	4297	2666	1910	1512

B/H	0.001 54	0.0013	0.0011	0.0010	0.0008	0.000 68
$\frac{B}{\mu_0 H}$	1194	1034	875	795	637	541

We must now plot values of μ_r (the second line) against magnetising force H, taken from the original table. Our plotting table is then

H	50	100	200	400	600	800
μ_r	796	4775	4297	2666	1910	1512
H	1000	1200	1400	1600	2000	2400
μ_r	1194	1034	875	795	637	541

The graph is plotted on the same horizontal axis of H in *Figure 6.8*.

This curve illustrates the wide variation which occurs in the value of relative permeability as the magnetising force changes. It also shows that there is a maximum value for μ_r which occurs at a relatively low value of H, after which there is a decline as saturation is approached.

MAGNETIC HYSTERESIS

Hysteresis is the name given to a 'lagging' effect displayed by the flux density B whenever there are changes in magnetising force H. If we start off with a piece of unmagnetised ferrous material and increase H in steps from zero, the flux density B will follow the normal magnetisation curve in the manner recently discussed. This is shown as the broken line in *Figure 6.9*. When H becomes sufficiently large the curve will bend over into the saturation region and reach the point A. If H is now slowly reduced, the values taken by B do not retrace themselves along

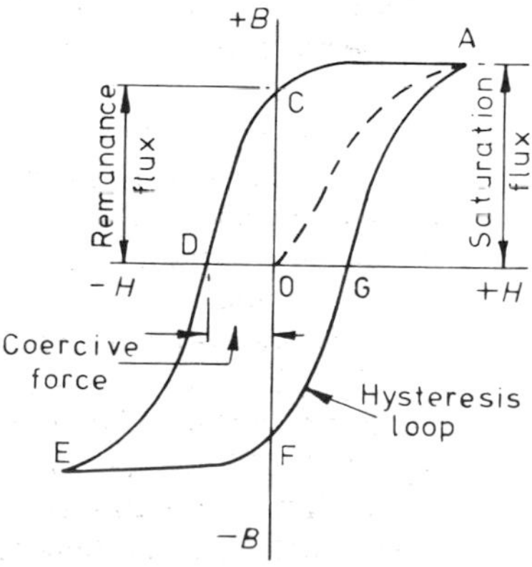

Figure 6.9

the broken line to 0 but remain fairly high until H is almost zero. The residual magnetic intensity at C when H has fallen from the saturation value to zero is called the *remanance flux density*. If now H is reversed and increases in the opposite (or negative) direction, the value of B falls fairly sharply along the curve C–D and at a certain value of $-H$ will become zero at point D. The reversed value of H required to reduce the magnetic intensity from its remanance value OC to zero is called the *coercive force*. Hence the length OD is a measure of the coercive force, just as the length OC is a measure of the remanance flux.

As the value of H continues round the cycle, saturation (in the reverse direction) is again reached at point E, and if H is now again reversed the curve becomes a complete loop ACDEFGA. Throughout the traversing of the cycle, B lags behind H as though the flux was resisting the change that the magnetising force was imposing upon it. This lagging effect is called hysteresis, and the complete magnetisation curve is known as a *hysteresis loop*.

The relative dimensions of the loop and hence its area are not constant but depend upon the magnetic properties of the material and the greatest value of the magnetising force reached.

HYSTERESIS LOSS

Hysteresis results in a dissipation of energy which appears as a heating of the magnetic material. It can be proved that the energy wasted in this way is proportional to the area of the loop, so for small energy loss a small loop area is required.

The dissipation of energy represents the work done in orientating and re-orientating the magnetic domains to follow the imposed variations in H. For magnetic materials which are subject to rapid reversals of magnetism, such as transformer cores, a small loss is essential and it is important that the area of the loop be kept as small as possible. *Figure 6.10* illustrates typical loops for hard steel, soft iron, silicon steel and a ferrite material respectively.

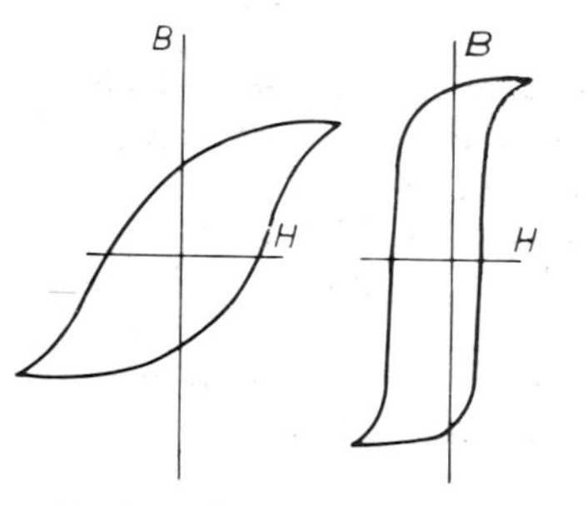

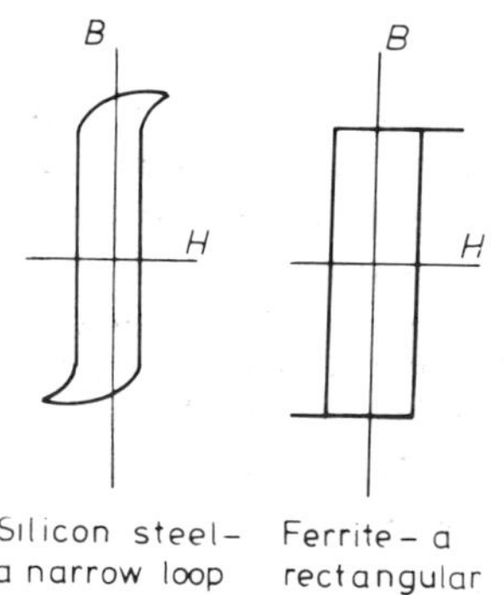

Figure 6.10

(8) Fill in the blank spaces in the following statements:

(a) The unit of flux density is . . . . . .

(b) The force acting between two parallel conductors carrying current is used to define the . . . . . .

(c) The product NI ampere-turns is equivalent to . . . . . .

(d) The permeability of free space is . . . . . . SI units.

(e) Of the four materials mentioned in connection with *Figure 6.10* . . . . would be most suitable for transformer cores.

(f) a material is saturated when increases of . . . . . . no longer result in increases in . . . . . .

(g) The coercivity of a ferrous material would be measured in . . . . . .

(h) The remanance of a ferrous material would be measured in . . . . . .

(9) The following table gives related values for B and H for four different ferrous materials. Plot, to a common base of magnetising force H, the B-H curves for these materials. (Keep these graphs: you will use them in later examples.)

→H	200	400	600	800	1000
Soft iron	1.1	1.35	1.45	1.52	1.54
Silicon iron	0.95	1.19	1.28	1.34	1.36
Cast iron	0.05	0.13	0.20	0.25	0.3
Mild steel	0.10	0.25	0.41	0.60	0.78

	1200	1400	1600	1800	2000
Soft iron	1.56	1.60	1.61	1.62	1.63
Silicon iron	1.37	1.38	1.40	1.41	1.42
Cast iron	0.34	0.38	0.42	0.46	0.5
Mild steel	0.91	1.01	1.11	1.20	1.25

PROBLEMS FOR SECTION 6

Group 1

(10) The absolute permeability of a piece of iron is 3.142×10^{-4}. What is its relative permeability?

(11) What is the flux density in a magnetic field of cross-sectional area 30 cm^2 having a flux of 1.75 mWb?

(12) When an electromagnet produces a flux of 350 μWb, the flux density is 0.3 T. Calculate the cross-sectional area of the core.

(13) Two overhead power cables, each 1 km long, are spaced 6 m apart and carry currents of 500 A. What is the total force acting between the cables?

(14) The force acting between two parallel conductors which carry equal currents is found to be 0.05 N. If the conductors are spaced 20 cm apart, what current does each carry?

(15) A solenoid, 30 cm long, is wound with 1000 turns of wire. When the coil carries a current of 1.5 A, what is the field strength inside the solenoid?

(16) A solenoid, 10 cm long, is wound with 450 turns of wire. What current is required to establish a magnetising force of 2250 At/m inside the solenoid?

(17) A magnetising force of 410 At/m produces a flux density of 1.2 T in a sample of silicon iron. What is the relative permeability of the iron under this condition?

Group 2

(18) Calculate the magnetising force and the m.m.f. required to produce a flux density of 0.15 T in an air gap of length 5 cm.

(19) Determine the flux density produced by an m.m.f. of 8000 At applied to an air gap of length 1.5 cm.

(20) An air gap between two pole pieces is 0.5 cm in length and the area of the flux path across the gap is 10 cm^2. What m.m.f. is necessary to produce a flux of 0.65 mWb in the gap?

(21) Determine the value of the relative permeability of the following specimens under the given conditions:

Wrought iron: B = 1.6 T, H = 3500 At/m
Cast iron: B = 0.75 T, H = 6000 At/m
Silicon iron: B = 1.0 T, H = 450 At/m

(22) Show that the force acting between two parallel conductors spaced d metres apart in air and carrying currents I_1 and I_2 respectively is given by

$$F = 2 \times 10^{-7} \times \frac{I_1 \times I_2}{d} \text{ N}$$

(23) Three conductors A, B and C lying parallel in the same plane are spaced 10 cm apart in air. Determine the force per metre on each conductor if, taking them in order, A and C carry 3000 A each in one direction, when B carries 6000 A in the opposite direction.

7 Electromagnetic induction

Aims: At the end of this Unit section you should be able to:
State Faraday's laws of electromagnetic induction.
State Lenz's law.
Describe the production of an induced e.m.f. due to a changing magnetic field.
Explain the motor and the generator principle.
State the effects of self- and mutual inductance.
Describe the principle of the transformer.
Calculate the energy stored in a magnetic field.

There are two laws relating to electromagnetic induction, those of Faraday and of Lenz.

Faraday's law states: (a) whenever the magnetic flux linking with an electrical circuit is changing in magnitude, an e.m.f. is induced in the circuit; (b) the magnitude of the induced e.m.f. is directly proportional to the rate of change of flux linkages, or to the rate at which the flux is cut.

Lenz's law states: the direction of the induced e.m.f. is such as to *oppose* the change producing it.

We will examine each of these laws in turn.

When a change of flux occurs and that flux links with a conductor, whether in the form of a straight length of wire, or a solenoid, an e.m.f. is produced in the conductor. There has been a change in the linkages which the lines of magnetic flux are making with the conductor. In *Figure 7.1(a)* a magnet, for example, has been thrust into the coil of wire. While the magnet is actually *moving* relative to the coil, the magnetic flux affects the free electrons in the wire and they tend to move to one end or other of the coil. The direction in which they move, and hence the direction in which the induced e.m.f. acts at the terminals, depends upon whether the flux is emanating from a North pole or a South pole of the magnet and whether the flux is increasing or decreasing in intensity. There will be no induced e.m.f. if the magnet is stationary.

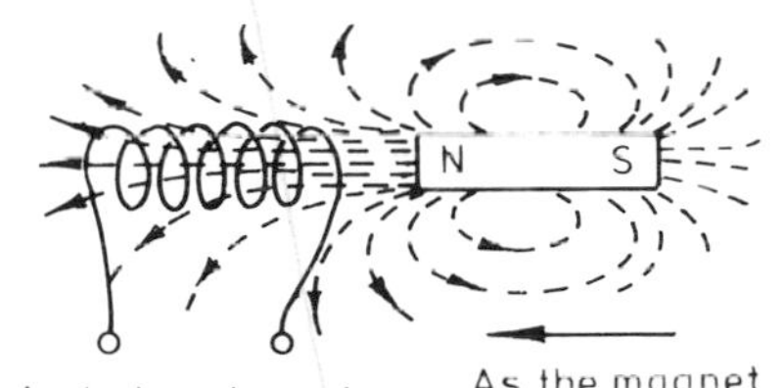

(a)

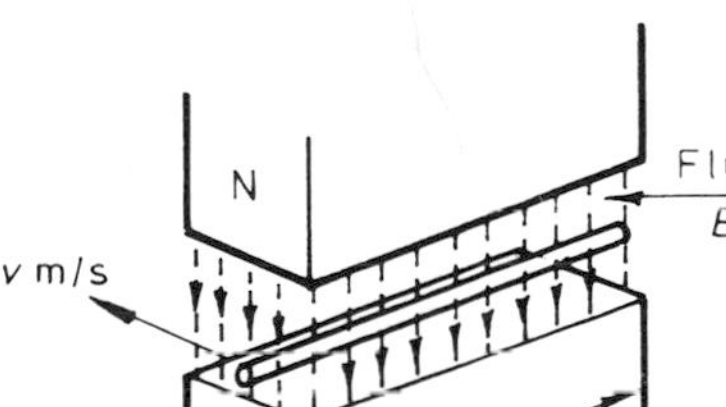

(b)

Figure 7.1

In *Figure 7.1(b)* the relative motion of conductor and magnetic flux has been reversed. This time a straight piece of wire is moved through a fixed magnetic field. The effect is exactly as it was for the previous case: an e.m.f. is induced between the ends of the wire so long as it is moving relative to the magnetic lines of flux. This then explains the meaning of the first of Faraday's laws.

The second law tells us that the magnitude of the induced e.m.f. is proportional to the *rate* at which the flux is cut. Clearly, the rate of cutting will depend upon the velocity with which the conductor moves through the field. Faraday's law tells us that if we double the velocity we shall double the induced e.m.f. and so on proportionally. Also, the magnitude of the e.m.f. must depend upon the field density B (since more lines will be cut for a given velocity of movement), and also upon the length of the conductor actually within the field. In *Figure 7.1(b)* the active length of the conductor is ℓ metres and it is moving at a velocity of v m/s at right-angles to the magnetic flux B. In 1 s the conductor cuts through an area $v\ell$ m^2 and the flux cut by the conductor is $Bv\ell$ Wb. Therefore the rate of change of flux linkages equals $Bv\ell$ Wb/s and the induced e.m.f.

$$e = Bv\ell \text{ volts}$$

We have already noted in the previous section that flux is not measured in terms of lines but in terms of the induced e.m.f. The unit of magnetic flux can be defined as follows: when unit flux of 1 Wb links with a circuit of 1 turn in 1 s, or when a conductor cuts flux at the rate of 1 Wb/s, an induced e.m.f. of 1 V appears in the circuit. Hence

$$1 \text{ Wb} = 1 \text{ V} \times 1 \text{ s}$$

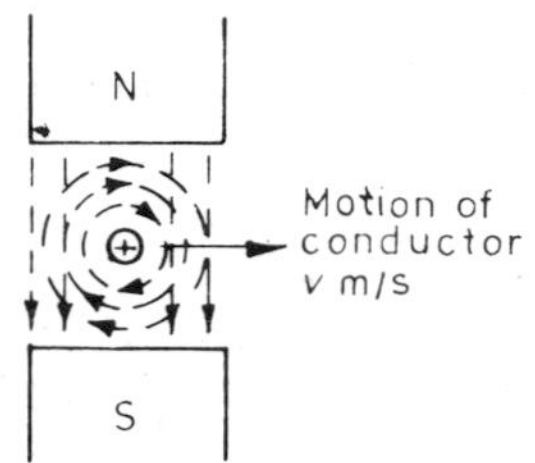

Figure 7.2

Lenz's law states that the direction of the induced e.m.f. is such as to *oppose* the change producing it. The direction of the e.m.f. and of the resulting current flow in the case of the conductor forming part of a closed circuit may therefore be determined by considering Lenz's law. Suppose the conductor, seen in cross section in *Figure 7.2*, moves to the right and a current flows in it as the result of the induced e.m.f. Then this current will set up its own concentric rings of flux surrounding the conductor. These lines are shown superimposed on the main field lines in the diagram; so as the conductor moves to the right there is an increase in the flux on its left and a decrease on its right. The current which flows then produces its own lines in such a direction that the change is opposed, i.e. they attempt to decrease the flux on the left and increase it on the right. This will happen if the direction of action of the concentric lines is clockwise. Hence the direction of current flow, and the direction of the induced e.m.f. must be *into the page* as the cross on the end of the conductor indicates.

Example (1). A conductor of length 0.25 m moves at right-angles to a magnetic field of flux density 0.1 T at a velocity of 5 m/s. What will be the e.m.f. induced across the conductor ends?

Induced e.m.f. $= e = Bv\ell$ V

$= 0.1 \times 5 \times 0.25$

$= 0.125$ V

We have assumed so far that the conductor moves through the field perpendicularly to the lines of magnetic flux. The next example deals with the situation where the conductor moves through the field at some angle other than 90°.

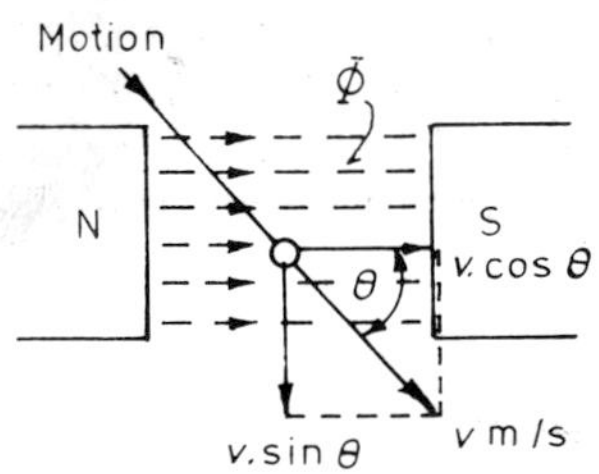

Figure 7.3

Example (2). A conductor moves with a velocity of 20 m/s at an angle of 60° to a magnetic field produced between two square-faced poles of side length 0.015 m. If the flux on the pole face is 0.5 μWb, find the magnitude of the induced e.m.f.

Figure 7.3 illustrates the situation. As the conductor is moving at an angle to the flux lines, the rate at which the flux is cut will be *less* than it would be if the direction of motion was at right-angles to the field. The e.m.f. is generated only by the *component* of the velocity which is perpendicular to the flux, and from the figure this is clearly equal to $v \sin\theta$, where θ is the angle between the direction of the flux and the direction of motion. Hence

Induced e.m.f. = e = $B\ell v.\sin 60°$ V

We now require B:

$$B = \frac{\Phi}{A} = \frac{0.5 \times 10^{-6}}{0.015 \times 0.015} = 0.0022 \text{ T}$$

$$\therefore e = 0.0022 \times 0.015 \times 20 \times 0.866$$

$$= 0.000\,58 \text{ V } (0.58 \text{ mV})$$

You should now be able to tackle the next two problems on your own.

(3) An e.m.f. of 0.25 V is induced in a conductor of length 12 cm which is moved perpendicularly to a magnetic flux of 0.5 T. What is the velocity of the conductor?

(4) A conductor, length 0.2 m, is driven at 2.5 m/s at an angle of 30° to a magnetic flux having a uniform density of 1.5 T. Calculate the induced e.m.f. What will the e.m.f. be when the flux density is halved and the velocity increased by 50%?

THE GENERATOR PRINCIPLE

Since the direction of the induced current is such that it opposes motion in the field (Lenz's law), it is natural for us to expect that energy must be expended in order to move a conductor through a field. It is, in fact, simply because we are expending energy to generate an electric current in this way that opposition to the mechanical movement of the conductor occurs. We are not getting something for nothing. We get our electricity in *exchange* for the work we have to do pushing the conductor through the field.

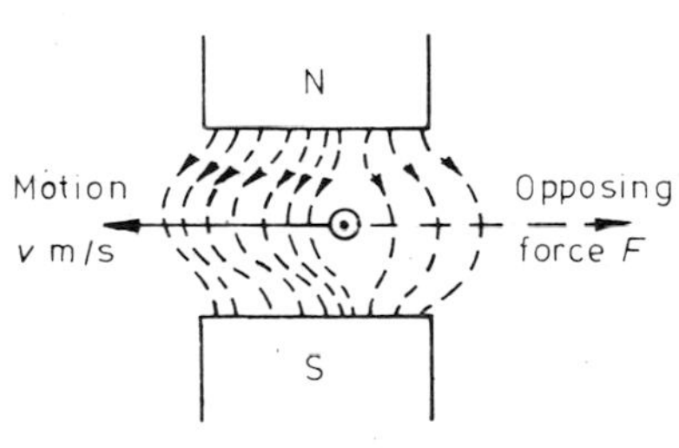

Figure 7.4

Look at *Figure 7.4*. Here a conductor is moving in a field, the generated e.m.f. being $Bv\ell$ V and the result circuit current I A. The magnetic field which is the resultant at any instant of the field lines and the concentric lines around the conductor due to the current is shown in the figure, and this field produces a force F N which opposes the motion; we are pushing against the 'resistance' of the crowded lines of flux on the left of the figure, as it were. To maintain the motion at a velocity v m/s and so generate electrical power eI W, a mechanical driving force must be applied in the direction of motion. Mechanical power is then transformed into electrical power and we have an elementary electrical generator or dynamo. Now

$$\text{Mechanical work done per second} = Fv \text{ J}$$
$$= Fv \text{ W}$$

So for an output power of eI W we must have

$$Fv = eI$$

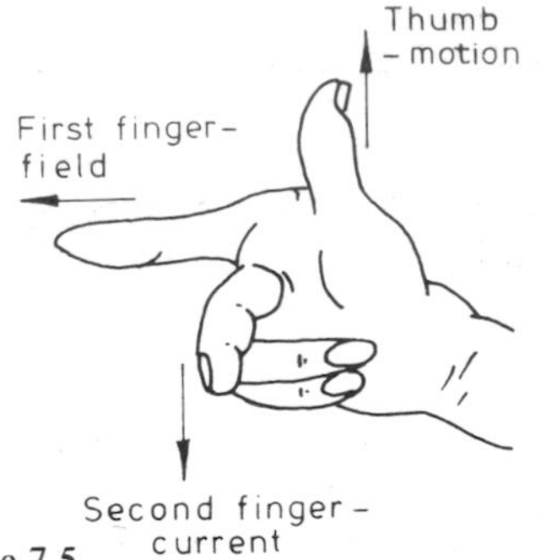

Figure 7.5

But $e = Bv\ell$ $\therefore$ $Fv = Bv\ell I$

and so $F = BI\ell$ N

There is a convenient rule for remembering the relative directions of the field, the motion and the induced e.m.f. (or current) when a generator is being considered. This is known as *Fleming's right hand rule* (or the geneRator rule) which states that if the thumb, first and second fingers of the right hand are extended mutually at right-angles, the First finger being parallel to the *f*ield and thuMb parallel to the direction of *m*otion, then the seCond finger will indicate the direction in which the induced e.m.f. will act and the *c*urrent flow. *Figure 7.5* illustrates this rule for you.

THE MOTOR PRINCIPLE

If a conductor placed in a magnetic field receives current, not as a result of its motion in the field, but from an external source, it will experience a mechanical force tending to move it out of the field. The result now is that the crowding of the lines on the left of the diagram tend to push the conductor towards the weaker part of the field on the right; hence, if it is allowed to do so, the conductor will move in that direction.

This is the motor principle where electrical power is transformed into mechanical motion, so this time we have an elementary electric motor.

Let the conductor move a distance d metres at right-angles to the field under the action of the force. Then

$$\text{Work done} = \text{Force} \times \text{Distance}$$

$$= BI\ell \times d \text{ J (newton-metres)}$$

But ℓd is the area A swept out by the conductor, hence

$$\text{Work done} = BIA \text{ J}$$

$$= \Phi I \text{ J, since } \Phi = BA$$

$$\text{Then work done} = \text{Flux cut (Wb)} \times \text{Current (A)}$$

The direction of the force this time can be found from *Fleming's left hand rule* which relates the Field with the *f*irst finger, the *c*urrent with the seCond finger and the thuMb with the *m*otion (force direction).

Example (5). A conductor lying perpendicular to a magnetic field of flux density 0.3 T carries a current of 100 A. Find the force acting on the conductor in newtons per metre run.

$$F = BI\ell \text{ N}$$

$$= 0.3 \times 100 \times 1 \text{ when } \ell = 1 \text{ m}$$

$$\therefore F = 30 \text{ N per metre run}$$

(6) A conductor of length 18 cm is required to exert a force of 10 N when situated in a field of flux density 1.2 T. What must be the current in the conductor?

(7) Complete the following statements:

(a) The induced e.m.f. is proportional to the . . . . . of flux linkages.

(b) The direction of the force on a current-carrying conductor is determined by the use of Fleming's . . . . . rule.

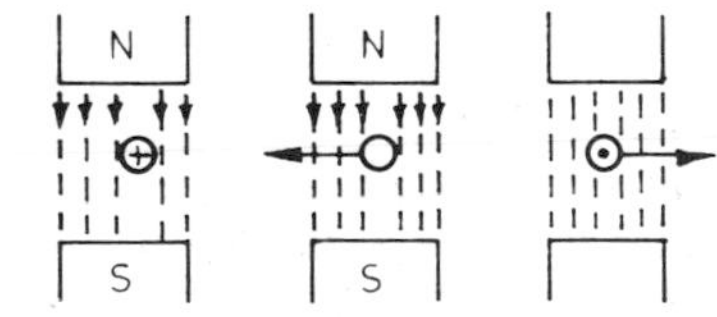

Figure 7.6

(c) All other things being equal, the greatest e.m.f. is induced when the conductor cuts flux at . . . . .

(d) Volts × seconds = ...

(8) In each of the diagrams of *Figure 7.6* fill in the missing quantity in the *generation* of an e.m.f.

SELF-INDUCTANCE

We have learned that a flow of current in a circuit is accompanied by a flux linking with the circuit. A change in the current causes a change in flux linkages and so, by Faraday's law, an e.m.f. is induced in the circuit. This is called the *self-induced e.m.f.* or the e.m.f. of *self-induction*. If the current is increasing the direction of the e.m.f. will be such as to oppose the increase. If the current is decreasing the e.m.f. will tend to maintain it at its original level. This is in accordance with Lenz's law. The effects of self-induction are felt *only* when the current is changing, so we may consider that an electrical circuit has a property which opposes *current change*, as well as resistance which simply opposes current flow. We define this opposition which results from the action of a self-induced e.m.f. as the *self-inductance*, or simply the *inductance*, of the circuit.

When unit flux, 1 Wb, links with a circuit of 1 turn in 1 s, an e.m.f. of 1 V is induced in the circuit. So a flux of Φ Wb linking with a coil of N turns in t seconds will induce an e.m.f.

$$e = \frac{\Phi N}{t} \text{ V}$$

and by our definition, the number of flux linkages will be

$$\frac{\Phi N}{t} = N.\frac{\Phi}{t} \text{ Wb } t/\text{s}$$

The ratio Φ/t represents the average rate of change of flux with respect to time (Wb/s). Now we may write

$$e = N.\frac{\Phi}{t} = N\left[\frac{\Phi}{I} \times \frac{I}{t}\right]$$

where the ratio Φ/I is constant for an air-cored coil since Φ is proportional to I; and the ratio I/t is the average rate of change of current, A/s.

$$\therefore\ e = \frac{\Phi N}{t} = \frac{\Phi N}{I} \times \text{Rate of change of current}$$

The factor $\Phi N/I$ is called the *inductance* of the coil and is denoted by the letter L.

Hence the e.m.f. of self-induction $e = L \times$ Rate of change of I.

It should perhaps be mentioned here that this expression is often seen preceded by a negative sign, i.e. $e = -L \times (I/t)$. This is put in simply to remind us that the e.m.f. is opposing the change. It can normally be dispensed with in general calculations.

The unit of inductance is the *henry* (H), and it is defined by considering unit values in the above expression:

A circuit has an inductance of 1 H when an e.m.f. of 1 V is induced in it by a current changing at the rate of 1 A/s.

Example (9). A coil is wound with 1000 turns and a current of 5 A flowing in the coil produces a flux of 60 μWb. What is the inductance of the coil?

$$L = \frac{\Phi N}{I}$$

$$= \frac{60 \times 10^{-6} \times 1000}{5} \text{ H}$$

$$= 0.012 \text{ H}$$

Example (10). When a current of 3 A in a coil collapses uniformly to zero in 0.05 s, the induced e.m.f. is 500 V. What is the coil inductance?

The current changes by 3 A in 0.05 s. Its rate of change is therefore

$$3 \times \frac{1}{0.05} = 60 \text{ A/s}$$

$$L = \frac{\text{Induced e.m.f.}}{\text{Rate of change of current}}$$

$$= \frac{500}{60} = 8.33 \text{ H}$$

The inductance of a circuit obviously depends upon the form it takes and the opportunity there is for the flux to link with as much of the circuit as possible. A straight length of wire is only slightly inductive, but if it is wound into a compact coil with a great number of turns, the inductance is greatly increased. If an iron core is inserted in the coil the flux density is multiplied by a factor μ_r, and in this case very high values of inductance, up to many hundreds of henries, can be obtained.

(11) A coil having an inductance of 50 mH is carrying a current of 100 A. What is the self-induced e.m.f. when the current is (a) reduced to zero in 0.075 s, (b) reversed in 0.05 s?

(12) An average e.m.f. of 100 V is induced in a coil of 0.5 H when a current of 5 A is reversed. In what time did the current reverse?

INDUCTANCE OF A COIL

With certain restrictions we can obtain the inductance of a solenoid or coil in terms of its physical dimensions and the number of turns. You will recall that the magnetising force inside the solenoid is expressed as $H = NI/\ell$. Also $B = \mu_0 H$ and $\Phi = BA$.

From these we can obtain

$$\Phi = BA = \mu_0 HA$$

$$= \frac{\mu_0 NIA}{\ell} \qquad \text{since } H = \frac{NI}{\ell}$$

$$\text{But} \quad L = \frac{N\Phi}{I}$$

$$= \frac{N}{I} \times \frac{\mu_0 NIA}{\ell}$$

$$L = \frac{\mu_0 A}{\ell} . N^2 \ \text{H}$$

This result shows that for an air-cored solenoid the inductance L is *proportional to* N^2.

Mutual inductance

The magnetic flux which induces an e.m.f. in a coil need not come from a moving magnet; it can equally well be produced by a current flowing in a second coil placed in close proximity to the first. *Figure 7.7* shows a suitable arrangement. Here a voltage V_1 produces a current I_1 in the coil L_1. The resulting flux Φ links with itself and also with the adjacent coil L_2. Thus, when current I_1 changes, it produces a change in the flux linking with L_2 and an e.m.f. is induced in the second coil. As the only common factor between the coils is the flux Φ, the circuits are said to have the property of *mutual inductance*, and to be *mutually coupled* together.

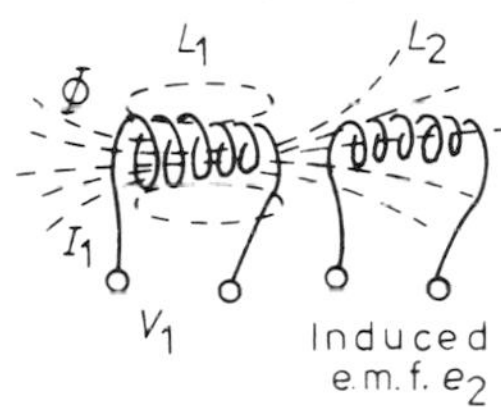

Figure 7.7

The unit of mutual inductance, like self-inductance, is the henry, and mutual inductance is defined as 1 H when an e.m.f. of 1 V is induced in the second coil by a current changing at the rate of 1 A/s in the first coil. It is common practice to call the first and second coils in such an arrangement the *primary* and *secondary* windings respectively.

As for the case of self-inductance it is not very difficult to show:

Secondary e.m.f. $e_2 = M \times$ Rate of change of primary current

where M is the mutual inductance.

> (13) What is the mutual inductance between two coils when a current of 5 A in one of them, being suddenly switched off, falls to zero in 0.01 s, and induces an e.m.f. of 1 V in the other?

THE TRANSFORMER PRINCIPLE

A transformer consists basically of two coupled insulated windings wound upon a closed iron core. The core, being a closed loop, carries almost all of the flux generated by a changing current in one of the coils, so that as *Figure 7.8* shows, the same flux links with the turns of the other coil and so induces the greatest possible e.m.f. The coils are referred to respectively as the primary and the secondary windings and they are wound usually either side by side or one on top of the other, the reason being to make the coupling between them as tight as possible.

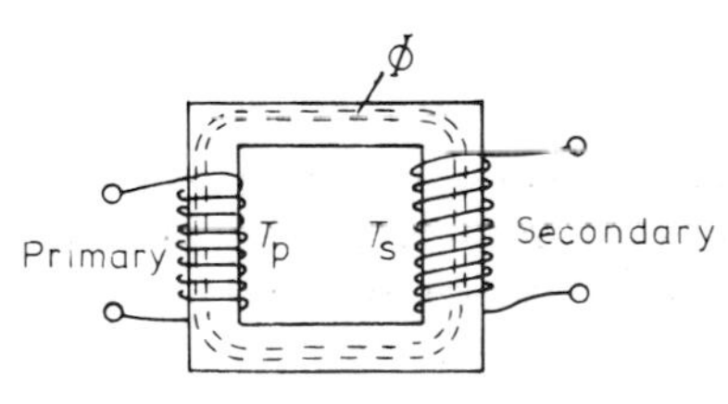

Figure 7.8

Let the number of turns on the primary and secondary coils be T_p and T_s respectively, and let an alternating voltage (that is, a voltage which is rapidly changing its direction) be applied to the primary so that the current and the flux Φ will also be alternating. The changing flux links with both windings and e.m.f.s are induced in both of them. If the transformer is ideally made so that all the flux generated by the primary cuts all the turns of the secondary, the induced *e.m.f. per turn* will be the same for both of them. The e.m.f. induced in the secondary will therefore be greater than, equal to or less than the e.m.f. induced in the primary according as to whether the secondary has more, the same or less turns than the primary respectively.

Flux Φ linking with turns T_p induces e.m.f. $e_1 = \dfrac{\Phi T_p}{t}$

Flux Φ linking with turns T_s induces e.m.f. $e_2 = \dfrac{\Phi T_s}{t}$

$$\therefore \text{Ratio } \frac{e_2}{e_1} = \frac{\Phi T_s}{\Phi T_p} = \frac{T_s}{T_p} = \text{Transformation ratio } N$$

As we shall learn in due course, e_1 is equal, but opposite in sign, to the applied primary voltage V_1, and clearly e_2 = the output voltage V_2 at the secondary terminals. Hence

$$V_2 = \frac{T_s}{T_p} \times V_1 = NV_1$$

When the secondary has fewer windings than the primary, N is less than one and the transformer *steps-down* the voltage. When the secondary has more turns that the primary, N is greater than 1 and the transformer *steps-up* the voltage. The terms step-up and step-down refer to the voltage transformation. When a load is connected to the secondary terminals, a secondary current I_2 will flow and power will be delivered to the load. Since for a perfectly efficient transformer $I_1 T_p = I_2 T_s$, an increase in voltage from primary to secondary must be accompanied by a *decrease* in the current between primary and secondary, and conversely. The ratio of primary to secondary current is therefore inversely proportional to the turns ratio N, that is

$$I_2 = \frac{T_p}{T_s} \times I_1 = \frac{1}{N} . I_1$$

(14) A transformer has 1000 primary and 3500 secondary turns. If the alternating primary voltage is 240 V, find the secondary voltage.

(15) A transformer has a transformation ratio of 5, and a 1000 Ω resistor is connected across its secondary terminals. If the primary alternating voltage is 10 V, find the secondary voltage and the currents flowing in both primary and secondary windings.

ENERGY STORED IN AN INDUCTANCE

Energy from the supply is required to create a magnetic field. When the field collapses this energy is given up in some form or other, often as a spark at the contacts of the switch breaking the circuit.

Suppose a current rises to I A in a time t in an inductance. Then

Average rate of change of current $= \dfrac{I}{t}$ A/s

Average induced e.m.f. $= L.\dfrac{I}{t}$ V

$$\text{Average current flowing in time } t \text{ s} = \frac{I}{2} \text{ A}$$

$$\text{Energy} = \text{Voltage} \times \text{Current} \times \text{Time}$$

$$= L.\frac{I}{t} \times \frac{I}{2} \times t \text{ J}$$

$$= \frac{1}{2}LI^2 \text{ J}$$

We have assumed for simplicity that the current built up uniformly in the circuit, but you may accept that the result obtained is true however the current rises.

The energy is stored in the magnetic field all the time the field is established. When the field collapses, less energy is returned to the circuit than was supplied during the build up of the field.

Example (16). Why is less energy returned when the field collapses?

Some of the energy is dissipated as heat in overcoming the resistance of the inductance windings - all conductors have resistance, remember. This resistive heat loss has to be made good from the supply at all times, irrespective of the stored energy in the field.

PROBLEMS FOR SECTION 7

Group 1

(17) A straight conductor 15 cm long moves at a speed of 10 m/s in a direction perpendicular to a magnetic field of flux density 0.5 T. Calculate the e.m.f. induced in the conductor.

(18) What is the effective length of a conductor which moves at a velocity of 250 cm/s at right-angles to a magnetic field of density 0.45 T, if the induced e.m.f. is 2 V?

(19) A straight conductor of effective length 0.3 m is moved, in turn, at various angles to the direction of a magnetic field of density 0.5 T. The angles in degrees are respectively 0, 30, 45, 60, 90, 120, 135, 150 and 180. If the velocity of the conductor is 5 m/s in each case, calculate the induced e.m.f.s and plot a graph of e.m.f. against a base of angle.

(20) Calculate the force acting on a 1 m length of conductor carrying a current of 10 A, if it is (a) perpendicular, (b) inclined at 30°, (c) parallel to a field of flux density 0.01 T.

(21) Two parallel wires spaced 5 cm apart each carry a current of 200 A. Calculate the force acting between them per metre run.

(22) A current of 4 A flowing in a solenoid of 1600 turns sets up a flux of 4.8 μWb. What is the inductance of the solenoid?

(23) A current of 3 A flows in a coil of 2500 turns. If the inductance of the coil is 0.5 H under this condition, find the value of the magnetic flux.

(24) The current in a coil changes from 10 A to 2 A in a time of 0.1 s. If the inductance of the coil is 1.5 H, what is the induced e.m.f.?

(25) The coils of an electric bell have an inductance of 1.2 H and carry a current of 250 mA. When the circuit is broken the e.m.f. induced in the coils is 50 V. In what time does the current fall to zero?

(26) Calculate the inductance of a coil of 100 turns wound on a non-magnetic ring having a mean circumference of 60 cm and a cross-sectional area of 12 cm^2.

Group 2

(27) The current flowing through a coil is suddenly changed so that the flux linking the turns is increased by 3 mWb in 0.1 s. If the coil is wound with 800 turns, calculate the induced e.m.f.

(28) A solenoid is 0.5 m in length and has a mean diameter of 20 cm. If it is wound with 1500 turns, calculate (a) the inductance, (b) the total flux if a current of 4 A flows, (c) the energy then stored in the magnetic field.

(29) A rectangular coil of 100 turns is rotated about a vertical axis at a constant rate of 50 rev/s in a magnetic field of density 0.2 T which is perpendicular to the axis of the coil. What is the greatest value of e.m.f. induced in the coil if the active length of each coil side is 10 cm and the coil sides are 3 cm from the axis?

(30) What is the mutual inductance between two coils when a current of 1 A in one of them, being suddenly switched off and falling to zero in 0.05 s, induces an e.m.f. of 2 V in the other?

(31) A double wound transformer of ratio 5 : 1 is to supply 50 V at 20 A at the secondary terminals. What voltage must be applied at the primary terminals, and what primary current will be drawn from the supply?

(32) A 400-660 V transformer has 2500 turns on the secondary winding. How many turns are there on the primary coil?

(33) The primary winding of a transformer is connected to a 240 V supply. If the ratio of primary to secondary turns is 15 : 2, calculate the primary and secondary currents when a lamp rated at 100 W is connected to the secondary terminals.

8 Alternating voltages and currents

Aims: At the end of this Unit section you should be able to:
Define the terms amplitude, period and frequency.
Understand the meaning of instantaneous, peak, average and r.m.s. values of an alternating waveform.
State the principle of the simple a.c. generator.
Use phasor and algebraic representation of sinusoidal quantities.
Determine the resultant of the addition of two sinusoidal quantities by graphical and phasor representation.

A current or voltage which is continually changing in direction is known as an alternating current or voltage, and a graph plotted to show how such a quantity changes with time shows what is called the *waveform* of that quantity. Two alternating currents, each having a different waveform, are shown by the two graphs of *Figure 8.1*. The currents increase to a maximum value in one direction before falling to zero, they then increase to a maximum value in the opposite direction before again falling to zero. We shall consider cases like those illustrated where the two maximum values are the same in each direction. One complete series of changes is called a *cycle*. In the figure the horizontal axis OT is a time axis, and in each case the time Ot is called the *period* or the *periodic time* of the waveform. One complete cycle of the alternation occurs in the periodic time.

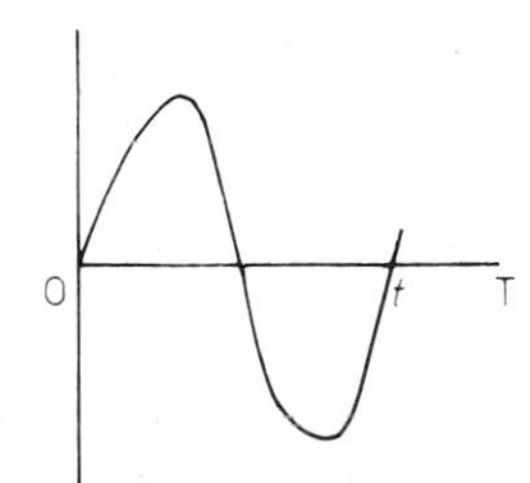

(a)

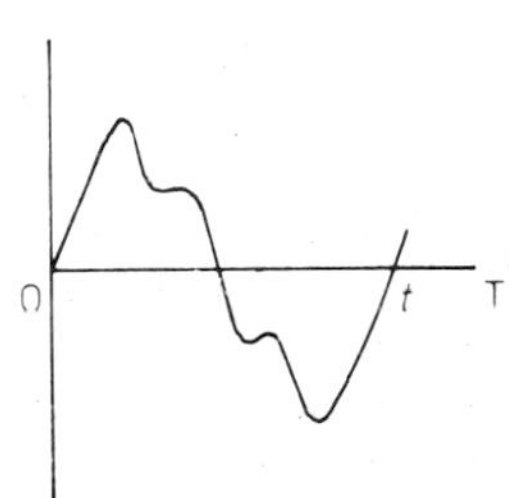

(b)

Figure 8.1

The number of complete cycles occurring per second is called the *frequency*. The unit for frequency is the *hertz* (Hz), and 1 Hz = 1 cycle per second.

Clearly from our definitions

$$\text{Frequency } f\,(\text{Hz}) = \frac{1}{\text{Periodic time } T}$$

(1) What is the period of the mains supply, frequency 50 Hz?

(2) What is the frequency of a radio transmission if the period of the signal is 2 μs? Give your answer in kHz, where 1 kHz = 1000 Hz.

The greatest value reached by the current or voltage in either half-cycle of the waveform is known as the *maximum* or *peak value*, denoted either by I_m or $\hat{I}$ in the case of current, or by V_m or $\hat{V}$ in the case of voltage.

The instantaneous value of the current (or voltage) is that value which represents the current (or voltage) at any stated instant of time. This can be any value between the limits $+\hat{I}$ and $-\hat{I}$ for current (or $+\hat{V}$ and $-\hat{V}$ for voltage), including zero, but the actual instant of time must be stated for an actual value to be calculated. Instantaneous values are indicated by small letters – for example, instantaneous current is represented by i.

For the moment we are interested only in the sinusoidal waveform

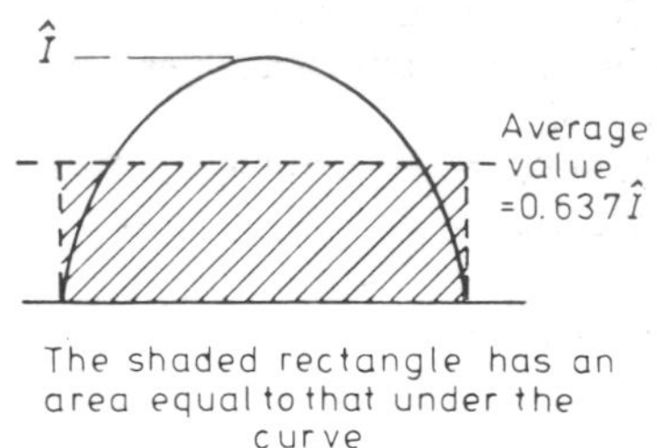

Figure 8.2

which is the form illustrated in *Figure 8.1(a)*, although you might bear in mind that all repetitive waves can be expressed as combinations of sinusoidal waves. If we consider a half-cycle of a sinusoidal wave as shown in *Figure 8.2* having a peak value $\hat{I}$, there is clearly an average or mean value to the current taken over the half-cycle period. Taken over a *complete* cycle the average value is zero, but if the wave is rectified (see Unit Section 12) so that it is made to flow in one direction only, the resulting fluctuating but unidirectional current will be equivalent in its effect to an average current having a value equal to the height of the broken line in the figure. If can be proved that the average height of a sine wave is equal to $2/\pi$ of the peak value, or about $0.637\hat{I}$.

MEASUREMENT OF ALTERNATING QUANTITIES

How should we measure alternating quantities like current and voltage? Clearly, a statement of the instantaneous value is of no practical use, and although it may at first appear promising, a statement of the average value is of little practical use either. If we are going to have a consistent system, we must relate the power that a certain alternating current, for example, will dissipate in a given circuit to the power that an equivalent direct current will dissipate in the same circuit. Based on the dissipation of energy, this is the value normally used for current and voltage measurement in a.c. circuits. It is called the *effective* value or the *root-mean-square* (r.m.s.) value of the alternating quantity.

When the instantaneous value of the current i flowing in a resistor R dissipates power, the instantaneous power is i^2R W. In *Figure 8.3* a current wave is shown in full line with its power waveform shown in broken line. Notice that the power waveform is wholly positive, since i^2 is positive whether i itself is positive or negative. Power dissipation in a resistance is *unaffected by the direction of current flow*. The shaded area under the power curve represents energy since it is the product of power and time; the average value of the power curve thus represents the effective power dissipated over one complete cycle.

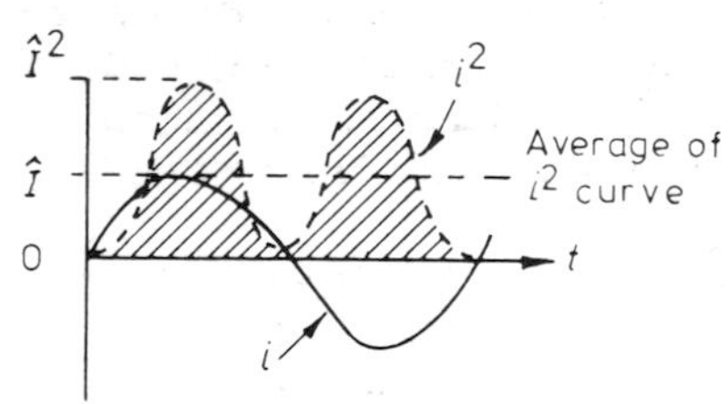

Figure 8.3

Let I be the *equivalent* direct current which when flowing through the same resistance R dissipates the same amount of power as the alternating current, i.e.

$$\text{Power} = I^2R \text{ W}$$

Then

$$I^2R = \text{average of the } i^2R \text{ values}$$

Since R is the same on both sides of this equality, we have

$$I^2 = \text{average of the } i^2 \text{ values}$$

so that

$$I = \sqrt{\text{average of the } i^2 \text{ values}}$$

which is the root of the mean (average) squared values of i, hence the 'root-mean-square value'.

From the figure, the mean value of the i^2 curve is $\hat{I}^2/2$, hence

$$\text{r.m.s. current } I = \sqrt{\frac{\hat{I}^2}{2}} = \frac{\hat{I}}{\sqrt{2}} = 0.707\hat{I}$$

Similarly

$$\text{r.m.s. voltage} = 0.707\hat{V}$$

Remember, these results are true *only* for sinusoidal waves.

The r.m.s. value is always implied when alternating quantities are given unless the contrary is expressly stated.

It is sometimes necessary to know the relationships between the peak, average and r.m.s. values of sinusoidal waveform:

The ratio $\frac{\text{Peak value}}{\text{r.m.s. value}}$ is the *peak factor*

The ratio $\frac{\text{r.m.s. value}}{\text{Average value}}$ is the *form factor*

You should be able to deduce that peak factor = $\sqrt{2}$ = 1.414, and that form factor = 1.11.

(3) An alternating current has a peak value of 10 A. What is its average and r.m.s. value?

(4) The r.m.s. value of mains electricity supply is 240 V. What is the peak value?

THE A.C. GENERATOR PRINCIPLE

Let a single-turn coil of rectangular shape be rotated with constant angular velocity in a uniform magnetic field, its axis of revolution being at right-angles to the magnetic flux, as shown in *Figure 8.4*. As the coil rotates, the cutting of the flux will be a continuous process and an e.m.f. will be induced in the side conductors of the coil as long as the rotation goes on. The magnitude of the e.m.f., however, will depend upon the instantaneous position of the coil as it is only the component of coil velocity *perpendicular* to the field lines which results in a generated

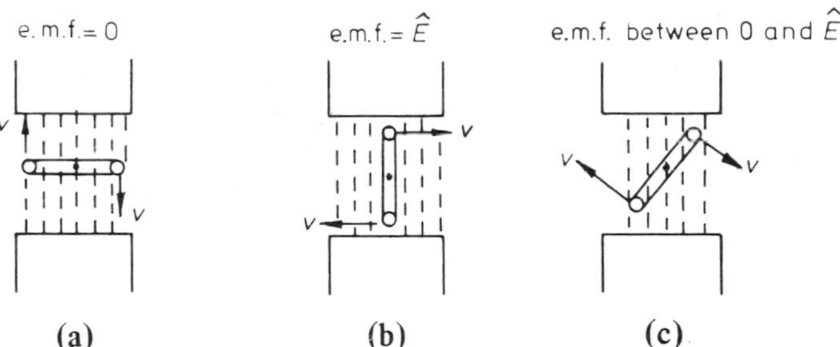

Figure 8.4

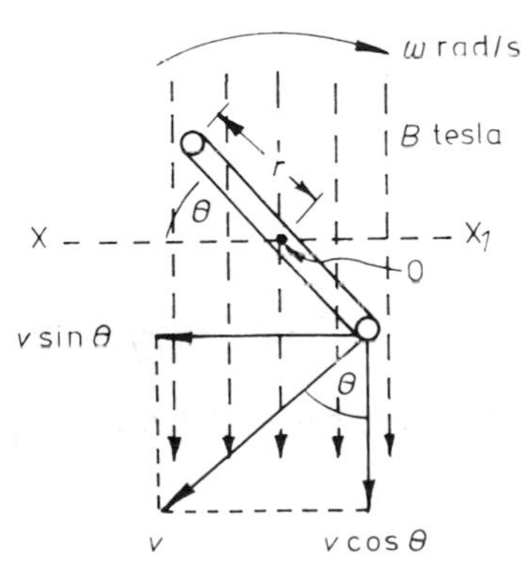

Figure 8.5

e.m.f. *Figure 8.4* shows three different positions of the coil: at (a) the side conductors are instantaneously moving parallel to the flux lines, hence no e.m.f. is being induced. At (b) the conductors are instantaneously moving perpendicularly to the flux lines, hence the maximum e.m.f. is being induced. Obviously (c) represents some intermediate position where the induced e.m.f. lies between zero and $\hat{E}$. *Figure 8.5* shows this general position in more detail.

The instantaneous induced e.m.f. is

$$e = B\ell v \text{ V}$$

where B is the field density and ℓ the length of conductor actively cutting the flux. Only the component of velocity v perpendicular to the flux lines will generate an e.m.f. and from the figure this is $v.\sin\theta$. Hence the e.m.f. generated in each side conductor is $B\ell v.\sin\theta$ and the total e.m.f. generated is twice this since the coil has two active side conductors effectively connected in series. So

$$e = 2B\ell v.\sin\theta \text{ V}$$

The greatest value of $\sin\theta = 1$ and this will occur when θ is 90°, that is when the side conductors are moving perpendicularly to the flux. Hence $\hat{E} = 2B\ell v$, and the equation of the generated e.m.f. becomes simply

$$e = \hat{E}.\sin\theta$$

This is the equation of a sinusoidal wave and relates the instantaneous e.m.f. e to the angle that the coil makes with the axis perpendicular to the flux lines.

It is not particularly convenient to work with angle θ for reasons which will soon be apparent. With angular coil velocity ω rad/s the conductors move through an angle $\omega t(=\theta)$ in a time t seconds from the horizontal reference position marked XOX_1, i.e. from the position when the induced e.m.f. is instantaneously zero. Substituting we get

$$e = \hat{E}.\sin\omega t \text{ V}$$

There is one more alternative form: one revolution of the coil clearly generates one cycle of the voltage waveform. But one revolution is 2π radians, and at f cycles per second the angular velocity $\omega = 2\pi f$ rad/s. Hence we can write

$$e = \hat{E}.\sin 2\pi ft \text{ V}$$

These last two forms for the expression representing an alternating voltage (or current by substituting i and $\hat{I}$) are of fundamental importance and you must make certain you remember them and understand their meaning.

Example (5). An alternating current is represented by the expression $i = 10 \sin 1570t$ A. What are the peak value, the frequency and the period of the current wave?

This problem is only a matter of comparison with the 'standard' form for a current wave, i.e.

$$i = \hat{I}.\sin 2\pi ft \text{ A}$$

Comparing $i = 10 \sin 1570t$ with this we have

$$\hat{I} = 10 \text{ A}$$

$$2\pi f = 1570 \text{ rad/s}$$

Hence

$$f = \frac{1570}{2\pi} = 250 \text{ Hz}$$

Then period $T = \dfrac{1}{f} = \dfrac{1}{250} = 0.004$ s or 4 ms

PHASORS

Imagine a line OA rotating in an anticlockwise direction about a point O at a constant angular velocity ω radians per second, as shown in *Figure 8.6*. Let the length OA be equal to the peak value of an alternating cur-

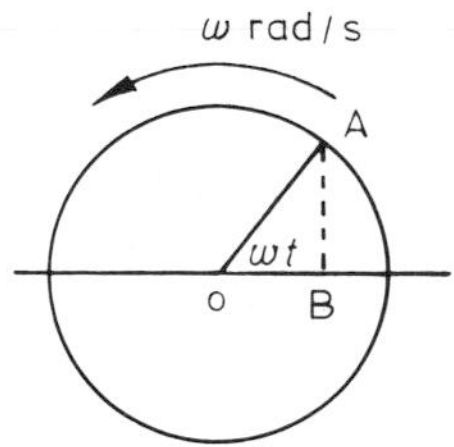

Figure 8.6

rent I. Starting from the horizontal position along OB the angle traced out in t s will be ωt radians, and the vertical projection of the line = AB will be expressed by $\hat{I}.\sin \omega t$. But this is the expression for the instantaneous value of the current i, hence

Length of the line OA $= \hat{I}$

Length of the projection AB = Instantaneous value i

It is now possible to draw a sinusoidal waveform as the projection of a number of perpendiculars such as AB. In *Figure 8.7* twelve positions of the line OA have been considered throughout one single revolution; to the right of this twelve equal intervals of time have been set out corresponding to the angle turned through by the line. Notice particularly how the time scale is expressed: at an angular velocity of ω rad/s one complete rotation (or cycle) occurs in $2\pi/\omega$ s. By projecting the successive vertical projections of AB across to the corresponding time interval, a series of points is obtained through which a continuous curve may be drawn to represent the sine wave. This is really just another way of representing the output e.m.f. of a single coil of wire rotating in a magnetic field. The line OA is called a *phasor*.

Any quantity which varies sinusoidally can be represented in this way as a phasor which rotates about a fixed point with a constant angular velocity, the number of revolutions occurring per second being equal to the frequency of the generated wave.

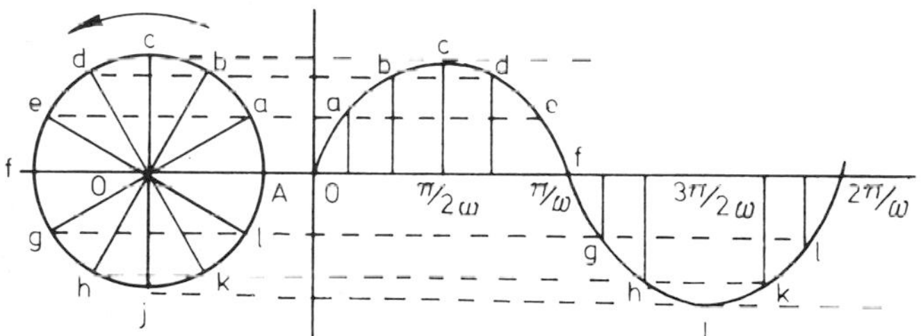

Figure 8.7

(6) An alternating voltage is represented by $e = 50 \sin 3142t$ V. Find the r.m.s. value of the wave, its frequency and periodic time.

(7) The domestic mains supply has an r.m.s. value of 240 V at a frequency of 50 Hz. Write down an expression for this wave, and find the amplitude of the voltage at the instant when $t =$ 0.006 s.

PHASE

In the discussion on phasor representation we assumed that the line OA started at time $t = 0$ in the horizontal position. The sine wave which was then derived from the rotation of OA started from the zero of the time axis with zero amplitude. If, however, the line had started in some other position, say at an angle of ϕ to the horizontal, as shown in *Figure 8.8*, a new sine wave would have been generated, displaced from the one above by the angle ϕ. The construction of this new wave is exactly similar to the previous example but would start from a different point.

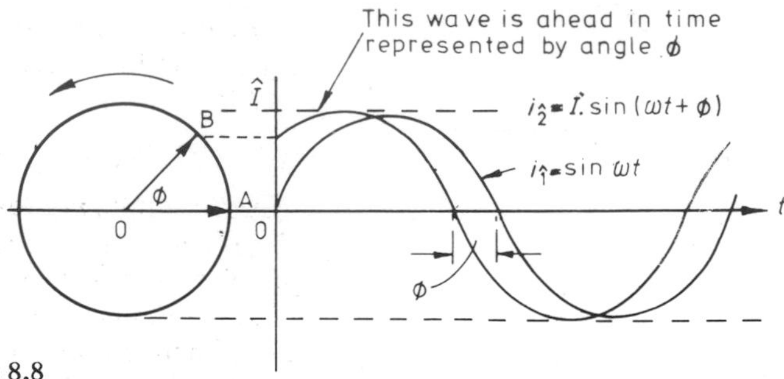

Figure 8.8

Both waves are drawn in *Figure 8.8*, the previous one being shown for purposes of comparison. For the wave generated by the line OB, when $t = 0, i_2 = \hat{I}.\sin \phi$, hence this wave is always *ahead* of the first wave by the angle ϕ. The equation for the second wave is therefore

$$i_2 = \hat{I}.\sin(\omega t + \phi)$$

and the angle ϕ is called the phase angle. As our direction of rotation of the phasor lines is anticlockwise, angle ϕ is a *leading phase angle*, because its generated wave is always ahead of the other wave $i_1 = \hat{I}.\sin \omega t$.

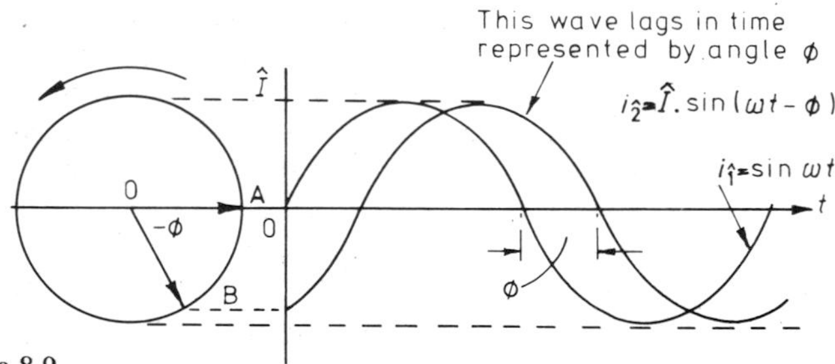

Figure 8.9

Similarly, *Figure 8.9* shows a case of a *lagging phase angle.* Phasor OB lags behind phasor OA by an angle ϕ. The generated waveforms on the right show the effect of the phase angle; waveform i_2 is always behind waveform i_1 by the angle ϕ.

Before we proceed any further, we shall summarise the contents of the last two headings.

A phasor is a line of length that represents (to a suitable scale) the peak (or r.m.s., since r.m.s. simply = 0.707 peak) value of an alternating current or voltage.

Phasors are taken to rotate anticlockwise, and usually carry an arrow-head indicating the end opposite the point of rotation.

The angle between two phasors shows the phase angle between wave-forms.

The horizontal line is taken as reference axis, and phase angles are measured as positive (leading) or negative (lagging) with respect to this.

Example (8). Draw phasor diagrams to represent the following currents:

$$i_1 = 300 \sin \omega t,\ i_2 = 200 \sin(\omega t + \pi/4),\ i_3 = 250 \sin(\omega t - \pi/2)$$

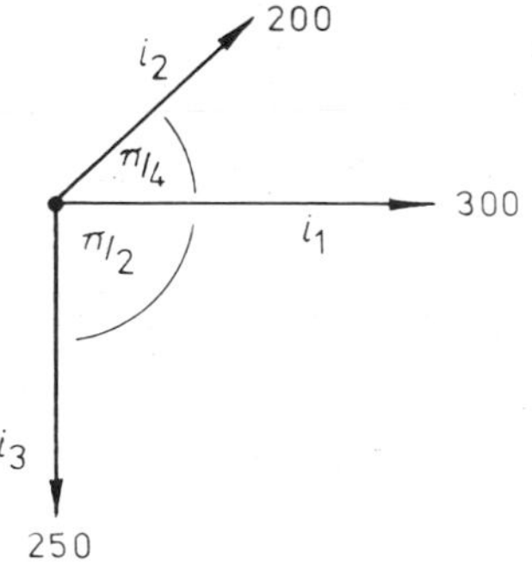

Figure 8.10

Always draw the phasors for the instant $t = 0$, so that i_1 then equals 0 and so becomes the reference phasor.

Also

$$i_2 = 200 \sin(\omega t + \pi/4), \quad i_3 = 250 \sin(\omega t - \pi/2)$$

Using a suitable scale, the phasors are drawn as in *Figure 8.10*. The reference phasor i_1 is drawn horizontally to the right of the point of rotation O, its length being 300 units representing its maximum value. i_2 leads i_1 by angle $\pi/4$ (or 45°) and is drawn accordingly, its length being 200 units. Finally i_3 lags behind i_1 by angle $\pi/2$ (or 90°) and has a length of 250 units.

ADDITION AND SUBTRACTION OF SINE WAVES

If we connect two sinusoidal voltages of the same frequency in series, simple arithmetic addition of the voltages or currents may only be made *when they are in phase*, that is, when the waveforms are zero at the same instant, and at their maximum values at the same instant. *Figure 8.11(a)* shows the meaning of in-phase quantities. Clearly, if we add these two sine waves together, we shall get a third sine wave in phase with the component waves and whose instantaneous amplitude is the sum of the ordinates of the component waves having due regard to their relative signs.

If there is any phase difference between the two waves, then their resultant sum (or difference) can only be plotted by addition (or subtraction) of their ordinate values at each instant of time. This is obviously a very laborious process and requires the component sine waves to be accurately drawn before the addition can begin. The resultant sum of the two out-of-phase waveforms of *Figure 8.11(b)* has been obtained in this way by taking the values of v_2 off by dividers and adding them on to the values of v_1 at the same respective instants. You will notice that this resultant waveform is another sine wave of the *same frequency* as the two component waves, having an amplitude greater than the component amplitudes and a phase angle, with respect to the reference wave, which is different from the angle ϕ between the component waves.

The addition or subtraction of sine waves is easily accomplished by using the phasor representation of the waves. These phasors are added or subtracted by the parallelogram rule, that is, the resultant is the *diagonal of the parallelogram* of which the component phasors form two adjacent sides.

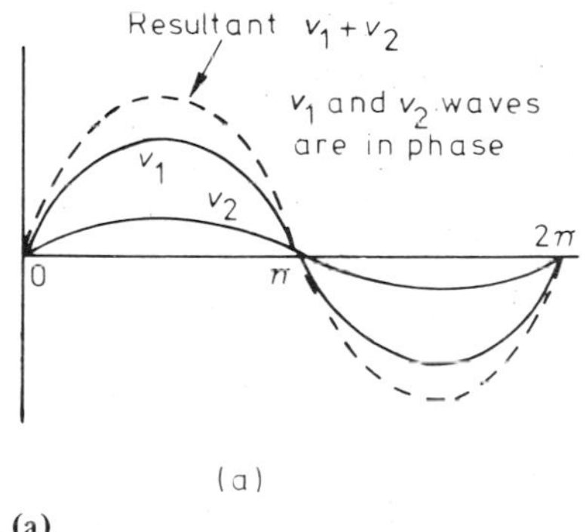

(a)

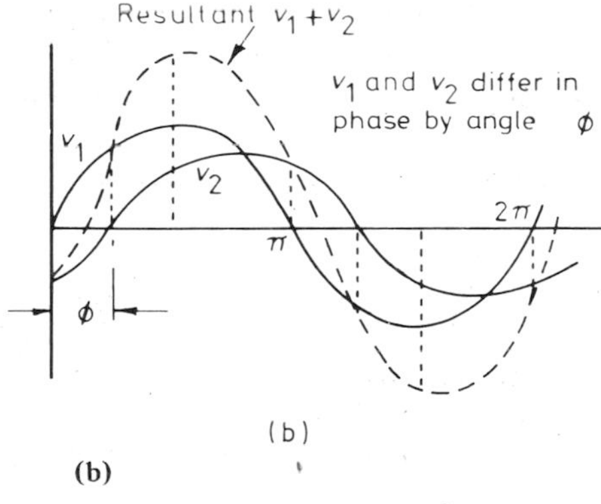

(b)

Figure 8.11

Example (9). Two alternating voltages are given by the equations $v_1 = 20 \sin 1000t$ and $v_2 = 30 \sin(1000t + \pi/3)$. Use a scaled diagram to find the sum of these two voltages, $v_1 + v_2$.

Figure 8.12 shows the two voltages:

v_1 is taken as our reference phasor and drawn to scale length 20 units.

v_2 is a phasor leading v_1 by $\pi/3$ (or 60°) and of scale length 30 units.

These phasors are, of course, to be considered as rotating about the point O at the angular velocity of 1000 rad/s, which corresponds to a frequency of about 160 Hz. From the figure, the

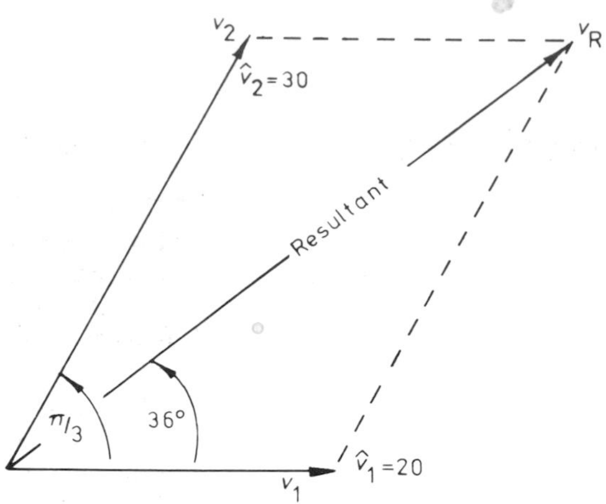

Figure 8.12

resultant v_R is measured and comes out to be about 44 units length. The phase angle of the resultant relative to v_1 is 36° (= 0.63 rad). Hence the equation for the sum of v_1 and v_2 is

$$v = 44 \sin (1000t + 0.63) \text{ V}$$

You should note that since ω is expressed in radians, that is, 1000 rad/s in the given equations, the phase angle ϕ of the resultant is expressed in radians, although the units are sometimes mixed. The answer could equally well have been written as

$$v = 44 \sin (1000t + \frac{36\pi}{180}) \text{ V} = 44 \sin (1000t + \frac{\pi}{5}) \text{ V}$$

(10) Determine the sum of $v_1 = 30 \sin \omega t$ and $v_2 = 40 \sin (\omega t + \pi/2)$ and the phase angle of the resultant relative to v_1.

(11) Two currents given by the equations $i_1 = 10 \sin (500t)$ and $i_2 = 15 \sin (500t - \pi/3)$ flow to a junction. Find (a) the equation of the current leaving the junction, (b) the frequency of the current, (c) the r.m.s. value of the current.

You would have worked the previous two problems by using scaled phasor diagrams. Both examples involved the addition of quantities, but subtraction can be obtained from phasor diagrams in exactly the same way if the phasor line for the quantity being subtracted is drawn in the opposite direction. *Figure 8.13* shows how the trick is performed, so you will have no difficulty with the next two problems.

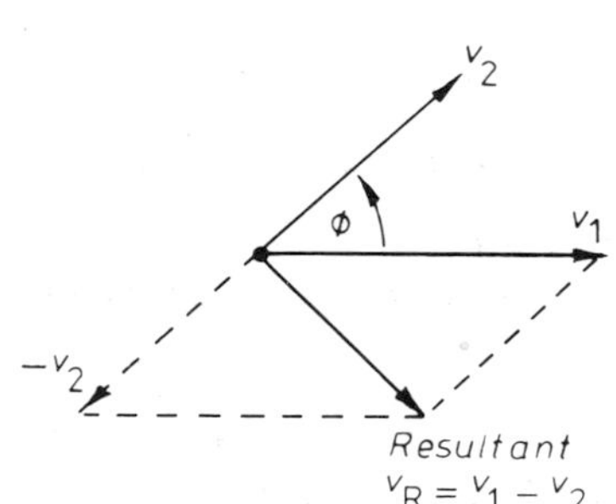

When subtracting phasor v_2 from v_1 reverse v_2 and find the resultant of v_1 and $-v_2$

Figure 8.13

(12) Two voltages are given by $v_1 = 4 \sin (800t)$ and $v_2 = 2 \sin (800t + \pi/4)$. Find the resultant $v_1 - v_2$ and express it in the form $V.\sin (800t + \phi)$.

(13) Two generators produce the following terminal voltages: v_1 is a sine wave with a peak voltage of 250 V and a frequency of 50 Hz. v_2 is also a sine wave of the same frequency producing an r.m.s. output of 100 V and lagging 45° in phase on v_1. If the two generators are connected in series, find the *two* possible resultant voltages in the form $v = V.\sin (\omega t + \phi)$.

PROBLEMS FOR SECTION 8

Group 1

(14) Find the periodic time of the following frequencies: (a) 500 Hz, (b) 5 kHz, (c) 100 kHz, (d) 1.5 mHz.

(15) The r.m.s. value of a sinusoidal wave is 200 V. What are its peak and average values?

(16) A sinusoidal current wave has an r.m.s. value of 10 mA. What are the maximum values of the current over one complete cycle?

(17) An alternating voltage has a peak value of 565 V. This voltage has a peak factor of 1.5 and a form factor of 1.2. Find the r.m.s. and average values of the voltage. (Note: this is a case of a non-sinusoidal wave).

(18) An alternating current is represented by $i = 20 \sin 6284t$ mA. Find the r.m.s. value of the current, the frequency and the periodic time.

(19) Write down an expression representing a sinusoidal wave which has an r.m.s. value of 100 V and a frequency of 40 Hz.

(20) Draw phasor diagrams to represent the following voltages:

$$v_1 = 500 \sin \omega t, \quad v_2 = 150 \sin (\omega t + \pi/3), \quad v_3 = 20 \sin (\omega t - \pi/6)$$

Group 2

(21) Write down an expression for an instantaneous voltage of peak value 660 V which leads the current by $\pi/3$ rad, the frequency being 50 Hz. Calculate the value of the voltage at a time $t = 0.008$ s.

(22) Using scaled diagrams, find the resultants and phase angles (relative to v_1 in each case and expressed as radians), for the following:

(a) $v_1 = 100 \sin \omega t$, $v_2 = 100 \sin (\omega t + \pi/2)$; $v_1 + v_2$
(b) $v_1 = 20 \sin \omega t$, $v_2 = 15 \sin (\omega t - \pi/2)$; $v_1 + v_2$
(c) $v_1 = 120 \sin 628t$, $v_2 = 80 \sin (628t - \pi/4)$; $v_1 - v_2$

(23) Add together the following currents, expressing the sum in the form $i = \hat{I} \sin (\omega t + \phi)$: $i_1 = 10 \sin (\omega t + 45^\circ)$, $i_2 = 6 \sin \omega t$, $i_3 = 10 \sin (\omega t - 60^\circ)$.

(24) Two sinusoidal e.m.f.s of peak values 100 V and 50 V but differing in phase by 60° are induced in the same circuit. Find by means of a scaled diagram, or by calculation, the peak value of the resulting e.m.f.

(25) Prove that the phasor sum of the following three voltages is zero: $v_1 = 40 \sin (\omega t - 25^\circ)$, $v_2 = 40 \sin (\omega t + 95^\circ)$, $v_3 = 40 \sin (\omega t - 145^\circ)$.

9 Magnetic circuits

Aims: At the end of this Unit section you should be able to:
Relate the magnetic circuit to the electric circuit.
Define magnetic reluctance.
Apply the data from magnetisation curves to the solution of series magnetic circuits.
Discuss magnetic screening.
Understand the constructional features of iron-cored inductors.
Further discuss losses in magnetic materials.

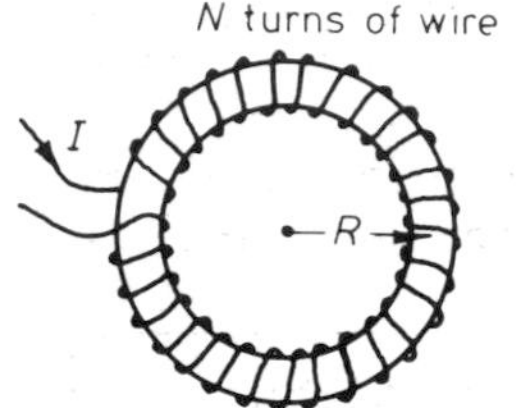

Figure 9.1

The field inside a solenoid is relatively uniform throughout its length, and the magnetising force H is given to a good approximation by NI/ℓ At/m. If a solenoid is bent into the form of a closed ring, or *toroid*, and uniformly wound with wire as shown in *Figure 9.1*, all the magnetic flux paths set up when a current I flows in the coil are completely enclosed throughout their lengths by all the turns of the coil, and we have the equivalent of an 'endless' solenoid. If the toroid is an iron ring or made of some other ferrous material, the flux density B is increased by a factor μ_r.

Now flux is maintained by the magnetomotive force m.m.f. = NI At, and for a flux path of length ℓ metres the magnetising force $H = NI/\ell$ At/m. If the ring of *Figure 9.1* is thin in comparison with its mean circumference, then

$$H = \frac{NI}{2\pi R} \quad \text{At/m}$$

where R is the mean radius.

The closed ring forms what we call a *magnetic circuit*. Such magnetic circuits and the problems associated with them are made understandable if a comparison is made with the simple electric circuit. The ampere-turns give rise to the m.m.f. which produces and maintains the magnetic flux. This may be compared with the e.m.f. in an electric circuit which produces and maintains the flow of current round the circuit. The magnetic flux may be compared with the current in the electrical circuit, although you must realise that nothing 'flows' in the magnetic circuit comparable to the electron flow in circuit wires. We now require a quantity analogous to electrical resistance. In a magnetic circuit this is called *reluctance*, denoted by S. For a given m.m.f. the flux produced in a circuit can reasonably be expected to depend upon

(a) the relative permeability of the material,
(b) the length of the magnetic path,
(c) the cross-sectional area of the magnetic path.

We may set up an 'Ohm's law' for magnetic circuit on this basis which will be analogous to that for electric circuits:

$$\text{Current } I = \frac{\text{e.m.f. } E}{\text{Resistance } R}\ ; \quad \text{Flux } \Phi = \frac{\text{m.m.f. } NI}{\text{Reluctance } S}$$

Figure 9.2. shows the comparison between the two circuits.

(1) Can you deduce, using the general magnetic relationships, what the unit of reluctance is?

Let the magnetic circuit of *Figure 9.1* be a thin iron ring of uniform cross section A m^2 and mean circumference (the length of the flux path) ℓ metres. Then since

$$H = \frac{NI}{\ell} \text{ At/m}, \quad \Phi = BA \text{ Wb}, \quad B = \mu_o\mu_r H \text{ T}$$

$$S = \frac{\text{m.m.f.}}{\Phi} = \frac{NI}{\Phi} = \frac{H\ell}{BA} = \frac{\ell}{\mu_o\mu_r A} \text{ At/Wb}$$

The last expression here verifies our assumptions given in the list: reluctance is seen to be inversely proportional to the permeability and to the cross-sectional area of the flux path, and directly proportional to the length of the flux path.

We can now make a table of comparisons between the various electric and magnetic quantities, and their relationships, to fix it in our minds.

Electric circuit	*Magnetic circuit*
e.m.f. E (V)	m.m.f. NI (At)
	Magnetising force H (At/m)
Current I (A)	Flux Φ (Wb)
Resistance R (Ω)	Reluctance S (At/Wb)
$I = \frac{E}{R}$	$\Phi = \frac{\text{m.m.f.}}{S}$
$R = \frac{\rho\ell}{A}$	$S = \frac{1}{\mu_o\mu_r}\frac{\ell}{A}$

You are reminded to use these comparisons with thought and care. As we have noted, nothing flows in a magnetic circuit in the way that electrons flow in a wire. Also, in an electric circuit, insulation confines the current to a definite path through the conductor, but it is impossible to confine all the magnetic flux paths to the actual magnetic circuit. There are always flux lines which stray into the surrounding space. Further, electrical resistance is constant, apart from small variations due to temperature changes, but reluctance depends upon μ_r and this can vary enormously according to the degree of working flux density.

SERIES MAGNETIC CIRCUITS

The usual problem associated with a magnetic circuit is to find the m.m.f. or the magnetising force H which gives rise to a certain flux in a circuit of given permeability or reluctance. This is like finding the e.m.f. necessary to give rise to a certain current in a circuit of given resistance. Unlike resistance, however, reluctance changes with variations in μ_r and so it is necessary to know μ_r (or the ratio of B to H), for the conditions under which the magnetic material is being used. Unless, therefore, the actual working value of μ_r is given in the problem, it becomes neces-

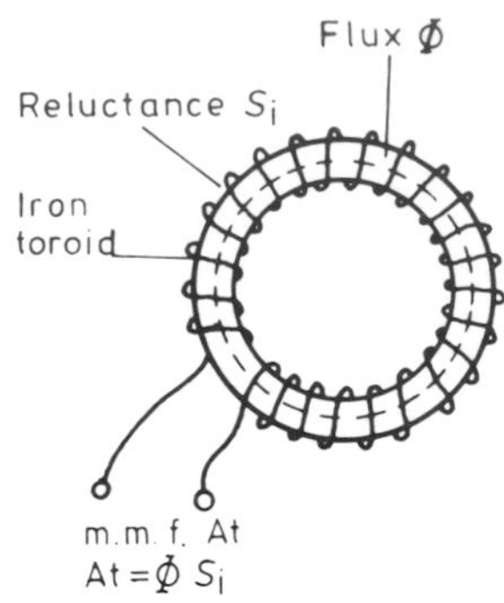

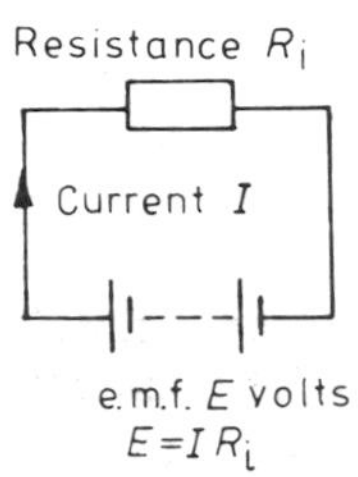

Figure 9.2

sary to find it from a study of the appropriate magnetisation curve of the material being used. You will require the magnetisation curves that you drew for Problem (9) at the end of Section 6 for some of the following problems.

We consider first of all the case of the simple closed ring wound as in *Figure 9.1* for an introduction to what are known as series magnetic circuits.

Figure 9.2 shows the magnetic circuit and its electrical counterpart. As the magnetic circuit is a completely closed ferrous ring the reluctance will be small, so the equivalent electrical circuit will be one having a small resistance. Hence, from the figure

$$\text{e.m.f.} = IR_i; \ \text{m.m.f.} = \Phi S_i$$

and from these simple comparisons we can solve problems relating to the basic closed magnetic circuit.

Example (2). A uniform ring of mild steel has a cross-sectional area of 5 cm² and a mean circumference of 15 cm. Find the m.m.f. necessary to produce a flux of 0.5 mWb in the ring.

We first tabulate all the details we have been given:

$$A = 5\ \text{cm}^2 = 5 \times 10^{-4}\ \text{m}^2$$

$$\ell = 15\ \text{cm} = 15 \times 10^{-2}\ \text{m}$$

$$\Phi = 0.5\ \text{mWb} = 0.5 \times 10^{-3}\ \text{Wb}$$

Then

$$\text{Flux density } B = \frac{\Phi}{A} = \frac{0.5 \times 10^{-3}}{5 \times 10^{-4}} = 1.0\ \text{T}$$

Referring to the magnetisation curve for mild steel (or interpolating from the given tables) we see that for $B = 1.0$ T, $H = 1400$ At/m.

$$\therefore \text{m.m.f.} = H\ell = 1400 \times 15 \times 10^{-2}$$

$$= 210\ \text{At}$$

We could get this m.m.f. in a variety of ways: 210 At is the product of current and turns, so 1 A flowing in 210 turns, or 0.5 A flowing in 420 turns would be two possibilities. The choice in practice depends, of course, upon the application. In nearly all electronic applications, a great number of turns carry a small current.

Example (3). An iron ring of mean circumference 25 cm is uniformly wound with 1000 turns of wire. When a current of 0.2 A is passed through the coil a flux density of 0.35 T is set up in the iron. What is the relative permeability of the iron under these conditions?

Again we set down a table of the given information:

$$N = 1000, \ I = 0.2\ \text{A}, \ B = 0.35\ \text{T}$$

$$\ell = 25\ \text{cm} = 0.25\ \text{m}$$

Then

$$H = \frac{NI}{\ell} = \frac{1000 \times 0.2}{0.25} = 800 \text{ At/m}$$

But

$$B = \mu_o \mu_r H$$

$$\therefore \mu_r = \frac{B}{\mu_o . H} = \frac{0.35 \times 10^7}{4\pi \times 800}$$

$$= 348$$

Try the next two problems on your own.

(4) A uniform ring of mild steel has a cross-sectional area of 5 cm^2 and a mean circumference of 12 cm. What current will be required in a coil of 1500 turns wound on the ring to produce a flux of 0.75 mWb?

(5) An iron ring has a mean diameter of 12 cm and a cross-sectional area of 4 cm^2. It has a current of 2 A flowing in a coil uniformly wound around the ring and the flux produced is 0.6 mWb. If the relative permeability of the iron under these conditions is 500, find (a) the reluctance, (b) the number of turns on the coil.

CIRCUITS WITH AIR GAP

A practical magnetic circuit rarely consists of a completely closed ring, for the flux is contained within the ring and no North or South poles are apparent. If a radial cut is made in the ring, forming a narrow air gap, a discontinuity is produced and North and South poles are established across the gap. The flux may now be utilised as, for example, a tape recording head or the rotor of an electrical machine. Air gaps cut in this way are usually filled with a non-magnetic material, such as brass, to prevent the ingress of iron particles and other unwanted dust.

Suppose a radial air gap is cut across the simple closed ring just discussed. Then the magnetic circuit and its equivalent electrical circuit will be as represented in *Figure 9.3*. The reluctance S_i of the iron path will be low as before, but the reluctance S_g of the air gap, even if this is narrow, will be high. The circuit is therefore equivalent to an electrical circuit which has two resistances, one of high and one of low value, in series across the source of e.m.f. So

$$\text{e.m.f.} = I(R_i + R_g), \quad \text{m.m.f.} = \Phi(S_i + S_g)$$

Now I is common to all parts of a series electrical circuit, so Φ is common to all parts of a series magnetic circuit. The flux threading the iron path passes across the air gap and re-enters the iron again on the other side. The total m.m.f. acting in the circuit will be the sum of the m.m.f.s of each part, just as the sum of the volts-drop in the two resistances of the electrical circuit will be equal to the battery e.m.f. Hence the ampere-turns required to produce a given total flux Φ is ΦS where S is the total reluctance ($S_i + S_g$).

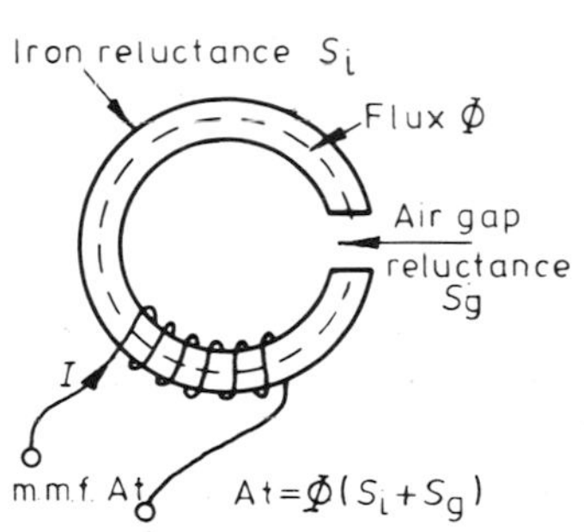

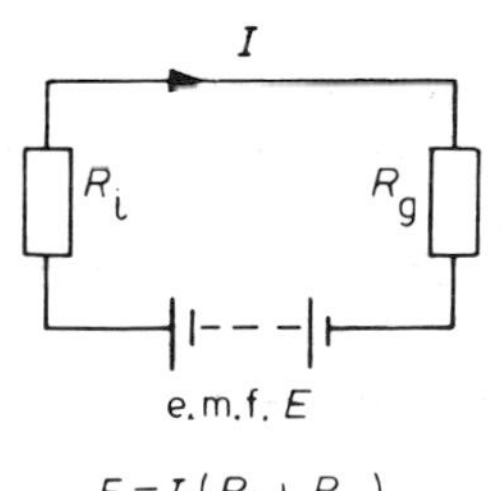

Figure 9.3

Example (6). The ring of Example (2) has a radial gap 2 mm wide cut into it. Calculate the m.m.f. now required to maintain the flux of 0.5 mWb in the ring.

In examples such as this we must find the m.m.f. necessary to maintain the flux in each part of the circuit, gap and iron.

(a) For the iron path

$A = 5 \times 10^{-4}\ \mathrm{m}^2$, $\ell_i = 14.8 \times 10^{-2}$ m (the circumference less the 2 mm air gap)

$\Phi = 0.5 \times 10^{-3}$ Wb

As before flux density $B = 1.0$ T, and so for $H = 1400$

$$\therefore \text{ m.m.f. for the iron path } = 1400 \times 14.8 \times 10^{-2}$$

$$= 207 \text{ At}$$

(b) For the air gap

$A = 5 \times 10^{-4}\ \mathrm{m}^2$, $\ell_g = 2\ \mathrm{mm} = 2 \times 10^{-3}$ m

$\Phi = 0.5 \times 10^{-3}$ Wb

The flux density in the gap will, of course, be the same as that in the iron, i.e. 1.0 T. To find H we shall have to use the air relation

$$H = \frac{B}{\mu_o} = \frac{1.0 \times 10^7}{4\pi} = 795\,775$$

$$\therefore \text{ m.m.f. for the gap } = 795\,775 \times 2 \times 10^{-3}$$

$$= 1591 \text{ At}$$

$$\therefore \text{ Total m.m.f. required } = 207 + 1591 = 1798 \text{ At}$$

You will notice from this example that the slightly reduced iron path required for all practical purposes the same m.m.f. as the closed ring, 207 compared with 210 At. In many cases where the air gap length is negligible compared with the total flux path, time can be saved by taking the m.m.f. for the iron path to be the same as that for the iron before the ring is cut. You will also notice the large m.m.f. needed to maintain the flux across the air gap compared with that in the iron.

Now try the following similar problems.

(7) A magnetic core in the form of a closed ring has a mean length of 20 cm and a cross section of 1 cm². The permeability of the iron is 2400 and a coil of 2000 turns is wound uniformly around the ring to create a flux of 0.2 mWb. What current is required in the coil?

If an air gap 1 mm wide is cut radially through the iron, what *increase* in the current will be needed to maintain the flux at the same value?

(8) A soft iron bar, 30 cm long, is bent into the form of a ring but with the ends separated 1.5 mm apart in air. The bar is wound with 500 turns of wire which carries a current of 0.5 A. What is the flux density in the air gap, given that μ_r under the conditions is 300?

(9) A table relating B to μ_r for a sample of iron is as follows:

B (T)	0.8	1.0	1.2	1.4
μ_r	2300	2000	1600	1100

Find the ampere-turns required to produce a flux of 0.4 mWb in a ring of this material which has a mean circumference of 60 cm and a cross section of 4 cm^2. If a saw cut 1 mm wide was made in the ring, how many extra ampere-turns would be necessary to establish the same flux in the gap?

MAGNETIC CIRCUIT MATERIALS

All components such as transformers, chokes, loudspeakers, recording heads, and so on, utilise magnetic circuits, and each uses the material and the constructional form applicable to its function in life. When iron cores are used for transformers and chokes in particular, two fundamental losses make their appearance. One of these we have already mentioned: hysteresis loss. The other is *eddy current* loss. Eddy current loss is energy dissipated as heat in the metal of the core when an alternating current flows in the energising coil. The alternating flux, as well as producing voltage in the coil, produces voltages in the core, causing small local currents to circulate. These induced currents will be large if the core is made of a solid material for they will be flowing in a conductor with a very small resistance. To reduce this effect as much as possible, the core is made up of a great many thin plates, or laminations, interleaved with each other and generally insulated by a thin coat of paint or paper on one side of each lamination. This process does little to affect the magnetic properties of the core, but circulating currents cannot flow easily between the laminations and are consequently restricted in their magnitude.

As the frequency increases, the thickness of the laminations has to be reduced; when it becomes impracticable to make laminations any thinner, core loss is reduced by using so-called iron-dust (granulated iron) cores. Such cores are used at radio frequencies to provide cores for transformers and inductances, as well as tuning screws.

MAGNETIC SCREENING

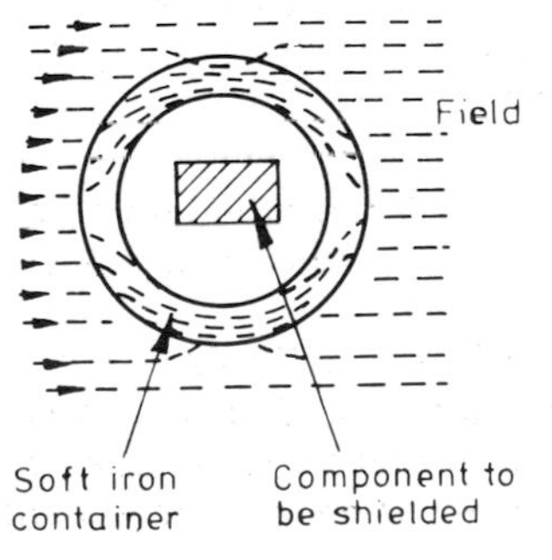

Figure 9.4

Lines of magnetic flux prefer to pass through ferrous materials rather than air. If a component needs to be shielded from surrounding magnetic fields it is placed in a soft iron box or cylinder which completely surrounds it, rather as shown in *Figure 9.4*. Most of the flux associated with the external magnetic field will then make its way through the soft iron, leaving the space inside the protective container almost free of magnetic influence. The material for such magnetic screens is usually an alloy having a very high value of relative permeability, commercially known as *mu-metal*. It is specially heat treated after being formed to the required shape, and must be carefully handled in use to avoid its shielding qualities being impaired. You will see such a shield used around the neck of a cathode ray tube in an oscilloscope, and around the recorder head in a tape recorder, as typical examples.

PROBLEMS FOR SECTION 9

Note. In those problems marked with an asterisk, you will have to refer to your B–H curves as necessary.

Group 1

(10)* A uniform mild steel ring has a mean circumference of 0.15 m and a cross-sectional area of 10^{-4} m^2. Find the m.m.f. necessary to produce a flux of 0.5 mWb in the ring.

(11) What current would be required in a coil of 500 turns wound uniformly around the ring of the previous problem to produce the flux?

(12) An iron ring of mean circumference 80 cm is uniformly wound with 1000 turns of wire. When a current of 0.5 A is passed through the coil, a flux density of 1.1 T is set up in the ring. What is the relative permeability of the iron under this condition?

(13)* A cast steel ring has a cross-sectional area of 3 cm^2 and a mean diameter of 6.4 cm. What m.m.f. is necessary to establish a flux of 0.09 mWb in the ring?

(14) The ring of Problem (10) has a radial air gap 2 mm wide cut into it. What m.m.f. is now necessary to maintain the flux of 0.5 mWb in the ring?

(15) An electromagnet has an iron path 1 m long and requires a flux density of 0.6 T in a 2 mm air gap cut across the magnetic circuit. If the relative permeability of the iron used is 2400 under this condition, and a current of 2 A flows in a coil wound around the iron, how many turns are required on the coil?

(16) A specimen of iron has $\mu_r = 6000$ when $B = 0.6$ T, and $\mu_r = 2000$ when $B = 1.2$ T. If the relationship between μ_r and H is linear between these points, calculate the current needed in a coil of 1000 turns wound around a ring of the iron having a mean circumference of 20 cm, to produce a flux density of 0.9 T.

(17)* A mild steel rod 0.5 m in length and diameter 2.5 cm is bent to form a ring having a gap of 1.5 mm left between its ends. What m.m.f. is needed to maintain a flux density of 0.7 T across the air gap?

Group 2

(18) A magnetic circuit is in the form of an open rectangle having a mean length of 0.38 m and a cross section measuring 1 × 4 cm. A m.m.f. of 150 At produces a flux of 0.2 mWb in the circuit. Calculate (a) the flux density, (b) the relative permeability under this condition.

(19) A m.m.f. of 400 At produces a flux of 1.2 mWb in an iron circuit of mean length 80 cm and cross-sectional area 12 × 10^{-4} m^2. Find (a) the flux density, (b) μ_r, (c) the reluctance of the circuit.

10 Reactance and impedance

Aims: At the end of this Unit section you should be able to:
Understand phase relationships in purely inductive and capacitive circuits.
State the reactance of inductive and capacitive circuits.
Define impedance, and use impedance and voltage triangles.
Solve problems for series L–R *and* C–R *circuits.*

We have three basic electrical components which have been considered separately from a d.c. point of view in the previous sections of this course: the *resistor*, the *inductor* and the *capacitor*. The time has come to investigate what happens when these components are connected separately and in various combinations in an a.c. circuit.

Because the instantaneous values of alternating currents and voltages are functions of time, it might be reasonable to expect that certain components can change the time relationship (or phase) between current and voltage. Components which do this are referred to as *reactive components* to distinguish them from *resistive components* which do not change the phase relationship. Reactances appear in the form of inductors and capacitors.

In practice there are no such components as pure resistors, inductors or capacitors. For instance, all resistors have some inductance associated with them, even if only the connecting wires are considered; and for wire-wound resistors the inductance might well be appreciable. An inductor, being a coil of wire and very often quite a large coil, has resistance associated with it due to the material of the conductor from which the wire is made. And the same for a capacitor: the leads and plates have small resistive and inductive elements.

CIRCUIT WITH RESISTANCE

When the circuit contains only *pure* resistance, the current at any instant is directly proportional to the voltage, since Ohm's law must be obeyed. So if the applied voltage is a sine wave, the current waveform will also be a sine wave, being zero at the same instant the voltage is zero and at a maximum at the same instant the voltage is a maximum. Hence, the current and voltage are *in phase*. This is illustrated in wave and phasor form in *Figure 10.1*. Let

$$e = \hat{E}.\sin \omega t$$

But

$$i = \frac{e}{R} \quad \text{at any instant of time}$$

$$\therefore i = \frac{\hat{E}}{R}.\sin \omega t = \hat{I}.\sin \omega t$$

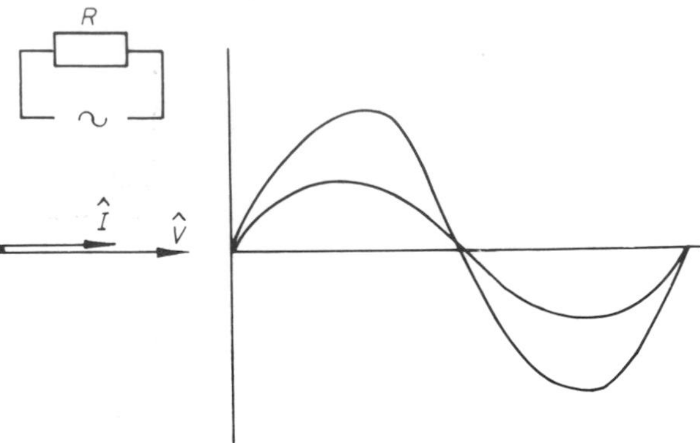

Figure 10.1

and this is a sine wave of maximum value $\hat{I}$ having the same frequency as the voltage wave and in phase with it.

We note then: *in a purely resistive circuit, current and voltage are in phase.*

CIRCUIT WITH INDUCTANCE

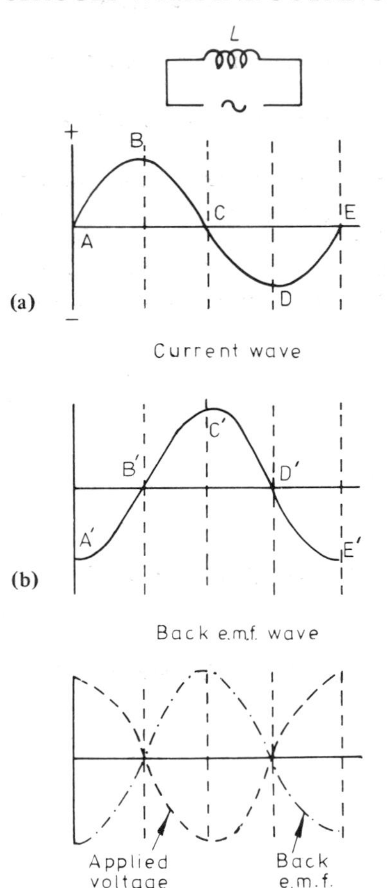

Figure 10.2

We have already learned that in an inductor, when the current changes, there is a self-induced e.m.f. which by Lenz's law acts in opposition to the change. This induced e.m.f., or *back e.m.f.*, is expressed by the formula

$$e = -L \times \text{rate of change of current}$$

the negative sign simply indicating that e acts in opposition.

Now when alternating current flows in a coil, there is a continual change in the current and hence a continual change in the back e.m.f. The above expression tells us that the greater the rate of change of the current, the greater the opposition provided, i.e. the greater the frequency of the applied voltage, the greater will be the coil opposition to the flow of current. This apparent resistance must not be confused in any way with the 'ordinary' resistance of the wire making up the inductor; we are, in fact, assuming that the coil has no resistance of this sort at all. The opposing effect of inductance to the flow of alternating current is called the *inductive reactance.* It is denoted by X_L and is measured in ohms.

Let us have a closer look at what goes on in the *pure* inductor. In *Figure 10.2(a)* we see a pure inductor, L henry, connected to an a.c. generator. The current wave is changing at its maximum possible rate at A (it is rising most steeply) in the positive direction; hence the self-induced e.m.f. will also be a maximum but in the opposite direction. At B the current is momentarily not changing, hence there is no back e.m.f. At C the current is again changing at its maximum possible rate but in a negative direction, so the back e.m.f. is also at its maximum, but acting in the positive direction. At D there is a zero change condition again. Thus the wave representing the back e.m.f. is as shown in *Figure 10.2(b)*, the corresponding conditions to instants A, B, C, etc., being A′, B′, C′, etc.

Now as the back e.m.f. *opposes* the applied voltage at any instant, the applied voltage waveform must be the same as that of the back e.m.f., but inverted. We can therefore sketch it as shown in *Figure 10.2(c)*.

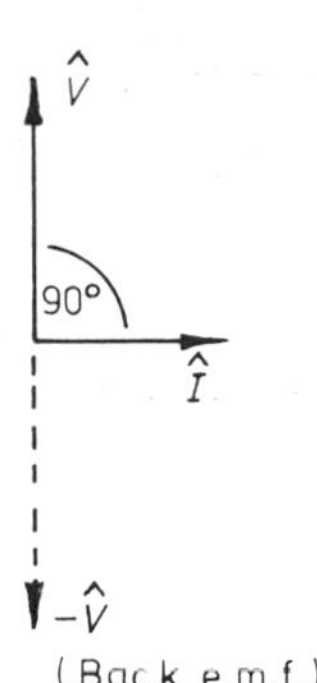

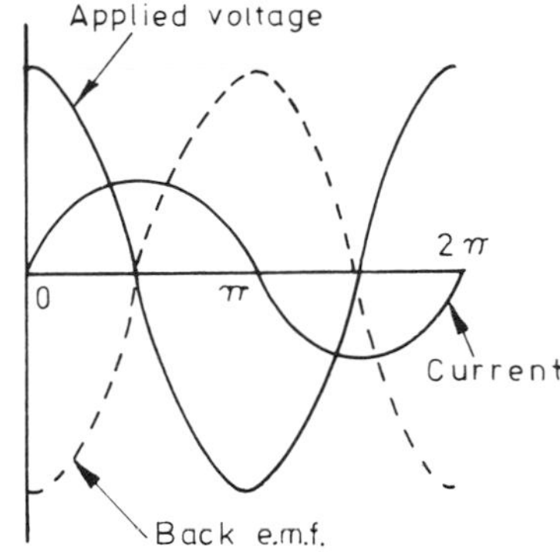

Figure 10.3

If we now compare the current wave at (a) with the applied voltage wave at (c), we notice that the current lags the voltage by 90°. Current and voltage are no longer in phase as they were in a pure resistor. This phase shift between current and voltage is a fundamental effect of inductance in a.c. circuits. *Figure 10.3* illustrates the effect in wave and phasor form.

We note then: *in a purely inductive circuit, current* I *lags 90° on applied voltage* V.

We want now to find the relationship between the current and voltage in the circuit.

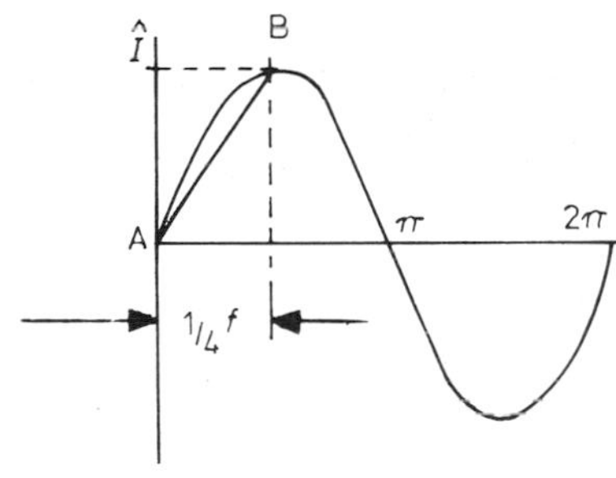

Figure 10.4

Let the current change from zero to $\hat{I}$ in one quarter-cycle of the current waveform, as from A to B in *Figure 10.4*.

So the change in current $= \hat{I} - 0 = \hat{I}$ A.

Time for 1 cycle $= 1/f$, hence the time for a quarter-cycle $= 1/4f$.

Then the average rate of change of current is represented by the straight line AB, and this is

$$\frac{\hat{I}}{1/4f} = 4f\hat{I}$$

Hence the average induced back e.m.f.

$$e = -L \times 4f\hat{I} = -4Lf\hat{I}$$

This back e.m.f. is equal and opposite to the applied voltage, so that

$$\text{Average applied voltage} = 4Lf\hat{I}$$

As we are considering a sine wave, peak value $= \pi/2 \times$ average value

$$\therefore \hat{V} = \frac{\pi}{2} \times 4Lf\hat{I}$$

that is

$$\hat{V} = 2\pi fL\hat{I} = \omega L\hat{I}$$

Using r.m.s. values instead of peak values we then get

$$V = \omega LI$$

$$\therefore \frac{V}{I} = \omega L = X_L \text{ the inductive reactance}$$

Hence

$X_L = \omega L$ ohms

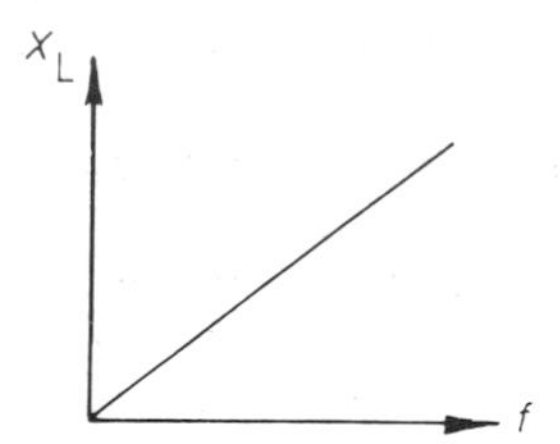

Figure 10.5

Compare this relationship between voltage and current with Ohm's law. The quantity ωL determines the r.m.s. current which flows through the inductor when an r.m.s. voltage V is applied. It is the apparent resistance of the inductor at a particular frequency, and is called the *reactance.*

Since X_L is proportional to frequency for a given L, a graph of X_L plotted against a base of frequency will be a straight line passing through the origin. This is shown in *Figure 10.5.*

Example (1). An e.m.f. of 10 V at a frequency of 1 kHz is applied to a coil of inductance 0.1 H. Find (a) the reactance of the coil, (b) the current flowing in the coil.

(a)

Reactance $X_L = 2\pi fL$

$\therefore$ at 1 kHz

$$X_L = 2\pi \times 10^3 \times 0.1$$
$$= 628\ \Omega$$

(b)

$$I = \frac{V}{X_L} = \frac{10}{628}$$
$$= 0.0318\text{ A (31.8 mA)}$$

Now try the following on your own.

(2) A coil of inductance 0.25 H is connected to a 50 Hz supply. What will be the reactance of the coil?

(3) A coil has a reactance of 50 Ω in a circuit with a supply frequency of 40 Hz. What is the inductance of the coil?

(4) *Without* using the formula for inductive reactance, complete the following table:

Frequency (Hz)	*Reactance* X_L
100	–
200	30
5 000	–
10 000	–
–	150

INDUCTIVE IMPEDANCE

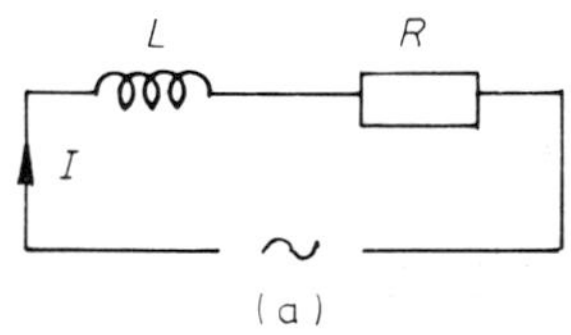

Figure 10.6(a)

No real inductor is without resistance, so we should expect to draw a circuit containing inductance rather as shown in *Figure 10.6(a)*, where the resistance R of the coil is considered as being in series with what up to now we have termed a pure inductance. We are, in a way, separating out the circuit into a pure resistance and a pure inductance, whereas in reality these two elements are intimately combined.

Now from what we have already learned

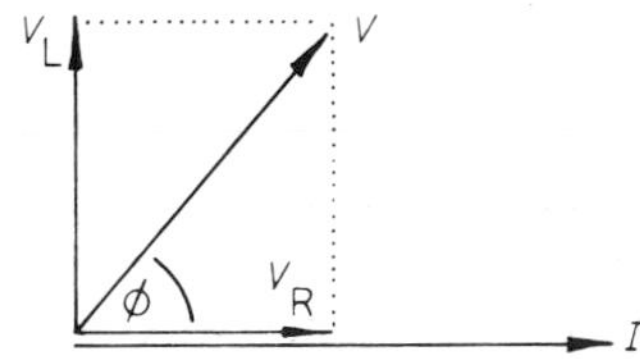

Figure 10.6(b)

(a) the voltage V_R across resistor R is in phase with the current;
(b) the voltage V_L across inductor L is leading the current by 90°

Note that current lagging voltage by 90° is equivalent to saying that voltage leads current by 90°.

Now with a series circuit, the sum of V_R and V_L must (phasor-wise, remember) equal the supply voltage V. As the current is common to all parts of the circuit, we use it as our reference phasor. In *Figure 10.6(b)*, therefore, we draw V_R in phase with I and V_L leading I by 90°. The phasor sum of these voltages (the diagonal of the parallelogram) is equal to V. Hence V leads the current by some phase angle ϕ which must lie *between* 0° and 90°.

(5) Under what circumstances will ϕ be 0° or 90°?

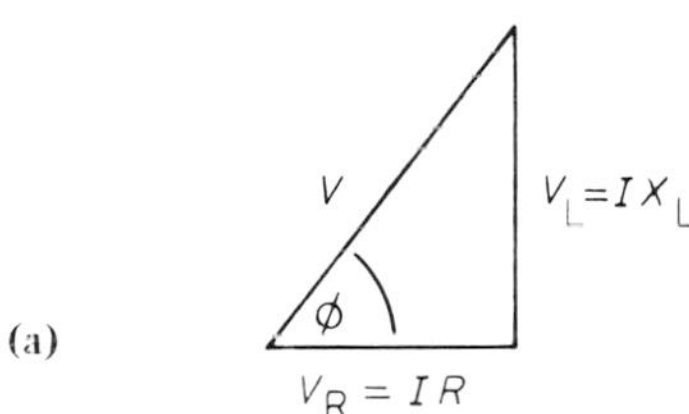

(a)

Looking again at *Figure 10.6(b)* we notice that we can represent the triangle which includes phase angle ϕ as a voltage triangle, and this is shown in *Figure 10.7(a)*. From this triangle, by Pythagoras

$$V = \sqrt{(V_R^2 + V_L^2)}$$

But $V_R = IR$ and $V_L = IX_L$

Also, let the ratio of supply voltage V to the current I be Z. Then

$$Z = \frac{V}{I} \quad \text{or} \quad V = IZ$$

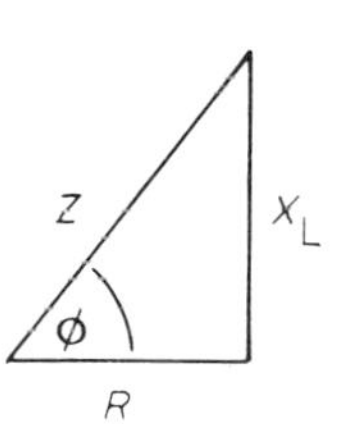

(b)

Figure 10.7

Since the current is common, we can draw a triangle similar to the voltage triangle and mark off the sides as R, X_L and Z respectively (see *Figure 10.7(b)*). This triangle is called an *impedance triangle*, and the voltage-current ratio for the circuit is called the *impedance Z*. Z is measured in ohms and is the combined effect of resistance and reactance acting together in one circuit. By Pythagoras

$$Z = \sqrt{(R^2 + X_L^2)} \quad \text{and} \quad \tan\phi = \frac{X_L}{R}$$

The next worked examples will illustrate the use of the impedance triangle.

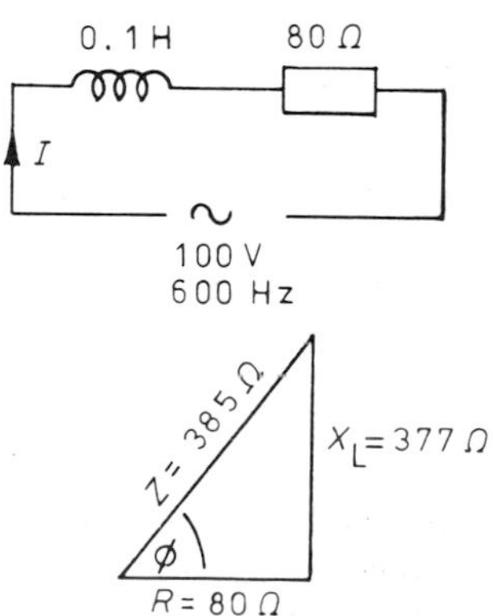

Figure 10.8

Example (6). A coil of inductance 0.1 H and resistance 80 Ω is connected to a 100 V, 600 Hz supply. Calculate the circuit impedance and the current taken from the supply. What is the phase angle between supply voltage and current?

Figure 10.8 illustrates the problem. We first calculate the reactance X_L.

$$X_L = 2\pi fL = 2\pi \times 600 \times 0.1$$
$$= 377\ \Omega$$

Also

$$R = 80\ \Omega$$

$$\therefore \text{Impedance } Z = \sqrt{(80^2 + 377^2)} = 385\ \Omega$$

$$\text{Current } I = \frac{V}{Z} = \frac{100}{385} = 0.26\ \text{A}$$

From the impedance triangle we get $\tan\phi = \dfrac{X_L}{R} = \dfrac{377}{80}$

$$= 4.712$$

$$\phi = 78°$$

Clearly, this is the angle by which I lags V.

Example (7). An alternating voltage represented by $v = 250 \sin 1000t$ volts is applied to a coil of resistance 150 Ω and inductance 500 mH. Find the impedance of the circuit, the current flowing, and the voltage across R and L respectively.

Applied voltage $v = 250 \sin 1000t$ V. This is a wave with a peak value $\hat{V} = 250$ V and $\omega = 1000$ rad/s.

$$X_L = \omega L = 1000 \times 0.5 \text{ (500 mH} = 0.5 \text{ H)}$$

$$= 500\ \Omega$$

Also $R = 150\ \Omega$

$$\therefore \text{Impedance } Z = \sqrt{(150^2 + 500^2)} = 522\ \Omega$$

$$\text{Current } I = \frac{\text{r.m.s. voltage}}{\text{impedance}}$$

$$= \frac{250}{\sqrt{2} \times 522} = 0.339 \text{ A}$$

Voltage across $R = IR = 0.339 \times 150 = 51$ V

Voltage across $L = IX_L = 0.339 \times 500 = 169$ V

These are, of course, r.m.s. quantities. Notice that the *arithmetical* sum of these is 220 V which is not the applied r.m.s. voltage, i.e. $250/\sqrt{2} = 177$ V. The voltages across R and L must be added phasorwise, so that from the voltage triangle (*Figure 10.9*) we have

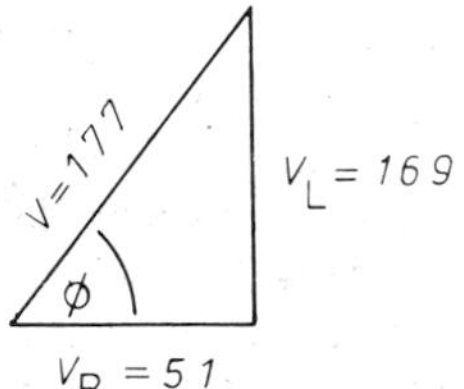

Figure 10.9

$$V = \sqrt{(V_R^2 + V_L^2)} = \sqrt{(51^2 + 169^2)} = 177 \text{ V as required.}$$

(8) What is the impedance of a coil which has a resistance of 10 Ω and a reactance of 12 Ω?

(9) A coil of negligible resistance takes a current of 3.2 A when connected to a 200 V, 50 Hz supply. Find the inductance of the coil.

(10) A coil of inductance 200 mH and resistance 40 Ω is connected to a 50 V, 50 Hz supply. Find the circuit impedance, the current flowing and the phase angle.

(11) In a series R–L circuit the applied voltage is 100 V and the voltage across the resistor is 50 V. What is the voltage across the inductor?

CIRCUIT WITH CAPACITANCE

We turn now to a circuit containing a *pure* capacitance. Let the voltage wave applied to the capacitor be as shown in *Figure 10.10*.

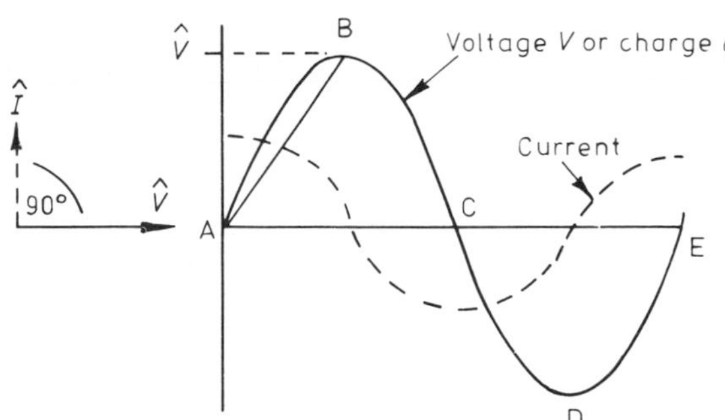

Figure 10.10

Since the charge at any instant is given by $q = Cv$ where v is the instantaneous voltage, charge q is directly proportional to v and so the curve of capacitor charge is identical with the voltage curve. We can say, in fact, that the voltage and charge are *in phase.*

Now, dividing by time t:

$$\frac{q}{t} = C.\frac{v}{t}$$

But q/t is the change of charge per second, which is the current flowing in the circuit. Therefore

$i = C \times$ rate of change of charge (or voltage)

Returning to the curve, at A the voltage (or charge) is changing at its maximum possible rate and in a positive direction, and so the capacitor is receiving its maximum charging current. As the voltage rises towards B the rate of increase (the steepness of the curve) gets less and so the charging current decreases until at B the voltage change is momentarily zero and the charging current is also zero.

From B to C the voltage falls, the current is reversed and the capacitor is discharged. The current now increases to its maximum negative value when the voltage is decreasing at its maximum rate at C.

Following a similar argument through the remainder of the input cycle, the current wave is seen to be as shown in the broken line in the diagram. We notice this time that the current leads the applied voltage by 90°. This is the opposite effect to the case of inductance, where the current lagged on the voltage by 90°. This phase shift of 90° is a fundamental effect of capacitance is an a.c. circuit.

We note then: *in a purely capacitive circuit, current* I *leads the applied voltage by 90°.*

We want now to find the relationship between the current and voltage values in the circuit.

Let the voltage rise from zero to $\hat{V}$ in one quarter-cycle of the voltage waveform, as from A to B in *Figure 10.10.*

The change in voltage $= \hat{V} - 0 = \hat{V}$ volts.

Time for 1 cycle $= 1/f$, hence the time for a quarter-cycle $= 1/4f$.

Then the average rate of change of voltage is represented by the straight line AB, and this is

$$\frac{\hat{V}}{1/4f} = 4f\hat{V}$$

Now we know that the increase in charge q coulomb for a voltage change v volts is

$$q = Cv = it$$

$$\therefore \quad i = C \times \frac{v}{t}$$

Then the average current = C × rate of change of voltage

$$= 4Cf\hat{V}$$

Now

$$\hat{I} = \frac{\pi}{2} \times \text{average current}$$

$$= \frac{\pi}{2} \times 4Cf\hat{V}$$

Using r.m.s. values

$$I = 2\pi CfV$$

and so

$$\frac{V}{I} = \frac{1}{2\pi fC}$$

The ratio V/I is the capacitive reactance X_c. X_c is measured in ohms. Hence

$$X_c = \frac{1}{\omega C}$$

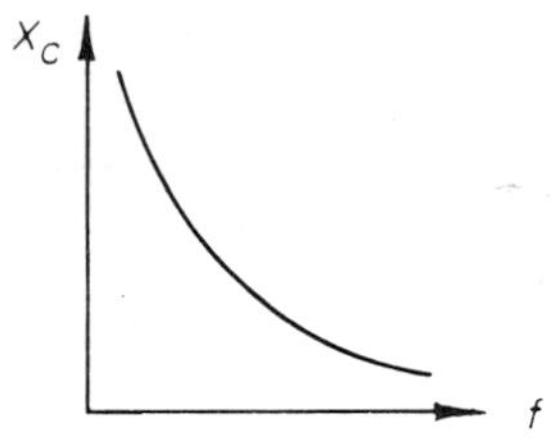

Figure 10.11

Compare this relationship between voltage and current with Ohm's law. The quantity $1/\omega C$ determines the r.m.s. current which flows in a capacitor when an r.m.s. voltage V is applied. It is the apparent resistance of the capacitor at a particular frequency, and is called the *reactance.*

We notice this time that X_c is inversely proportional to the frequency, hence X_c will decrease as the frequency increases. The graph of the variation is shown in *Figure 10.11.*

Example (12). A voltage wave represented by $v = \sin \omega t$ is connected in turn to (a) a pure inductance, (b) a pure capacitance. What is the expression for the current wave in each case?

(a) In a pure inductance, current lags the voltage by 90°. This means that we must introduce a phase shift term in the current expression which indicates a 90° lag. Hence

$$i = \sin(\omega t - 90^\circ) \quad \text{or} \quad i = \sin(\omega t - \pi/2)\text{ A}$$

(b) In a pure capacitance, current leads the voltage by 90°. To indicate this we must write the current expression as

$$i = \sin(\omega t + 90^\circ) \quad \text{or} \quad i = \sin(\omega t + \pi/2)\text{ A}$$

Example (13). Calculate the reactance of a 1 μF capacitor when connected to a circuit of frequency (a) 100 Hz, (b) 5000 Hz. What current would flow in the circuit in each case if the applied voltage was 10 V?

$C = 10^{-6}$ F

For f = 100 Hz

$$X_c = \frac{1}{2\pi \times 100 \times 10^{-6}} = \frac{10^6}{2\pi \times 100}$$

$$= 1590\ \Omega$$

For f = 5000 Hz

$$X_c = \frac{1}{2\pi \times 5000 \times 10^{-6}} = \frac{10^6}{2\pi \times 5000}$$

$$= 31.8\ \Omega$$

Notice how the capacitive reactance decreases as f increases.
When $X_c = 1590\ \Omega$,

$$I = \frac{V}{X_c} = \frac{10}{1590} = 0.0063 \text{ A } (6.3 \text{ mA})$$

When $X_c = 31.8\ \Omega$

$$I = \frac{V}{X_c} = \frac{10}{31.8} = 0.314 \text{ A } (314 \text{ mA})$$

The following test examples will get you familiar with the capacitive reactance expression and its effects in an a.c. circuit.

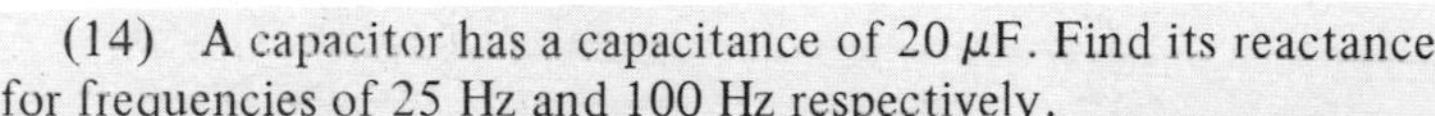

(14) A capacitor has a capacitance of 20 μF. Find its reactance for frequencies of 25 Hz and 100 Hz respectively.

(15) What value of capacitance will have a reactance of 3180 Ω when connected to a 600 Hz supply?

(16) Two similar capacitors, connected in parallel, take a total current of 250 mA when connected across a 100 V, 1000 Hz supply. Find the value of each capacitor.

(17) The two capacitors of the previous problem are connected in series across the same supply points. What current will now be drawn from the supply?

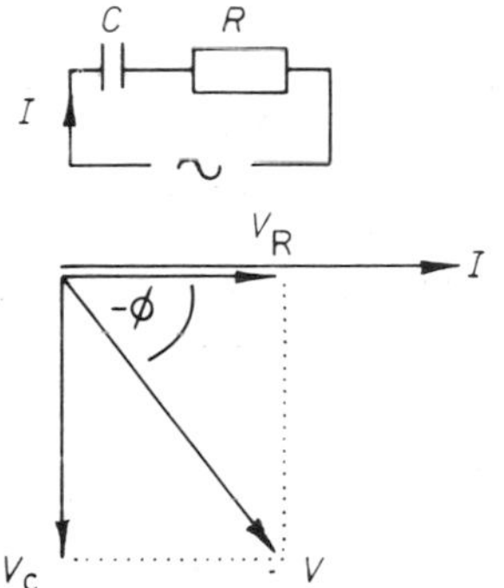

Figure 10.12

CAPACITIVE IMPEDANCE

We should expect the effect of capacitance and resistance in series in a circuit to lead to an effective impedance Z, for there will be a combined effect of reactance and resistance acting in the circuit.

The current is the common quantity again, so we can use current as our reference phasor. This is shown in *Figure 10.12.* From what we have already discovered

(a) the voltage V_R across resistor R is in phase with the current,
(b) the voltage V_c across the capacitor C lags the current by 90°.

In the figure we represent V as a phasor in phase with I, and V_c as a phasor lagging I by 90°. The phasor sum of these two voltages must equal the applied voltage V. Hence V lags the current I by some phase angle ϕ which must lie between 0° and −90°.

(18) Under what circumstances would ϕ be exactly 0° or −90°?

From the voltage triangle

$$V = \sqrt{(V_c^2 + V_R^2)}$$

But $V_c = IX_c$ and $V_R = IR$. Then if

Impedance Z = Supply voltage V/Circuit current I

we can sketch the impedance triangle as in *Figure 10.13*. You will notice that this is similar to the impedance triangle for inductance and resistance in series, except that capacitive reactance X_c is in the opposite direction to inductive reactance X_L. This leads to some interesting effects when a circuit contains both capacitance and inductance, as we shall discover in due course.

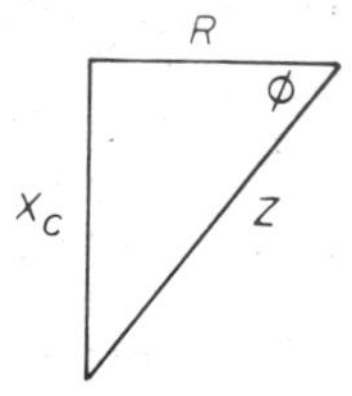

Figure 10.13

$$Z = \sqrt{(R^2 + X_c^2)} \quad \text{and} \quad \tan\phi = \frac{X_c}{R}$$

Example (19). A resistor of 40 Ω is connected in series with a capacitance of 50 μF across a 110 V supply. If the current flowing is 2 A, what is the frequency of the supply? What is the voltage across C and across R?

If 2 A flows with an applied voltage of 110 V, Z = 110/2 = 55 Ω. Now

$$Z = \sqrt{(R^2 + X_c^2)}$$

$$\therefore X_c = \sqrt{(55^2 - 40^2)} = 37.75\ \Omega$$

$$X_c = \frac{1}{2\pi fC} \quad \text{and so} \quad f = \frac{1}{2\pi CX_c}$$

Substituting values

$$f = \frac{10^6}{2\pi \times 50 \times 37.75}\ \text{Hz}$$

$$= 84.3\ \text{Hz}$$

Voltage across $R = IR = 2 \times 40 = 80$ V

Voltage across $C = IX_c = 2 \times 37.75 = 75.5$ V

We can check these results by seeing if the phasor sum of 80 V and 75.5 V comes to 110 V, i.e.

$$V = \sqrt{(V_R^2 + V_c^2)} = \sqrt{(80^2 + 75.5^2)} = 110\ \text{V}$$

You should be able to show that the current leads the voltage by an angle of 43.3°.

PROBLEMS FOR SECTION 10

Group 1

(20) Find the reactance of a coil of inductance 0.1 H when it is connected to an a.c. supply of frequency: (a) 50 Hz, (b) 80 Hz, (c) 1 kHz.

(21) An inductor has a reactance of 377 Ω when connected to a 120 Hz supply. What is its inductance?

(22) At what frequency will a coil of inductance 80 mH have a reactance of 302 Ω?

(23) Calculate the reactance of a 0.5 μF capacitor at frequencies: (a) 50 Hz, (b) 800 Hz, (c) 2 kHz.

(24) A capacitor has a reactance of 36 Ω when connected to a 50 Hz supply. What is its capacitance?

(25) At what frequency will a capacitor of 1000 pF have a reactance of 19 890 Ω?

(26) What is the impedance of a coil which has a resistance of 5 Ω and a reactance of 12 Ω?

(27) An a.c. circuit of impedance 12.5 Ω is made up of a coil connected in series with a resistor of 1.5 Ω. If the resistance of the coil itself is 6 Ω, calculate its reactance.

(28) What current is taken from a 240 V, 50 Hz supply by a coil of inductance 0.05 H and resistance 15 Ω? What is the phase angle between voltage and current?

(29) A coil, when connected to a 12 V d.c. supply, draws a current of 3 A, but when connected to a 100 Hz a.c. supply of 50 V takes a current of 10 A. Find (a) the resistance, (b) the reactance, and (c) the inductance of the coil.

(30) Five 10 μF capacitors are connected (a) in parallel, (b) in series, to a 100 V, 50 Hz supply. What will be the circuit current in each case?

(31) A capacitor is wired in series with a resistor of 100 Ω across a 50 V, 600 Hz supply. The current flowing is 200 mA. Calculate (a) the p.d. across the capacitor, (b) its capacitance, (c) the phase angle.

Group 2

(32) A 1 μF capacitor is wired in series with a 300 Ω resistor across an a.c. supply of 15 V. If a current of 25 mA flows in the circuit, what is the supply frequency?

(33) The impedance of a coil is measured as 500 Ω at a frequency of 796 Hz and as 800 Ω when the frequency is doubled. Find the inductance and the resistance of the coil.

(34) A 100 V, 60 W lamp is to be operated on 250 V, 50 Hz mains. Calculate the value of (a) a resistor, (b) an inductor (assumed to be of negligible self-resistance), required to be connected in series with the lamp.

(35) When connected to a 220 V, 50 Hz supply, an inductor draws a current of 5 A. When a resistance of 10 Ω is added in series, the current falls to 4.4 A. What is the resistance and inductance of the inductor, and what is the phase angle between voltage and current?

(36) A voltage represented by $v = 282.8 \sin 3142t$ is applied to a circuit of impedance 50 Ω, and the current lags the supply voltage by 20°. Find (a) the frequency, (b) the peak current, (c) the component values used in the circuit.

11 Power and resonance

Aims: At the end of this Unit section you should be able to:
Determine the power in an a.c. resistive circuit.
Explain graphically that the average power dissipated in a purely inductive or capacitive circuit is zero.
Solve problems of power dissipation in series L–R *and* C–R *circuits.*
Use phasor diagrams to solve simple series L, C *and* R *circuits.*
Define series resonance.
Solve problems associated with series resonance.

POWER IN A.C. CIRCUITS

In a d.c. circuit we have expressed the power dissipation in three forms:

Volts × amperes = VI W

Current squared × resistance = I^2R W

Voltage squared ÷ resistance = $\frac{V^2}{R}$ W

In an a.c. circuit these expressions are true only for instantaneous values of current and voltage, that is, i and v. By using the power expression $P = vi$ we can trace the power curve in any a.c. circuit by multiplying together corresponding values of voltage and current taken from a number of points on the sine waves representing the voltage and current. We shall do this for the three cases of pure resistance, pure inductance and pure capacitance connected in turn into an a.c. circuit.

Power in a pure resistance

When an alternating voltage $v = V.\sin \omega t$ is applied to a circuit of resistance R Ω, the current which flows is in phase with the voltage and is expressed by $i = I.\sin \omega t$. The curve of *Figure 11.1* show these voltage and current waveforms.

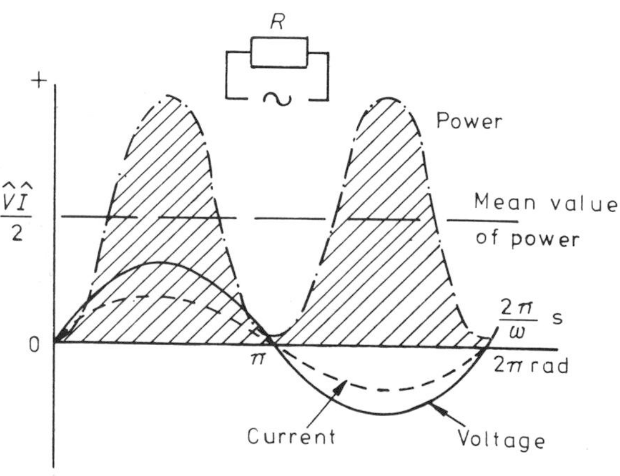

Figure 11.1

We obtain the power curve by multiplying together instantaneous values of v and i and the result is shown in the broken line curve traced on the same axes as the v and i waves. We make a note of two points:

(a) The product v times i is always positive, since v and i are either simultaneously positive or simultaneously negative, so the power curve is always positive.

(b) The power curve is another sine wave having twice the frequency of the current or voltage wave (there are two complete cycles of the power curve to one complete cycle of the voltage or current), and it is symmetrical about an axis having a mean height of $\hat{V}\hat{I}/2$ W.

Now the area shown shaded under the power curve is the product of power and time, and so represents energy expended. The mean or average power over a cycle is $\hat{V}\hat{I}/2$ which can be written as $(\hat{V}/\sqrt{2}) \times (\hat{I}/\sqrt{2})$. But $\hat{V}/\sqrt{2}$ and $\hat{I}/\sqrt{2}$ are the r.m.s. values of voltage and current, V and I, respectively. Therefore

Power dissipated over one cycle $= VI$ W

or

$$I^2R = V^2/R \text{ W}$$

The power dissipated in a purely resistive circuit is therefore identical with the power dissipated in a d.c. circuit, except that the r.m.s. values of the alternating voltage and current replace the direct current values. This is as it should be, of course, since we have based our definition of r.m.s. values on the equivalence to power dissipated in d.c. circuits.

Power in a pure inductance

Figure 11.2 shows the current and voltage curves for a purely inductive circuit. The current curve lags 90° behind the voltage, and the power delivered to the circuit during a complete cycle is found as before by multiplying together the instantaneous values of the current and voltage waves throughout the cycle. If at any given instant the current and voltage have the same sign, for example, as between 0 and $\pi/2$ rad, the power curve will be positive. When these quantities have opposite signs, for example, as between $\pi/2$ and π rad, the power curve will be negative.

Plotted in this way, the power curve is again a sine wave of twice the frequency of the current or voltage wave, but this time is symmetrically disposed about the horizontal axis, half of the shaded area being above

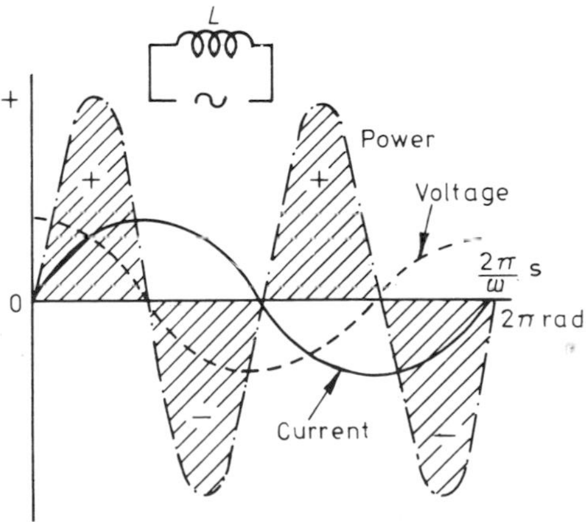

Figure 11.2

and half below the time (or angle) axis. Again energy is represented by the shaded areas. When the power curve is positive and above the axis, energy is being delivered to, and stored in, the magnetic field associated with the inductance. When the power curve is negative, the magnetic field is collapsing and energy is being returned to the source of supply. Remember there is no resistance in the circuit (an ideal example), so energy cannot be dissipated as heat. It must therefore continually interchange between the source and the magnetic field.

Since the power curve is symmetrical about the horizontal axis, un like the previous case of a resistive load where the curve was wholly above the axis, the energy delivered to the circuit during one quarter-cycle of the input current is exactly equal to the energy returned to the circuit during the succeeding quarter-cycle, and so the total power supplied to the circuit over a complete cycle is zero.

Power in a pure capacitance

Figure 11.3 shows the voltage and current waves for a purely capacitive circuit. The current wave leads the voltage by 90° and the power delivered to the circuit is again found by multiplying together the instantaneous values of current and voltage throughout the cycle.

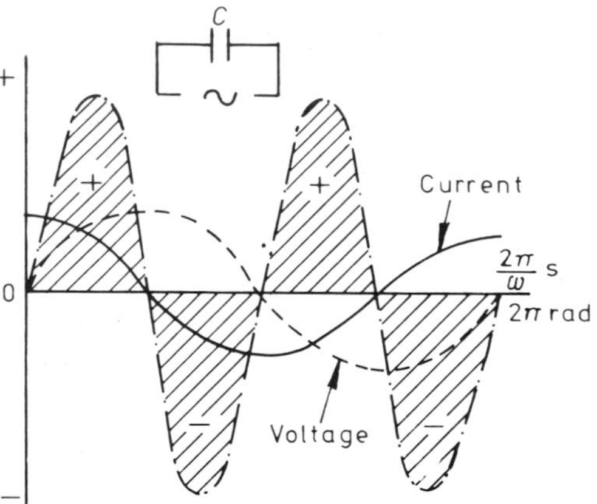

Figure 11.3

The resulting power curve is shaded in the figure and once again it is a sine wave symmetrically disposed about the horizontal axis. During the first quarter-cycle of the input waveform, the plates of the capacitor are charged in a positive direction; during the next quarter-cycle they are charged in a negative direction. Electric charges therefore move backwards and forwards round the circuit (constituting a current flow), and the energy stored in the electric field over one quarter-cycle of input is returned to the supply during the following quarter-cycle. The capacitor consequently absorbs no energy from the supply over a complete cycle, and so the total power supplied to the circuit over the cycle is zero.

We summarise:

(a) In a purely resistive circuit all the energy supplied is dissipated in the resistance, usually in the form of heat. Calculations are made, using the usual expressions for power, current and voltage being expressed in their r.m.s. values.

(b) In a purely reactive circuit, inductive or capacitive, all energy supplied during each quarter-cycle of the input wave is returned to the circuit during the succeeding quarter-cycle. Hence the total energy supplied and the power dissipated is, in both cases, zero.

(1) A current represented by $i = 282.\sin \omega t$ flows in a resistor of value 100 Ω. What power is dissipated in the resistor?

(2) A resistor of 500 Ω is connected in parallel with a capacitor of 10 μF across an alternating supply of 250 V. What power does the circuit consume?

POWER IN SERIES CIRCUITS

What happens in the context of power dissipation when an a.c. supply is connected to a series *L-R* or a series *C-R* circuit? We have already encountered these circuit arrangements in the previous Unit section, and dealt there with the impedance *Z* of such circuits.

Since power is dissipated only in the resistive part of the circuit, we need concern ourselves only with the power expression

$$P = I^2 R \text{ W}$$

to arrive at the solution. The thing we have to remember, however, is that the current *I* flowing depends upon impedance *Z*; that is

$$I = \frac{V}{Z}$$

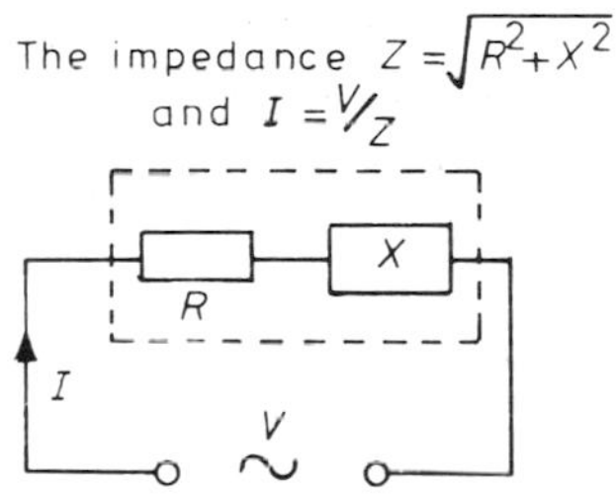

Figure 11.4

so it is necessary first of all to determine *Z* from a knowledge of the resistive and reactive components of the impedance. *Figure 11.4* illustrates the situation. After that, all we need is the application of the basic power expression given above. A couple of worked examples will best make the method clear.

Example (3). The coil of an electrically operated relay is supplied from a 50 V, 500 Hz source. At this frequency the coil is equivalent to an inductance of 0.5 H in series with a resistance of 800 Ω. How much power is being dissipated in the coil?

To use the power equation $P = I^2R$ we must calculate *I*. To do this we require the impedance of the circuit *Z*.

$$X_L = 2\pi f L = 2\pi \times 500 \times 0.5$$

$$= 1571\ \Omega$$

Also $R = 800\ \Omega$

$$\therefore \quad Z = \sqrt{(R^2 + X_L{}^2)} = \sqrt{(800^2 + 1571^2)}$$

$$= 1763\ \Omega$$

$$I = \frac{V}{Z} = \frac{50}{1763} = 0.0284 \text{ A}$$

$\therefore$ power dissipated $= I^2R = 0.0284^2 \times 800 = 0.64$ W

Example (4). A 100 W, 110 V lamp is required to be used on a 240 V, 50 Hz supply. What capacitance must be connected in series with the lamp in order that it will operate properly?

We treat the lamp as being purely resistive, so that the circuit will be as sketched in *Figure 11.5(a)*.

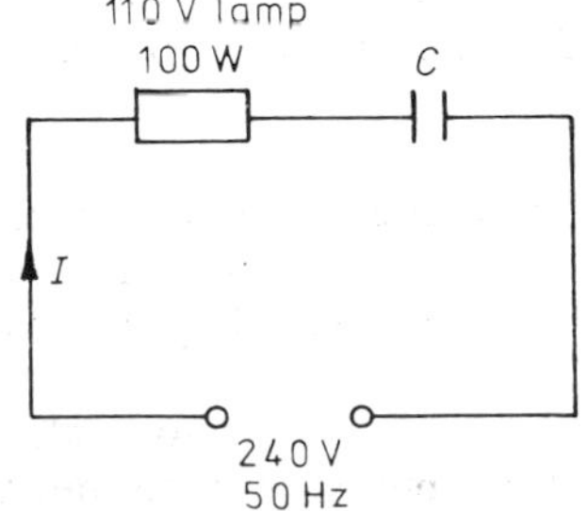

Figure 11.5(a)

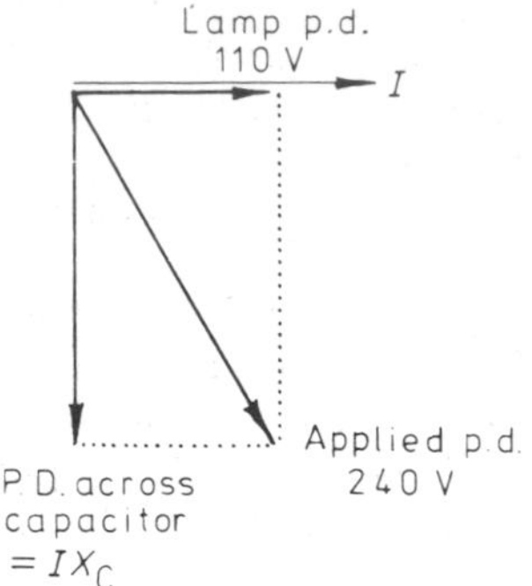

Figure 11.5(b)

The power dissipated in the lamp is 100 W at 110 V, hence the current taken by the lamp is

$$I = \frac{\text{Power}}{\text{Volts}} = \frac{100}{110} = 0.91 \text{ A}$$

From the phasor diagram of *Figure 11.5(b)*

$$IX_c = \sqrt{(240^2 - 110^2)} = 213.3 \text{ V}$$

$$\therefore \quad X_c = \frac{213.3}{0.91} = 234.4\ \Omega$$

$$\therefore \quad C = \frac{10^6}{2\pi f X_c} = \frac{10^6}{2\pi \times 50 \times 234.4}\ \mu\text{F}$$

$$= 13.6\ \mu\text{F}$$

This last example illustrates a method of dropping the voltage from 240 V to 110 V without a waste of energy; the capacitor 'loses' the excess voltage without any consumption of energy itself.

For certain reasons, however, it is more usual to employ a 'choking' or 'starter' coil for this purpose. Such a coil consists of wire wound on a laminated iron core and so designed that its inductive reactance is large compared with its resistance. The power it consumes is then relatively small but its impedance is high enough to provide the required reduction in voltage.

Now try the next two problems on your own.

(5) A 4 μF capacitor and a 150 Ω resistor are wired in series across a 30 V, 250 Hz supply. Calculate the circuit impedance, the current flowing and the power dissipated in the circuit.

(6) The power taken by a series L-R circuit when connected to a 100 V, 50 Hz supply is 200 W, and the current flowing is 3.5 A. Calculate the circuit resistance and the inductance.

RESONANCE IN A SERIES CIRCUIT

You will recall that we sketched the curves representing inductive and capacitive reactance against a base of frequency in Unit Section 10; and to refresh your memory you should glance back at *Figures 10.5* and *10.11* respectively.

You will also recall that in series circuits the voltage across R is IR volts represented by a phasor in phase with the current; the voltage across L is IX_L volts represented by a phasor leading the current by 90°; and the voltage across C is IX_c volts represented by a phasor lagging on the current by 90°.

The time has come to connect all three elements in series as shown in *Figure 11.6(a)* The voltage V applied to the circuit will be the phasor sum of the three separate voltages IR, IX_L and IX_c, but the actual appearance of the overall phasor diagram will clearly depend upon the relative magnitudes of these voltages. The three possible cases have been illustrated in *Figure 11.6(b)*.

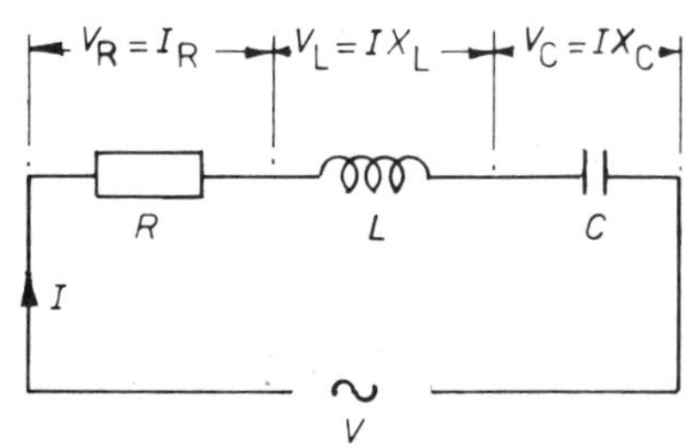

Figure 11.6(a)

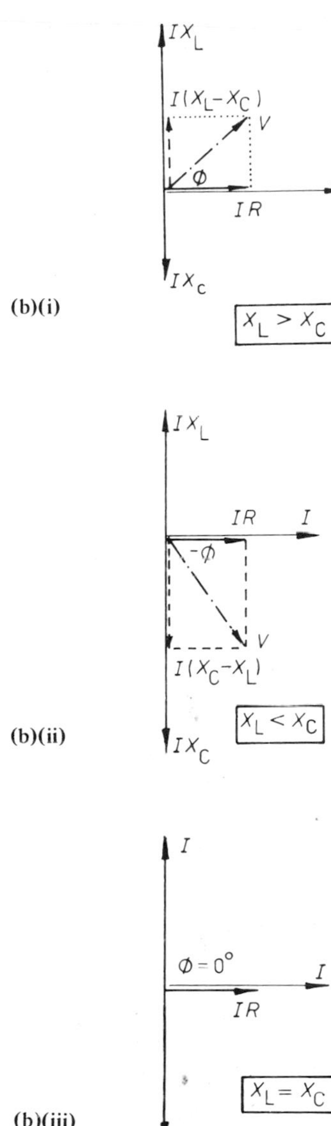

(b)(i)

(b)(ii)

(b)(iii)

Figure 11.6

In diagram (i) X_L is assumed greater than X_c; hence the effective reactance acting in the circuit is $X_L - X_c$, a straight algebraic subtraction since the phasors concerned are acting in direct opposition. The supply voltage V is then the phasor resultant of IR and $I(X_L - X_c)$, leading the current by phase angle ϕ. That is to say, the inductive reactance predominates in the circuit.

In diagram (ii) we assume that X_c is greater than X_L. This time the effective reactance in the circuit is $(X_c - X_L)$, again a straight algebraic subtraction since the phasors concerned are acting in opposition. Hence the supply voltage is the phasor sum of IR and $I(X_c - X_L)$, lagging the current by phase angle $-\phi$. So the capacitive reactance predominates in the circuit.

The important condition which calls for our particular attention is the one shown in diagram (iii), where $X_L = X_c$. In this situation, the voltages IX_L and IX_c are equal and in phase opposition, so cancelling out. The voltage phasor V is then in phase with current I and the circuit behaves as a pure resistance R. This effect is known as *series resonance*, and when any series circuit containing resistance, inductance and capacitance behaves as a pure resistance, it is said to be in a state of *electrical resonance*. The frequency at which resonance occurs is called the resonant frequency and it is not difficult to calculate what it is.

Let the resonant frequency be f_0. Then since the reactances are equal at this frequency, we have

$$X_L = X_c$$

$$2\pi f_0 L = \frac{1}{2\pi f_0 C}$$

$$\therefore \quad f_0^2 = \frac{1}{4\pi^2 LC}$$

$$f_0 = \frac{1}{2\pi\sqrt{LC}}$$

As this formula contains only L and C, the resonant frequency is clearly unaffected by any resistance present in the circuit.

You will notice from the phasor diagrams of *Figure 11.6(b)* that the resonant condition represents the minimum circuit impedance; in fact, at frequency f_0

$$Z = R$$

This could be used as a definition for series resonance, but a more general statement is given by defining resonance as that condition for which the current and voltage in the circuit are in phase.

Example (7). What is the resonant frequency of a circuit made up of a 100 μH coil of resistance 5 Ω connected in series with a 100 pF capacitor? What current would flow at resonance if the applied voltage was 1 mV?

$$L = 100 \times 10^{-6} = 10^{-4}\text{ H}, C = 100 \times 10^{-12} = 10^{-10}\text{ F}$$

$$f_0 = \frac{1}{2\pi\sqrt{(10^{-4} \times 10^{-10})}} = \frac{1}{2\pi\, 10^{-7}} = \frac{10^7}{2\pi}$$

$$= 159 \times 10^3\text{ Hz}$$

$$= 159\text{ kHz}$$

At resonance $Z = R$

$$\therefore \quad I = \frac{V}{Z} = \frac{10^{-3}}{5} = 0.2 \text{ mA}$$

This is the greatest current possible in the circuit. At all other frequencies the current falls below 0.2 mA.

(8) Find the resonant frequency for a 180 μH coil connected in series with a 300 pF capacitor.

(9) What capacitor would you connect in series with a 500 mH coil so that resonance would be obtained at 2 kHz?

(10) Draw a phasor diagram and use it to show that when the reactance of a series L-C-R circuit is equal to the resistance, the phase angle will be +45° or –45°.

REACTANCE CURVES

We return for a moment to the graphs of X_L and X_c plotted against frequency. The reactance-frequency characteristic for an inductance is reproduced in *Figure 11.7*. Since the equation for reactance $X_L = 2\pi fL$, the graph of X_L against f is (for any given L) a straight line passing through the origin.

The reactance curve for a capacitance is also reproduced in the figure. The equation for this curve can be written as $X_c = -1/2\pi fC$, the negative sign indicating the opposing effect of this reactance to that of X_L. The graph then lies in the lower right-hand quadrant of the co-ordinate axes as shown.

The resultant reactance when the inductance and capacitance are wired in series is shown by the broken line, this being the curve of $X_L + X_c$. At one frequency this sum must be zero, that is, when the positive and negative reactances are equal. This is the resonant frequency f_0. At frequencies below f_0 the negative component predominates and the circuit is capacitive, i.e. has current leading voltage, or a negative phase angle. Above f_0 the circuit is inductive, i.e. has current lagging voltage, or a positive phase angle. At f_0 the current and voltage are in phase.

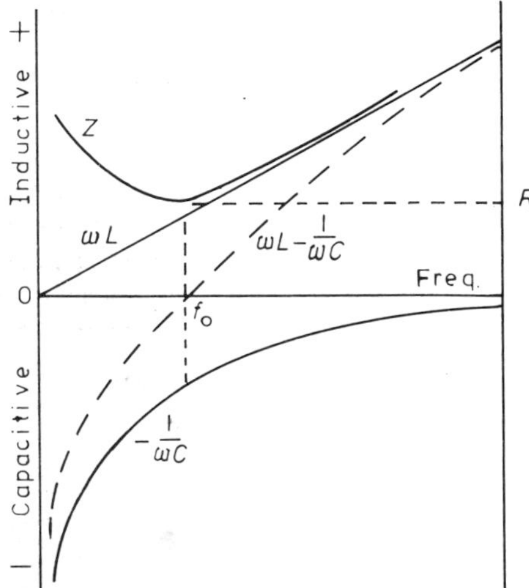

Figure 11.7

The circuit impedance has also been plotted on the figure. It is seen to reach its lowest point at frequency f_0 when it becomes equal to the resistance R.

(11) A series circuit, when supplied from a source of frequency 150 Hz, has a resistance of 30 Ω, an inductive reactance of 20 Ω and a capacitive reactance of 40 Ω. Draw, after the manner of *Figure 11.7*, to a base axis of 100–600 Hz, curves to show the variations in inductive and capacitive reactance as the frequency is changed from 100 Hz to 600 Hz. From your graphs, estimate the resonant frequency. (Hint: you don't *have* to work out what L and C actually are. This will save you a lot of effort.)

VOLTAGES AT RESONANCE

In certain circumstances it is possible for the voltages set up at resonance across L and C to be very much greater than the applied voltage V. This may appear a little surprising at first, but remember that these voltages are acting in phasor opposition at resonance and so their sum at resonance is zero, or very nearly so in practice.

Let the current at resonance be I_0, then the voltages developed across R, L and C respectively will be

$$V_R = I_0 R, \quad V_L = I_0 \omega L, \quad V_c = -\frac{I_0}{\omega C}$$

At resonance $V_L = -V_c$, $V_R = V$ (the applied voltage), and $I_0 = V/R$. The voltage across each reactance is then $\omega L\,(V/R)$ or $(1/\omega C)\,(V/R)$ which we can write as

$$V.\frac{\omega L}{R} \quad \text{or} \quad V.\frac{1}{\omega CR}$$

The applied voltage V is consequently multiplied by a factor $\omega L/R$ across the inductor and by a factor $1/\omega CR$ across the capacitor. If R is small, either of these factors can be much greater than unity, hence V_L or V_c can be many times the applied voltage V. You will learn in due course that these factors are called the 'quality' or 'goodness' factors of the coil and capacitor respectively, symbolised Q. For the time being, you will notice that Q represents the ratio of the *reactance* of either component to the circuit *resistance*.

Example (12). A coil of resistance 20 Ω and inductance 50 mH is wired in series with a capacitor of 0.1 μF across a 50 V variable frequency source. Find (a) the resonant frequency, (b) the current at resonance, (c) the voltages developed across either reactance at resonance.

Here $L = 50 \times 10^{-3}$ H, $C = 0.1 \times 10^{-6} = 10^{-7}$ F. Therefore

$$f_0 = 2\pi \frac{1}{\sqrt{(50 \times 10^{-3} \times 10^{-7})}} = \frac{10^5}{2\pi \times \sqrt{50}}$$

$$= 2250 \text{ Hz} \quad (\text{or } 2.25 \text{ kHz})$$

At resonance $I_0 = \frac{V}{R} = \frac{50}{20} = 2.5$ A

Voltage across $L = I_0 \omega L = 2.5 \times 2\pi \times 2250 \times 50 \times 10^{-3}$

$= 1767$ V

Voltage across $C = I_0 . \frac{1}{\omega C} = 2.5 \times \frac{1}{2\pi \times 2250 \times 10^{-7}}$

$= 1768$ V

Notice the extremely high voltages developed across C and L.

(13) A coil of inductance 10 H and resistance 300 Ω is used with a series capacitor to resonate at a frequency of 50 Hz. The capacitor working voltage is marked as 2000 V. Would this be adequate for a supply voltage of 240 V at 50 Hz?

PROBLEMS FOR SECTION 11

Group 1

(14) A voltage given by $v = 100 \sin \omega t$ is applied to a resistor of 2500 Ω. What power is dissipated in the resistor?

(15) A 200 μF capacitor is wired in series with an 8 Ω resistor across a 10 V, 50 Hz supply. What power is dissipated in the circuit, and what is the phase angle?

(16) A coil has a reactance of 1600 Ω and draws a current of 25 mA from a 50 V a.c. supply. What power is dissipated by the coil?

(17) A coil has an inductance of 30 mH and a resistance of 30 Ω. Calculate (a) its impedance, (b) the current drawn, (c) the power dissipated, when it is connected to a 25 V, 200 Hz supply.

(18) A 10 V, 24 Hz supply is connected to an inductor of 2 H having a resistance of 400 Ω. Calculate (a) the circuit impedance, (b) the current flowing, (c) the phase angle, (d) the power absorbed.

(19) A coil draws 8 A and dissipated 1.2 kW when connected to a 240 V, 50 Hz supply. What is its impedance and effective resistance?

(20) The solenoid of a magnetically operated switch is designed to work on a 100 V, 50 Hz supply, and is equivalent at this frequency to an inductance of 2 H in series with a 250 Ω resistor. What power is consumed in the solenoid when the switch is energised?

(21) A 100 V, 100 Hz a.c. supply is applied to an inductive circuit. The current flowing is 2 A and the power dissipated is 120 W Calculate the resistance and the inductance of the circuit.

(22) The current flowing in an inductance is 1.2 A when the applied voltage is 240 V. If the power absorbed is 135 W, what is the phase angle between voltage and current?

Group 2

(23) Find the resonant frequency of a circuit made up of a 180 μH coil in series with a 100 pF capacitor.

(24) A 20 mH coil of resistance 50 Ω is connected in series with a 200 pF capacitor. A supply of 200 mV at the resonant frequency is applied to the circuit. Find (a) the resonant frequency, (b) the current flowing, (c) the voltage across the capacitor, (d) the power dissipated.

(25) A 50 mH coil, resistance 5 Ω, in series with a 5 μF capacitor, is wired across a 100 mV variable frequency supply. Find (a) the resonant frequency, (b) the maximum current drawn, (c) the power dissipated.

(26) An inductor of 50 mH and 20 Ω resistance is connected in series with a 100 μF capacitor across a 100 V, 50 Hz supply. What value of capacitor would you connect in series (or parallel) with the existing capacitor to give series resonance? What current would then flow?

(27) A coil of inductance 250 mH and resistance 25 Ω resonates with a series capacitor at 1 kHz. Find the voltage across the capacitor at the resonant frequency, the supply voltage being 20 V. A capacitor of 1500 V working is available; would this be suitable for use in this circuit?

12 A.C. to D.C. conversion

Aims: At the end of this Unit section you should be able to:
Distinguish between alternating current and fluctuating unidirectional current.
Understand the elementary principle of the diode.
Understand the principles of half- and full-wave rectification.

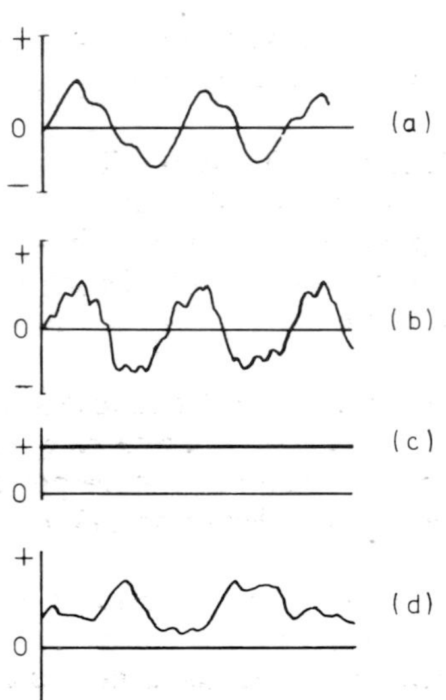

Figure 12.1

An alternating current is a current which is flowing first in one direction along a conductor and then, after a given time, reverses and flows for a further period of time in the opposite direction. As we recall, such a complete backwards and forwards movement of the charge carriers, (the electrons) constitutes one cycle of the alternating current. *Figure 12.1(a)* and *(b)*, for example, represent alternating currents.

On the other hand, a direct current is a current which flows always in one definite direction. Such a current flowing from the positive to the negative terminal of a battery (in the conventional sense, that is) through some form of resistance or load is generally a steady flow, maintaining a certain level for the whole length of time that the circuit is operating. The graph of such a current is shown in *Figure 12.1(c)*, and is known as a *unidirectional* (one-way only) current.

Now what about figure (d)? At first glance this looks like the alternating currents shown at (a) and (b), but on closer examination we notice that although it exhibits up and down fluctuations, it never crosses the horizontal axis. Like figure (c) the current it represents never *reverses* its direction; the electrons move forwards in a cyclic manner but they never turn round and move backwards. What we have here is a unidirectional current, even though it is a fluctuating one. Make certain you appreciate this important distinction between an alternating current and a unidirectional current. When a unidirectional is fluctuating wildly, it is very easy to confuse it with an alternating current. The criterion is: does it ever reverse its direction of flow?

In nearly all cases, electronic and electrical apparatus operates from steady d.c. supplies, as shown in *Figure 12.1(c)*. In many instances such supplies are obtained from cells or batteries; portable transistor radios, flashlamps, pocket calculators are familiar examples. But we do not normally expect to operate our television receivers from batteries, and certainly it would not be very economical or particularly practical, to operate, say, large computer systems or high-power transmitters, or domestic hi-fi equipment for that matter, from battery supplies. We use 'the mains' for all these things, and if we are to use the mains supply for such purposes, it is necessary to convert the alternating current (or voltage) into direct current (or voltage).

A.C. TO D.C. CONVERSION

To convert the sinusoidal alternating current flowing in resistor R of *Figure 12.2* into a unidirectional current it is necessary to eliminate one half or other of the alternations. The curve must either lie wholly

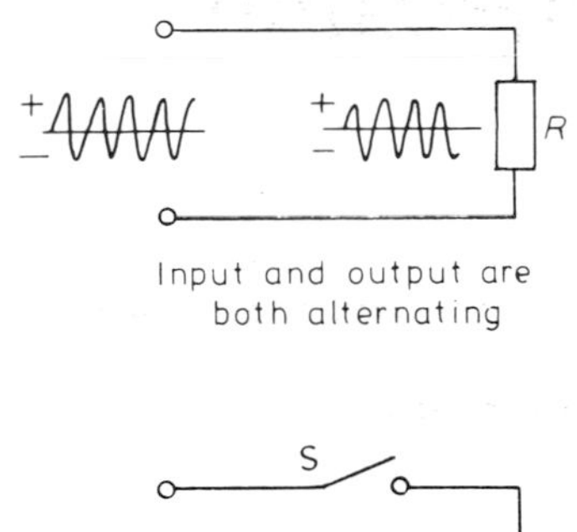

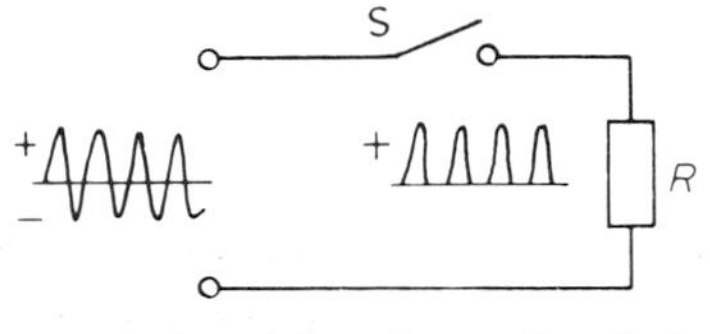

Figure 12.2

above the horizontal axis or wholly below it, but must not cross it. There can then be no question of current reversal. The obvious solution is to switch the circuit off whenever the current is about to reverse; if the switch S is switched on for each positive half-cycle of input current and switched off for each negative half-cycle, the resulting current through R will be a series of positive pulsations, that is, a current which continually goes on and off but never reverses in direction.

Now, if we tried any sort of manual switching even at the low frequency of the mains supply, we should have to operate the switch 100 times a second.

(1) The mains supply frequency is 50 Hz. Why would 50 operations of the switch per second not be satisfactory?

Further, not only would the speed of switching have to be right, it would also be necessary to keep in time with the alternations.

(2) Now it is perfectly feasible to design an electrically operated switch which will do the job automatically. Think of an ordinary electric bell or buzzer principle. Can you sketch a suitable electromechanical system that would perform the job efficiently? What would be its limitations?

However, whatever you may have 'invented' as a solution to Problem (2), such electromechanical methods are nowadays relatively rare. Automatic switching is carried out by devices called *diodes*, and the process of converting alternating into direct current is called *rectification*.

RECTIFIERS AND RECTIFICATION

We shall not be concerned in this section (apart from a few notes on the thermionic diode) with what goes on inside a diode; this is a matter for the electronics units of the course. Sufficient to say that a diode is a two-terminal device which turns up in a variety of shapes and sizes depending upon the particular application, and which has the property of allowing current to pass through it only in one direction. It behaves, therefore, quite unlike ordinary electrical conductors or resistors, which permit the flow of current irrespective of which way round you connect them into circuit. A few common examples of diodes are sketched in *Figure 12.3*.

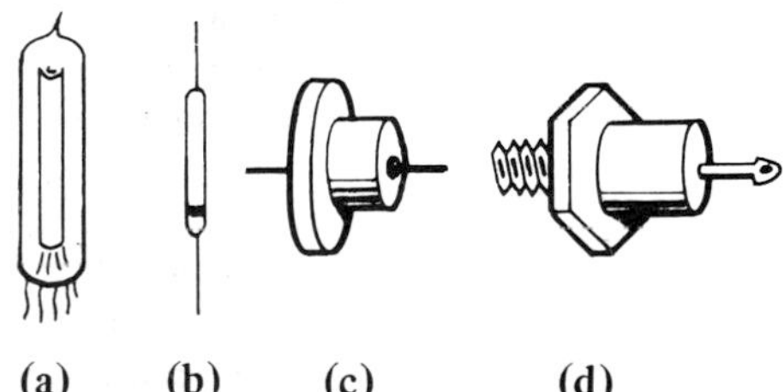

Figure 12.3 (a) (b) (c) (d)

The *thermionic* (heat operated) diode shown at (a) is little used in present day electronic apparatus. Its principle will, however, be briefly mentioned, as examples of it are still to be found in many pieces of apparatus. When certain materials such as tungsten or barium and strontium oxides are heated to a sufficiently high temperature in a vacuum, electrons are emitted from their surfaces. The effect is known

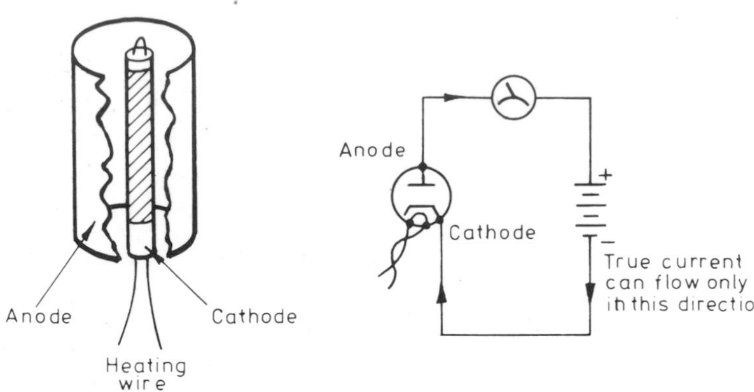

Figure 12.4

as *thermionic emission*. If a nickel tube is coated with barium or strontium oxide and then heated by means of a wire passing through the centre of the tube, the electrons are emitted at a temperature of some 800 °C, about red heat, and form a negatively charged cloud or space charge around the heated tube. The surface which supplies electrons in this way is called the *cathode*. If now, as shown in *Figure 12.4*, a metal electrode is placed to surround the cathode and this electrode is given a positive charge, the electrons in the space charge will be attracted to it, and a current will flow around the circuit as indicated in the circuit representation. The positive electrode is called the *anode*. Current can only flow from the cathode to the anode when the anode is at a positive potential with respect to the cathode. If the anode is negative, no current flows in the circuit. The thermionic diode is therefor a one-way device.

The modern diode is made either from germanium or silicon and is called a *semiconductor diode* or *p–n junction diode*. It is very compact, requires no heated cathode and is clearly much more convenient to use than the thermionic diode. Such diodes are illustrated in *Figure 12.3*, which shows a few of the forms they can take. The symbol for these diodes is shown in *Figure 12.5*. The arrowhead points in the direction in which current will conventionally flow through the diode. On this basis the circuit at (a) will permit the flow of current, but the circuit at (b) will not. We say that at (a) the diode is *forward biased*, at (b) the diode is *reverse biased*. In the forward direction its resistance is very small; in the reverse direction it is very large. The diode thus behaves as a switch.

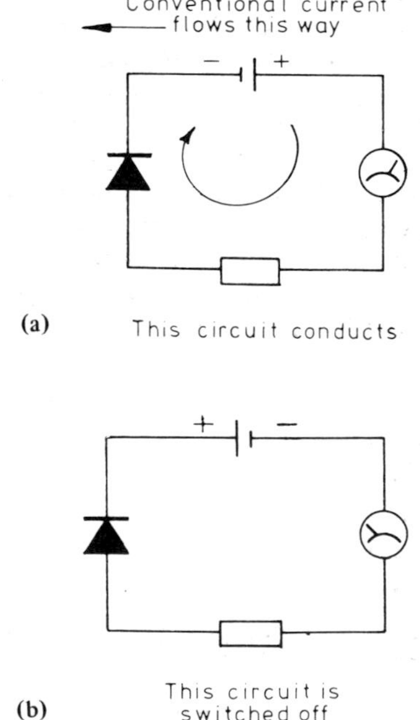

Figure 12.5

If we compare the direction of current flow in a semiconductor diode with that in a thermionic diode we can assign the terms anode and cathode to appropriate terminals of the semiconductor diode.

(3) Is the arrowhead of the semiconductor diode equivalent to the anode or the cathode of a thermionic diode?

Many diodes look like small resistors, and they are nearly always marked by a spot or coloured ring at one end. This end corresponds to the cathode of the diode. Keep in mind that this end has to be negative in order for the diode to switch on. If you make it positive, the diode will switch off.

We can now connect diodes into alternating current circuits and examine how they perform the job of rectification. We shall be interested in three circuit arrangements.

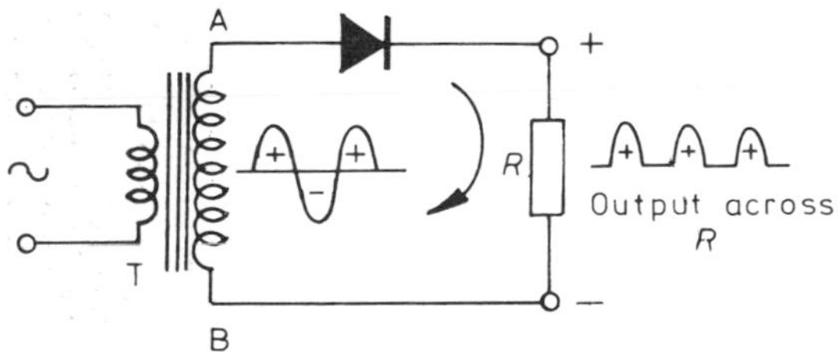

Figure 12.6

The half-wave rectifier

This circuit is shown in *Figure 12.6*. This includes a transformer T which is used (in general) for two purposes: it isolates the equipment from direct connection to the mains supply and so increases safety, and it enables the mains voltage to be either increased or decreased to suit the apparatus for which the rectified supply will finally be used. It is not directly associated with the process of rectification.

When terminal A is positive with respect to B, the diode conducts. The positive half-cycle of voltage across A–B therefore causes a current to flow round the circuit and a voltage will be developed across resistor load R corresponding to the form of the half-cycle. When the input polarity reverses, A will be negative with respect to B and the diode will switch off. Hence no current flows in the circuit and there is no output voltage across R.

The potential difference developed across R thus consists of half sine waves, and the circuit is referred to as a *half-wave rectifier*. The current through R is always in one direction in spite of the fluctuations; so our output is unidirectional.

Full-wave rectifier

The half-wave rectifier has the disadvantage that there is no output at all for half of the available time. The *full-wave rectifier*, as its name implies, enables us to use both halves of the input wave. The circuit is given in *Figure 12.7*. Two diodes are used with a transformer whose secondary winding is centre-tapped. We can treat the centre-tap as being a neutral point so that ends A and B swing alternately positive and negative about it. Each diode consequently conducts in turn when its particular anode happens to be positive with respect to the centre point. Following the direction of the resulting current flow as the diagram indicates, we notice that the current through R is, for both diodes, in the same direction. Our output voltage is therefore unidirectional, the spaces between the half sine waves in the half-wave rectifier now being filled in. The average output across R is therefore doubled, a much better arrangement altogether.

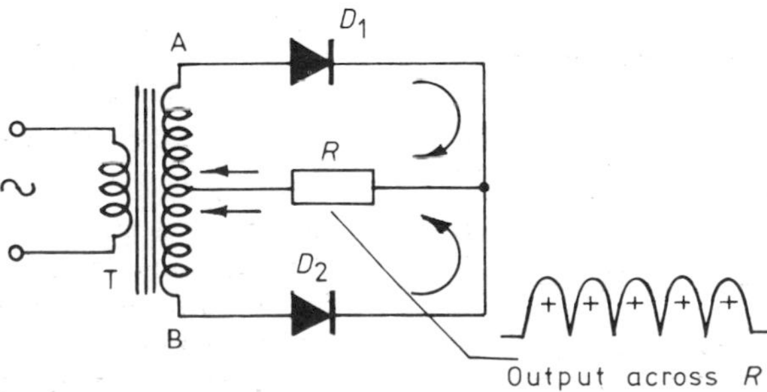

Figure 12.7

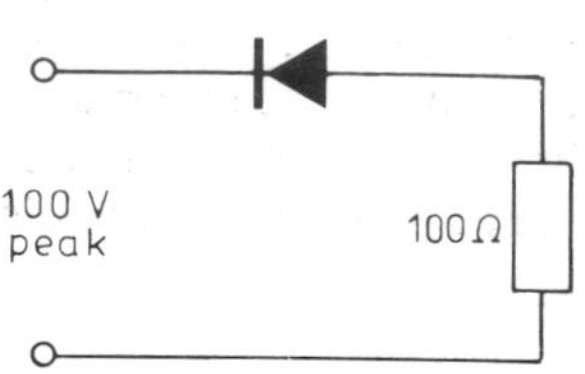

Figure 12.8

Example (4). *Figure 12.8* shows a half-wave rectifier circuit. The diode used has a constant forward resistance of 10 Ω and an infinite reverse resistance. For a 100 V peak input, calculate (a) the average current flowing, (b) the average voltage across the resistor, (c) the average voltage across the diode.

(a) When the diode conducts, the peak current flowing will be peak applied voltage divided by the total circuit resistance:

$$\text{Peak } I = \frac{100}{110} = 0.91 \text{ A}$$

The average value of a half sine wave is $0.637\hat{I}$, but as the output will have every alternate half-wave missing, the overall average falls to one-half of this, i.e.

$$\text{Average } I = 0.318 \times \hat{I} = 0.318 \times 0.91$$
$$= 0.29 \text{ A}$$

(b) The average current flowing in the resistor is 0.29 A, hence the average voltage across it will be $100 \times 0.29 = 29$ V.

(c) The average current through the diode is, as for the resistor, equal to 0.29 A. Hence the average voltage across it will be

$$0.29 \times 10 = 2.9 \text{ V}$$

(5) What will be the peak voltage across the diode (a) when it is switched on, (b) when it is switched off?

(6) Compare the power dissipated in the resistor with the power dissipated in the diode.

The bridge rectifier

This form of rectifier uses four diodes but does not require a centre-tapped transformer. It provides a full-wave output. The circuit of the *bridge rectifier* is shown in *Figure 12.9*. This time the diodes conduct in pairs: when terminal A is positive with respect to B, diodes D_1 and D_3

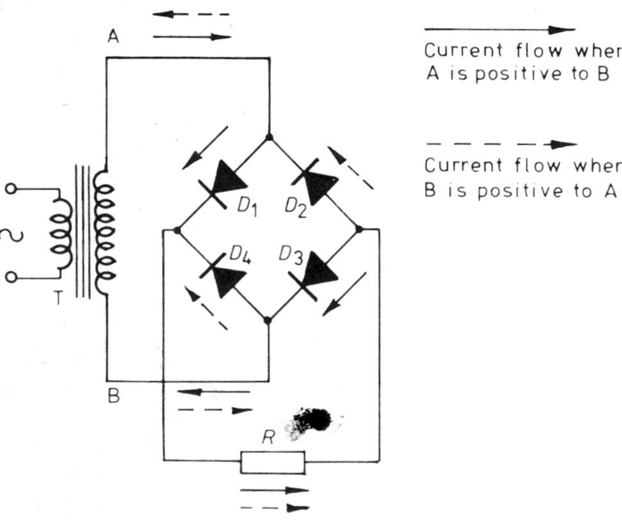

Figure 12.9

conduct in series, but the diodes D_2 and D_4 are switched off. When the input polarity reverses, D_2 and D_4 switch on in series, but D_1 and D_3 switch off. The current flow through R is, for each case, in the direction shown, so once again a unidirectional output voltage is obtained.

Go through the argument carefully and make sure you understand the working of the bridge circuit, as it has many applications in electronics.

SMOOTHING

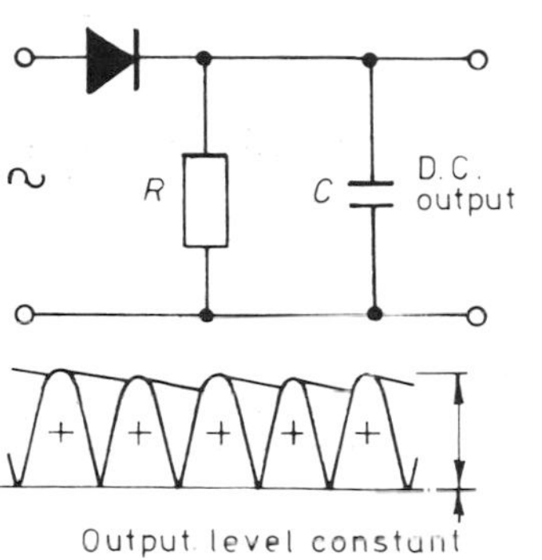

Figure 12.10

The pulsating output we obtain from the full-wave and the bridge rectifier circuits is not suitable as it stands for the operation of equipment which requires a steady d.c. output such as we should obtain from batteries. To smooth out the pulsations a large value capacitor is connected across the output of the rectifier (see *Figure 12.10*); the effect of this is to maintain the output voltage at a level which is very near to the peak of the output waveform. During each pulse of output voltage, the capacitor charges, and provided we do not draw off enough current between the pulses to discharge the capacitor appreciably, the level will remain reasonably constant. The output is now said to be *smoothed*. In practice a rather more involved smoothing arrangement is employed, but the principle is essentially one of maintaining the output level during the interval between the output pulsations.

PROBLEMS FOR SECTION 12

Only a few problems are set here, as this subject matter will be fully investigated in the electronics units of the course.

(7) The anode of a thermionic diode is at a voltage of 150 V d.c. and the current flowing through the valve is 2 mA. What power is being dissipated at the anode? How many electrons are flowing through the valve per second.

(8) A diode has a forward resistance of 50 Ω and an infinite reverse resistance. It is connected in series with a 100 Ω resistance and a 25 V, 50 Hz supply. Find (a) the average current flowing, (b) the average voltage across the resistor, (c) the average voltage across the diode.

(9) A sinusoidal voltage $v = 100 \sin 62.8t$ is applied to a circuit made up of a diode rectifier in series with a 30 Ω resistor. The resistance of the diode when conducting may be considered zero and when switched off as infinitely high. Sketch the current waveform over a complete input cycle, showing the appropriate scales. Calculate (a) the r.m.s. value of the supply voltage, (b) the r.m.s. value of the current.

(10) Refer to the half-wave rectifier of *Figures 12.6*. What would be the effect on the output waveform across R if a resistance was connected (a) in series with the diode, (b) in parallel with the diode? Assume the resistance value was about the same as R.

(11) Write down expressions for (a) average current, (b) r.m.s. current, in the load resistor R of the rectifiers shown in *Figures 12.7* and *12.9* respectively, taking the forward diode resistances to be r Ω and the peak input voltage from the transformers to be $\hat{V}$

13 Instruments and measurements

Aims: At the end of this Unit section you should be able to:
Describe the principles of working of moving coil and moving iron instruments and their limitations.
Explain the basic methods of current and voltage measurement.
Explain the need for shunts and multipliers.
Define calibration, observational and systematic errors in measurement.
Describe methods of measuring resistance and e.m.f.
Understand the principles of a.c. measurement.

One of the basic instruments for all electrical measurement is the moving coil galvanometer or sensitive microammeter, from which are derived:

(a) voltmeters and ammeters for direct current measurement by the addition of series and parallel resistors;

(b) voltmeters and ammeters for alternating current measurement by the addition of suitable rectifiers and transformers;

(c) voltmeters for high frequency measurements by the addition of valve or semiconductor detectors and amplifiers;

(d) multimeters which perform many of the above functions in one self-contained unit by the addition of suitable switching.

You will be mainly concerned at this stage with the moving coil and the moving iron instrument.

MOVING COIL METER

The principle underlying the operation of this instrument is the motor principle: when a coil carrying a current I is suspended in a strong magnetic field, a deflecting torque (turning force) acts on the coil and it rotates until the torque is balanced by a restoring couple, usually provided by the suspension system. *Figure 13.1* shows the general arrangement of nearly all instruments of this kind. The field is provided by a permanent magnet which has shaped pole pieces, between which is positioned a soft iron cylinder, so making the field in the air gap radial in form. The coil which is suspended to rotate in this gap thus moves in a field which acts always at right-angles to the direction of current flow

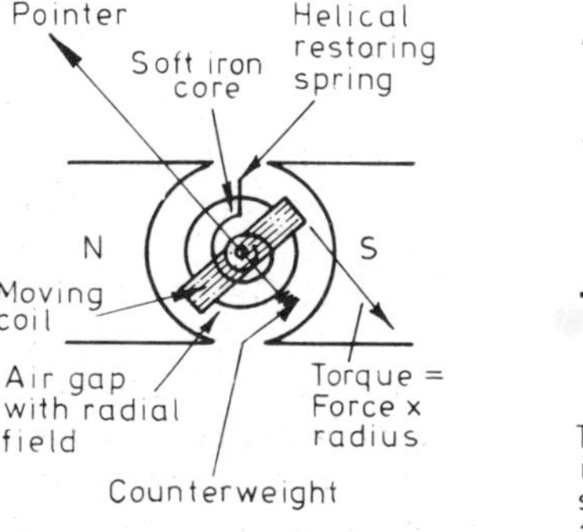

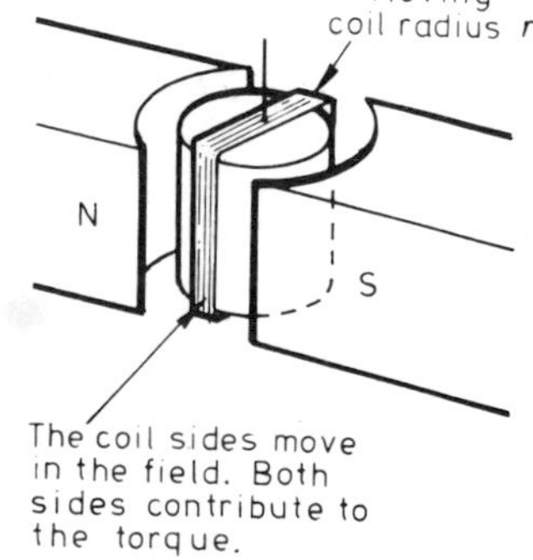

Figure 13.1

in the sides of the coil located within the air gap. From what we have already learned

Force on one conductor in the coil $= BI\ell$ newtons

Force produced by one conductor $= BI\ell r$ newton metres

$\therefore$ Total deflecting torque $= 2NBI\ell r$ newton metres

where N is the number of turns on the coil, and so $2N$ is the number of active conductors on both sides of the coil within the field.

Current is fed to the coil by flat helical springs; these springs also provide the restoring couple. When the deflecting force due to the current and the restoring force due to the springs are equal, a steady deflection from the original (rest) coil position is obtained. The angular deflection thus obtained is indicated to the user by a pointer attached to the moving coil which moves over a suitably calibrated scale. Let the deflection angle θ be proportional to the couple, then at the equilibrium position

Deflection angle $\theta \propto$ couple

i.e.

$$\theta = k.\,2NBI\ell r \quad \text{where } k \text{ is a constant}$$

$$\therefore\ I = \frac{\theta}{k2NB\ell r}$$

or

$$I = k_1\theta \quad \text{where } k_1 \text{ is also constant}$$

The deflection is thus proportional to the current in the coil, and so the scale of the instrument will be linear; that is, the spacing between the scale divisions will be uniform.

If the current happens to be an alternating current of a very low frequency the meter will be able to follow the alternations and will swing from side to side about the zero position of the pointer. If, however, the frequency exceeds some 10 Hz the coil will be unable to follow the variations due to mechanical inertia and the point will remain at the zero position. Hence a pure alternating current will not deflect a moving coil meter, which has, as a result, no application in a.c. measurements without the addition of some kind of rectifier.

Moving coil meters are available with full scale deflections (f.s.d.s) as low as 10 μA, but their coil resistance is quite high. An average, robust, general purpose meter would have a f.s.d. of from 1 to 10 mA.

MOVING IRON METER

There are two forms of this meter in general use: one uses magnetic attraction, and the other magnetic repulsion as the principle of operation. In both types a fixed coil carries the current to be measured and a magnetic field is set up by this coil when the current passes through it. The field strength is proportional to the current. A soft iron vane is attached to a spindle and pointer system fitted (as was the moving coil) with a controlling torque device, usually a helical spring system, so that the deflection of the pointer is determined by the force acting on the vane. In the repulsion form of the meter, the axis of the coil is made coincident with the spindle, and two soft iron vanes are situated axially along it. One of these vanes is fixed to the inside wall of the coil,

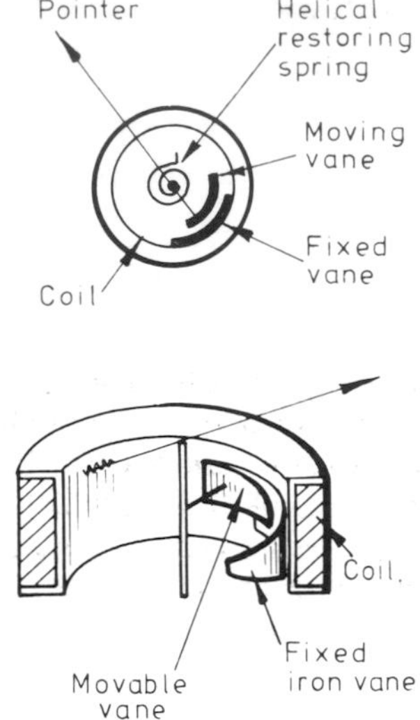

Figure 13.2

the other is movable and attached to the spindle. The construction is illustrated in *Figure 13.2*. When current flows through the coil both fixed and movable vanes are magnetised in the same direction so that mutual repulsion occurs. This repulsion moves the pointer over the scale which is suitably calibrated. The deflection this time is proportional to the product of the pole strengths of each magnet, which in turn is dependent upon the square of the number of turns (N) in the coil and the current (I) flowing through them. Hence

$$\theta = k(NI)^2$$

so that the pointer movement (and hence the scaling) is not linear but cramped at the upper end when the irons are widely separated.

As the deflection is proportional to I^2, and because $(-I)^2 = I^2$, the direction of the force between the vanes is always the same irrespective of the direction of current flow. The instrument therefore operates equally well on direct or low frequency alternating current. On alternating current the deflection is proportional to the mean value of I^2 and is therefore proportional to the r.m.s. current, so that moving iron meters respond to a.c. and indicate the r.m.s. value.

The moving iron meter has several advantages, two of which are the relatively simple construction of the movement, together with mechanical robustness and consequent cheapness compared with the delicate moving coil. The ability to be used directly for both d.c. and a.c. has already been mentioned. Where the superior accuracy, sensitivity and scale linearity of the moving coil meter is not an essential requirement, the moving iron meter is widely used.

(1) A moving coil meter has 100 turns and gives a f.s.d. when the coil current is 1 mA. Calculate the deflecting torque if the side of the coil has an active length of 1.5 cm, its width is 1.2 cm and the flux density in the gap is 0.15 T. (Note that one turn represents *two* active conductors.)

SHUNTS AND MULTIPLIERS

The basic moving coil meter will deflect fully, or indicate full scale deflection, for a very small current flow, typically of the order of 1 mA. Obviously, such instruments are very easily damaged if they are incorrectly used, and further, it is clearly necessary to be able to measure a range of currents (and voltages) and not to be restricted to the reading obtainable on the basic movement.

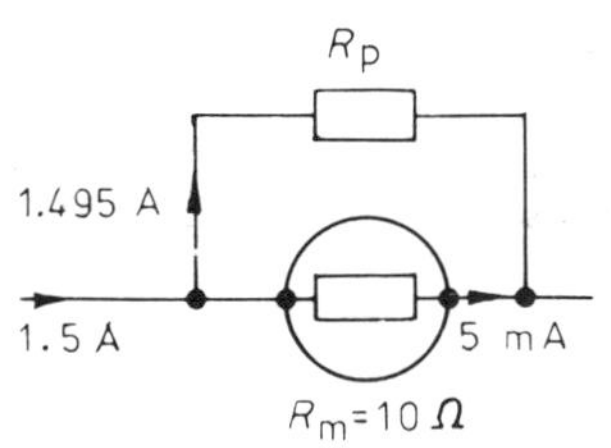

Figure 13.3(a)

For such a purpose the range of moving coil and (more rarely) moving iron instruments is extended by the use of *shunt* (parallel) or *multiplier* (series) resistors. To enable the basic instrument to read higher values of current a low resistance is connected in parallel with the instrument coil, as in *Figure 13.3(a)*. The excess current then passes through this shunt, leaving only the permissible fraction of the total circuit current I to pass through the meter coil.

Let I_m amps be the meter current and let R_m be the meter coil resistance. The voltage drop across the meter is then $I_m R_m$ volts, which is also the voltage across the parallel shunt resistor R_p. Hence

$$\text{Current in the shunt} = \frac{I_m R_m}{R_p}$$

Let the circuit current being measured be I. Then

$$I = I_m + I_s = I_m + \frac{I_m R_m}{R_p}$$

from which

$$R_p = \frac{I_m R_m}{I - I_m}$$

Figure 13.3(b)

To enable the basic instrument to read voltage, a high value series resistor is used as shown in *Figure 13.3(b)*. The value of this multiplier resistance R_s must be such that when the highest voltage V which it is required to measure is connected across terminals A–B, the current taken by the meter does not exceed its f.s.d. Let the symbols for meter resistance, meter current and circuit current be as above, then

$$I = I_m \quad \text{and so} \quad V = I(R_m + R_s)$$

and so

$$R_s = \frac{V - IR_m}{I}$$

There is no object in remembering these last two expressions. Any problems concerning shunts or multipliers are best dealt with by the straightforward application of Ohm's law.

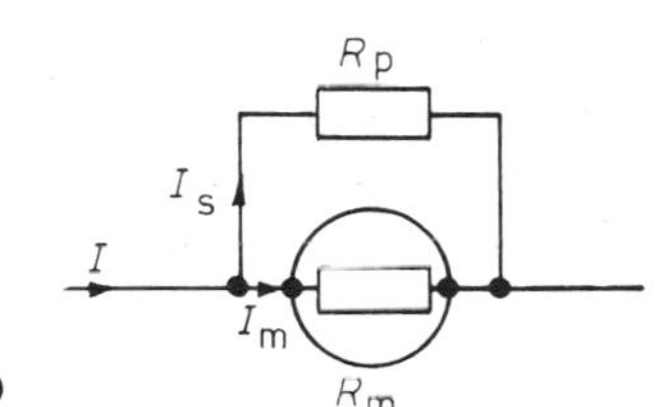

(a)

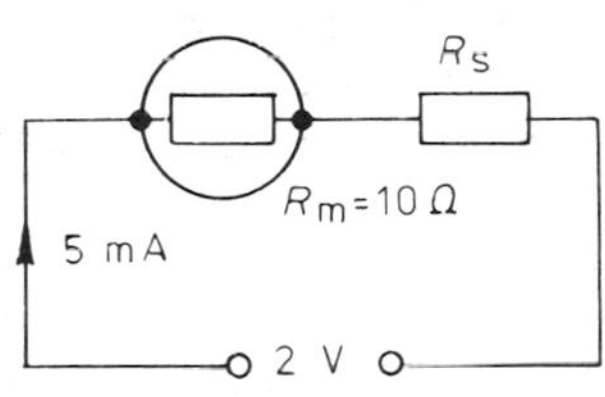

(b)

Figure 13.4

Example (2). A moving coil meter having an f.s.d. of 5 mA and a resistance 10 Ω is to be converted to an instrument reading full scale deflections of (a) 1.5 A, (b) 2 V, (c) 100 V. Calculate the value of the shunt or multiplier resistor required in each case.

We will work this problem from basic Ohm's law considerations.

(a) *Figure 13.4(a)* illustrates the situation. We require only 5 mA to flow through the meter when the circuit current is 1.5 A. Hence the current through the shunt R_p must be

$$1.5 - 0.005 = 1.495 \text{ A}$$

Now the voltage drop across meter and shunt

$$= 0.005 \times 10 = 0.05 \text{ V}$$

Applying Ohm's law

$$R_p = \frac{0.05}{1.495} = 0.0334\ \Omega$$

(b) *Figure 13.4(b)* illustrates this particular case. The current through R_s and R_m (10 Ω) in series must be 5 mA when 2 V is applied as shown. By Ohm's law

$$R_s + 10 = \frac{2}{0.005} = 400\ \Omega$$

$$\therefore \quad R_s = 390\ \Omega$$

(c) *Figure 13.4(b)* also illustrates this case, except that the applied voltage is 100 V. This time therefore

$$R_s + 10 = \frac{100}{0.005} = 20\,000\,\Omega$$

$$R_s = 19\,990\,\Omega$$

(3) A moving coil instrument has a resistance of 5 Ω and takes 25 mA to produce f.s.d. How can the instrument be adapted to measure (a) voltages up to 150 V, (b) currents up to 10 A?

(4) A moving coil meter takes 15 mA to produce f.s.d. and the p.d. across its terminals is then 0.075 V. What series resistor would be required to adapt the instrument for use as a voltmeter reading 0–100 V?

In both shunt and multiplier conversions care has to be taken to ensure that the resistors used are adequately rated so as not to overheat when carrying the full current applicable to the circuit conditions. Any such heating will cause a change in resistance, and so lead to inaccurate readings.

(5) Calculate the power dissipated in the meter coil and in each of the shunt or multiplier resistors used in Example (2).

Shunts and multipliers are not normally used with moving iron instruments since the coil can be wound with heavy or light gauge wire to suit the application.

CONNECTIONS AND ERRORS

An *ammeter*, as its name tells us, reads amperes (current). A *voltmeter* reads voltage (potential difference). The ammeter will measure any flow that goes through it, so in a series-parallel circuit, as shown in *Figure 13.5*, each ammeter will measure the current in that part of the circuit into which it is connected. If the parallel resistors are of different value, the ammeters will read different values. Ammeters must be connected in series with that part of a circuit you wish to test, and the current you wish to measure must pass through the instrument.

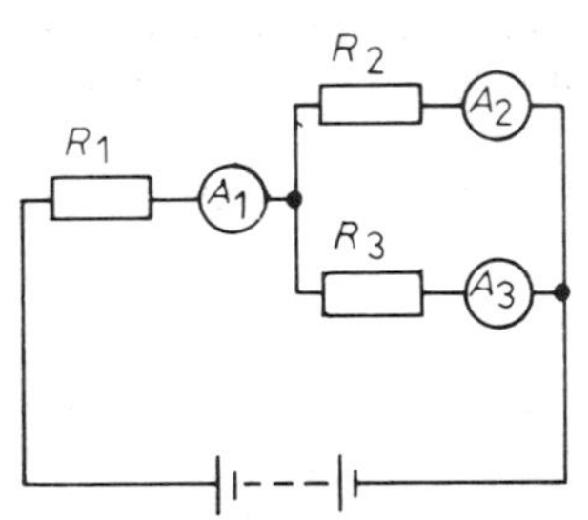

Figure 13.5

A voltmeter measures potential differences existing across various parts of a circuit, so in a series-parallel circuit as shown in *Figure 13.6* each voltmeter will measure the p.d. across the resistor to which it is connected. Voltmeters must be connected in parallel with that part of a circuit for which the p.d. is required, and the p.d. you wish to measure must be placed across the terminals of the instrument.

(6) Assuming perfect instruments, would any of the voltmeters shown in *Figure 13.6* show equal readings?

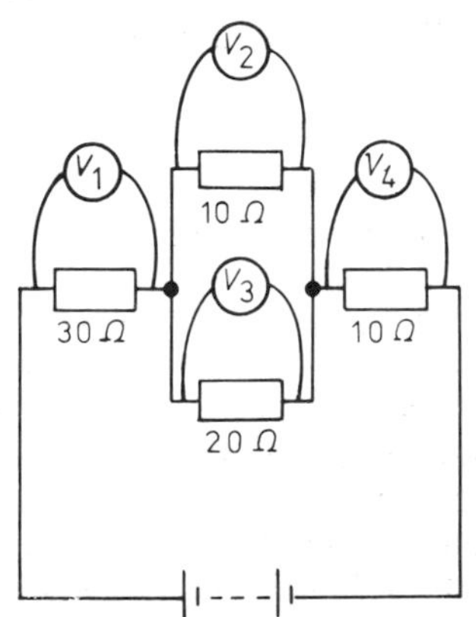

Figure 13.6

You would not normally be provided with a large number of separate instruments and be expected to distribute them about a circuit in the manner shown in *Figures 13.5* and *13.6*. You would probably be given at most, perhaps, a couple of *multimeters* (of which the Avometer is a familiar example) and you would apply these to selected parts of the circuit in turn, making sure that they are switched to a range appropriate to the measurement you expect to make. Multimeters are simply basic meter movements, usually of a sensitivity of 1 mA f.s.d. or better, provided with switched sets of shunt and multiplier resistors so that their ranges can be changed quickly to provide a variety of measurements, both d.c. and a.c. Have a good look at an Avometer and take a note of the very wide range of current and voltage measurements available.

When readings are taken from instruments of the type we are discussing, three fundamental forms of error are introduced. They are:

(a) *Calibration errors.* No instrument is perfect and what the pointer indicates on the scale is most probably not the exact value of current or voltage present in the circuit being tested. An industrial grade instrument, for example, has an accuracy ±2% of f.s.d., so that if such a meter having an f.s.d. of 100 mA indicated 50 mA, the actual current might be anywhere between 48 and 52 mA. Accuracy varies over the scale length.

(b) *Observational errors.* It is possible to misread the pointer position on the scale. An actual reading of 50 mA, for example, might easily be read as 49 or 51 mA if the eye is not positioned exactly above the pointer. This is a case of parallax error, and many meters have a mirror placed behind the pointer so that the effect is minimised. Again, it is sometimes difficult to judge the scale reading because of the way the scale is printed, making interpolation unavoidable, and so leading to guesswork.

(c) *Systematic errors*. These are errors introduced by the actual method of measurement employed. As an example, look at *Figure 13.7.* In figure *(a)* the voltmeter reads the p.d. across the resistor R correctly, but the ammeter reads not only the current in the resistor but also the current in the voltmeter. The presence of the voltmeter has therefore affected the current indicated on the ammeter. In figure *(b)* the ammeter correctly reads the current in the resistor, but the voltmeter reads the p.d. across the ammeter plus the p.d. across the resistor. The presence of the ammeter has therefore affected the voltage reading on the voltmeter. Neither method of connection will give the p.d. across the resistor and the current through it simultaneously correct.

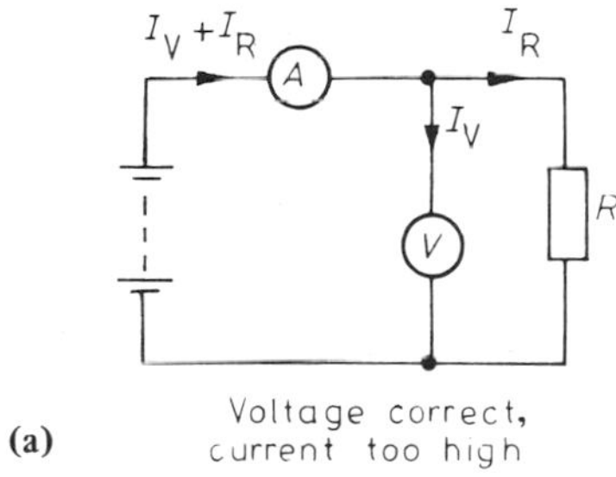

(a)

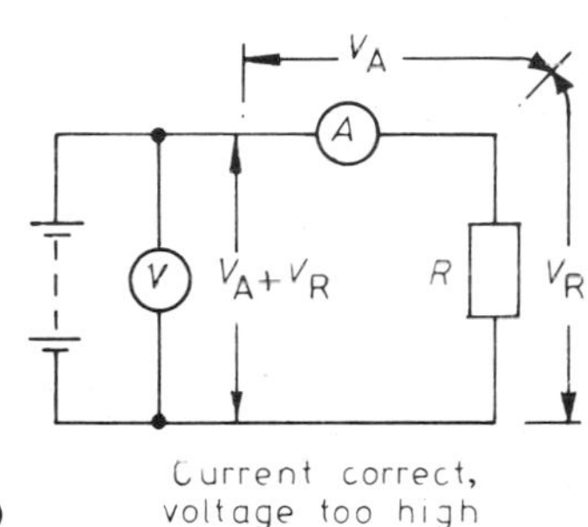

(b)

Figure 13.7

(7) Ideally, the ammeter should have . . . . . . resistance and the voltmeter . . . . resistance. Fill in the missing words.

(8) A voltmeter has an f.s.d. of 50 V and industrial grade accuracy of ±2 %. The scale is divided into 100 equal divisions and the observational accuracy is ±1 division. When this meter is used to measure the output of a power unit, the reading is recorded as being 30 V. What are the probable limits between which the voltage actually lies?

MEASUREMENT OF RESISTANCE

There are many ways of measuring resistance, and we shall mention a few of the more common of these.

Most multimeters, like the Avometer, have built-in ohmmeters so that a direct reading of resistance can be read from the meter scale. The basic principle of this sort of ohmmeter is shown in *Figure 13.8.* When switched to the 'Ohms' range, an internal battery is connected in series with the moving coil and an adjustable resistor R, usually marked 'Set zero ohms'. With the terminals A and B shorted together, R is adjusted so that the meter just reads f.s.d. which corresponds to the zero ohms position on the Ohms scale. If now an unknown resistor is connected to A and B, the meter will read some value less than f.s.d.,

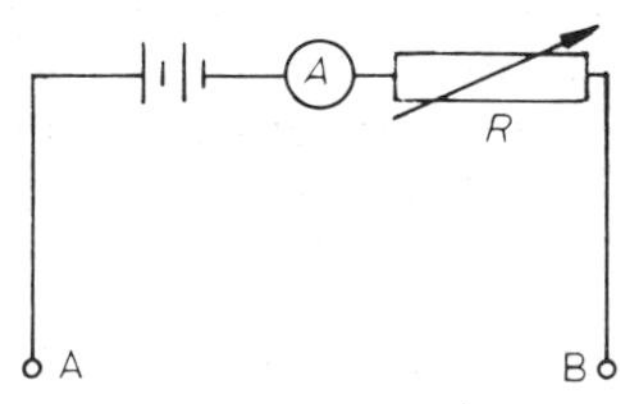

Figure 13.8

and by proper scaling can be made to indicate the value of the resistor directly on the scale. The higher the resistance, the greater must be the battery voltage to provide adequate indication. The scale is non-linear, but resistors can be measured to quite reasonable accuracy (within 2-5%) by this method.

Another simple method uses an ammeter and a voltmeter, connected as shown earlier in *Figure 13.7.* The limitations of this method have been mentioned, but if the ammeter is of low resistance and the voltmeter of very high resistance, the calculated value for the unknown resistor can be reasonably accurate. Calibration errors are spread if several readings for V and I are taken, and an average value for the resistor calculated.

Example (9). A resistance is being measured by the ammeter-voltmeter method and the circuit is wired as shown in *Figure 13.7(a).* The ammeter reads 0.35 A, and the voltmeter which has a resistance of 1000 Ω reads 9.3 V. Calculate the value of R (a) approximately, (b) exactly.

(a) Approximate value, ignoring any effect of the voltmeter resistance:

$$R = \frac{V}{I} = \frac{9.3}{0.35} = 26.57\ \Omega$$

(b) Accurate value, taking into account the effect of the voltmeter resistance:

$$\text{Voltmeter current} = \frac{\text{Voltmeter reading}}{\text{Voltmeter resistance}}$$

$$= \frac{9.3}{1000} = 0.0093\ \text{A}$$

$$\therefore \text{True current through } R = 0.35 - 0.0093 = 0.3407\ \text{A}$$

$$\therefore \text{Accurate value for } R = \frac{9.3}{0.3407} = 27.29\ \Omega$$

Notice from this example that although the resistance value was small compared with the resistance of the parallel voltmeter, the error introduced was about 0.7 Ω low on the true value when the voltmeter resistance was neglected. If the resistance of R had been comparable with that of the voltmeter, the error would have been considerable.

(10) Of the two possible circuit arrangements shown in *Figure 13.7*, one is best suited for the measurement of low resistances and one for the measurement of high resistances. Choose the correct circuit for each case and explain your reasons.

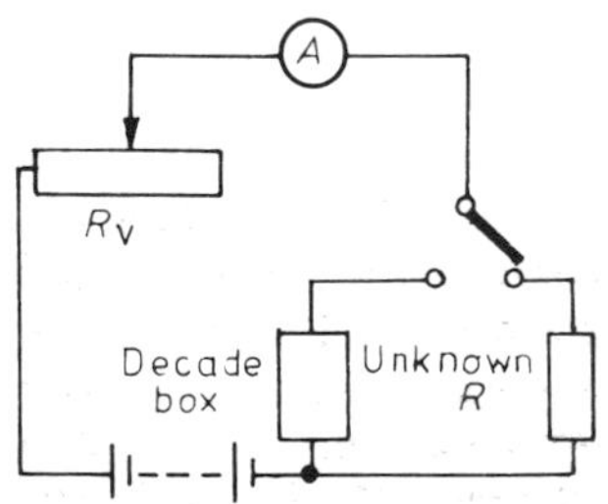

Figure 13.9

Substitution is a simple method which has the advantage that any error in the instrument is of no consequence. The unknown resistor is connected as shown in *Figure 13.9*. The variable resistor R_V is then adjusted to give any convenient reading on the ammeter. The switch is changed over to bring the decade box into circuit, and this in turn is adjusted until the same deflection is shown on the ammeter as before. The value given by the decade box is now equal to the value of the unknown resistor.

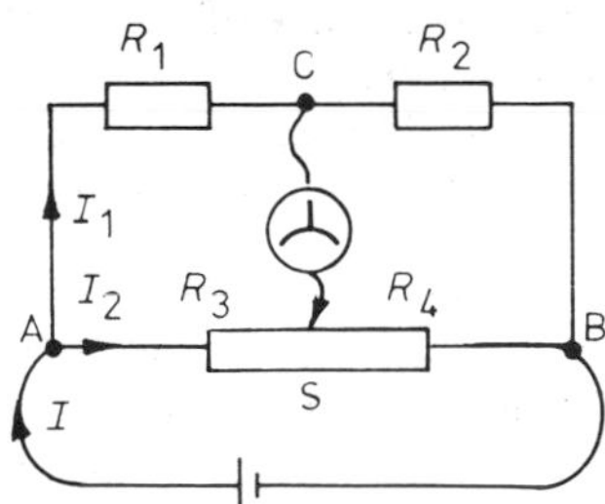

Figure 13.10

Wheatstone bridge: look at the circuit shown in *Figure 13.10*. Current entering the circuit at A divides, part flowing through the branch made up of R_1 and R_2 and part through the branch consisting of the potentiometer R_3R_4. The p.d. across both branches is the same, and equal to the applied p.d. If we move the slider S of the potentiometer from end A towards end B, there must be a position between A and B which is at the same potential as point C on the upper branch. At this point there is no p.d. acting between C and S and so the meter included in the connecting link will read zero current. Let the currents and resistance values be as shown in the figure.

Then p.d. between A and C = p.d. between A and S. Therefore

$$I_1R_1 = I_2R_3 \qquad \ldots\ldots (1)$$

Also p.d. between C and B = p.d. between S and B.

$$I_1R_2 = I_2R_4 \qquad \ldots\ldots (2)$$

Dividing out (1) by (2)

$$\frac{R_1}{R_3} = \frac{R_2}{R_4}$$

or

$$R_1 = R_2 \frac{R_3}{R_4}$$

So supposing R_1 is the unknown resistor, we can calculate its value if we know

(a) the values of R_2, R_3 and R_4

or

(b) the value of R_2 and the ratio of R_3 to R_4

There are two forms of the Wheatstone bridge that you are most likely to use in the laboratory, though very sophisticated forms exist for precision measurements. The so-called *metre bridge* is illustrated in *Figure 13.11(a)*. The heavy lines represent thick copper strips, and the line AB is a 1 m length of resistance wire having an overall resistance of about 2-5 Ω. The exact value is unimportant since, if the wire is uniform, the ratio of the resistances between A-S and S-B will be given by the ratio of the lengths ℓ_1 and ℓ_2. These lengths are measured by means of a metre rule fitted beneath the wire. With the unknown resistance X connected as shown, and a known resistance R connected to the opposite terminals (R can be a decade box if necessary), the slide contact S is moved along AB until the meter reads zero. By the previous reasoning, the value of X is then given by

$$X - R \cdot \frac{\ell_1}{\ell_2}$$

It is relatively easy to measure ℓ_1 and ℓ_2 to the nearest millimetre.

The greatest sensitivity and accuracy is obtained when 'balance', i.e. a zero meter reading, is found in the centre third of the wire AB.

An alternative form of the bridge is shown in *Figure 13.11(b)*. Here R_3 and R_4 form what are known as *ratio arms*. Each consists of three resistors of 10, 100 and 1000 Ω; hence the ratio R_3/R_4 can be given values of $\frac{1}{100}$, $\frac{1}{10}$, 1, 10 or 100, according to the size of the unknown

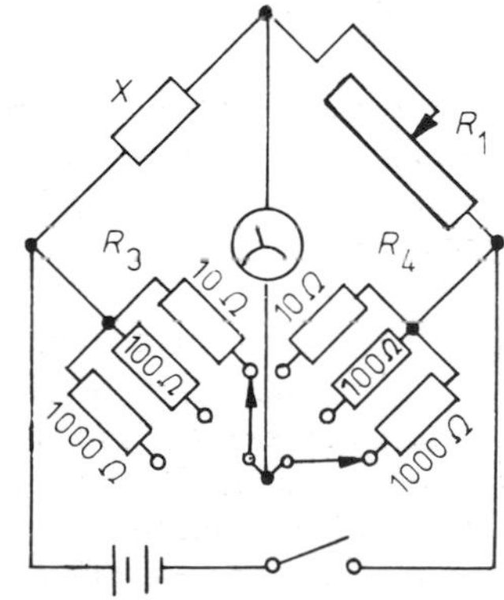

Figure 13.11

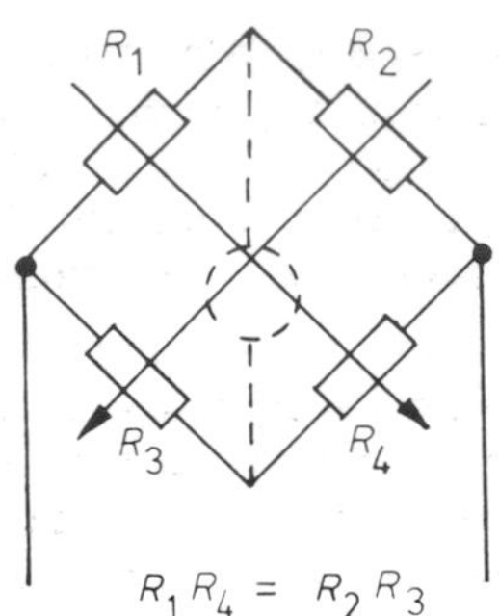

Figure 13.12

resistor X being measured. R_2 is a decade box, variable in steps of 1Ω from 1 to 9999 Ω. For a given setting of the ratio arms, balance is obtained by variation of the R_2 arm; the unknown resistance X is then calculated from the formula as derived previously:

$$X = R_2 \frac{R_3}{R_4} \quad \text{where } \frac{R_3}{R_4} \text{ is simply a ratio}$$

There is a simple way of remembering the balance conditions for a Wheatstone bridge circuit: look at *Figure 13.12* and imagine the bridge is balanced. Then, irrespective of which resistor is the unknown in reality, the balance condition is obtained by 'cross-multiplying' as indicated by the arrows, so that

$$R_1 R_4 = R_2 R_3$$

This simple rule will help you with some of the following problems.

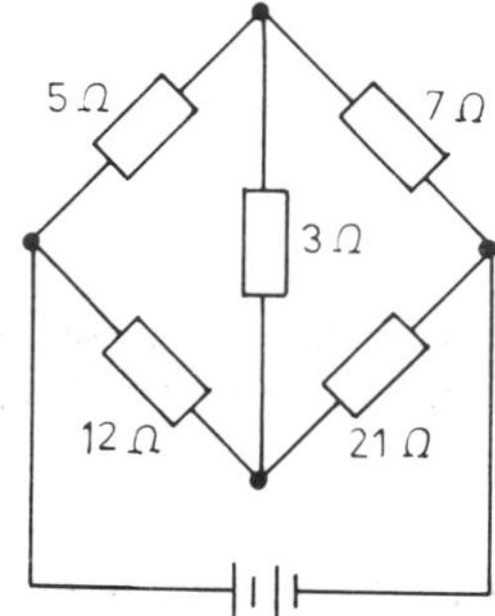

Figure 13.13

(11) An unknown resistor X is measured by a metre bridge as shown in *Figure 13.11(a)*. With $R = 250\ \Omega$, balance is obtained when $\ell_1 = 35$ cm. Find the value of X. If R was changed to 100 Ω, whereabouts along the slide wire would balance now be obtained?

(12) An unknown resistor X is to be measured using a ratio-arm bridge as shown in *Figure 13.11(b)*. When the ratio arms are arranged $R_3 = 1000\ \Omega$ and $R_4 = 10\ \Omega$, balance is obtained when R_2 is adjusted to 1543 Ω. What is the value of X?

(13) In the circuit of *Figure 13.13*, what change must be made in the 5Ω resistor branch in order that no current will flow through the 3 Ω resistor?

THE D.C. POTENTIOMETER

The potentiometer is used mainly for very accurate measurement of voltage, but it can also be adapted to measure resistance. Its advantage over the conventional voltmeter is that it draws no current when making a measurement.

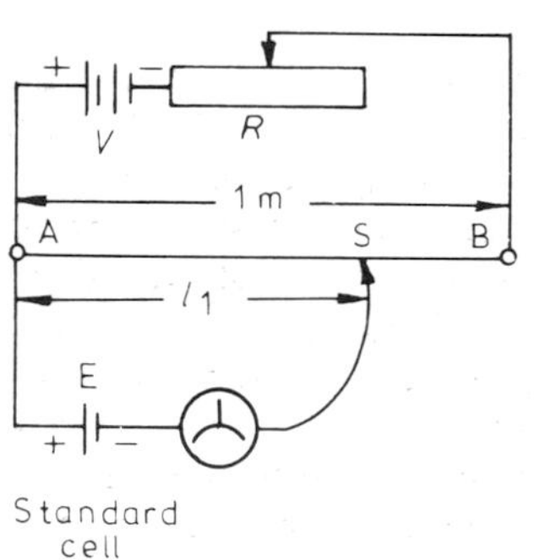

Figure 13.14

The principle is shown in *Figure 13.14*. A battery V of about 2 V e.m.f. is connected in series with a variable resistor R and a 1 m length of resistance wire AB. Also connected across part of the wire is a *Weston standard cell* (E) which has an accurately known e.m.f. of 1.0186 V, in series with a sensitive moving coil meter. R is adjusted so that the voltage across AB due to battery V is greater than the e.m.f. of cell E (usually about 2 V is maintained across AB). The sliding contact S is then moved along the wire until zero current passes through the meter. In this condition the p.d. across the wire section AS due to battery V must be exactly balanced by the e.m.f. of cell E, since no current is being drawn from E, i.e. the voltage across length ℓ_1 of the wire AB is 1.0186 V. Knowing length ℓ_1, the fall of potential per centimetre length of wire can be calculated as $1.0186/\ell_1$. The wire is now standardised.

The e.m.f. of any cell with e.m.f. less than the p.d. across AB can now be measured by substituting it for the standard cell E. Contact S is readjusted so that the meter again indicates zero current. Then the e.m.f. of the given cell is equal to (distance AS) × $1.0186/\ell_1$.

Resistance can be measured by potentiometer methods. A low resistance (much less than 1 Ω) cannot be measured accurately by the Wheatstone bridge (neither can resistances above some 50 000 Ω for

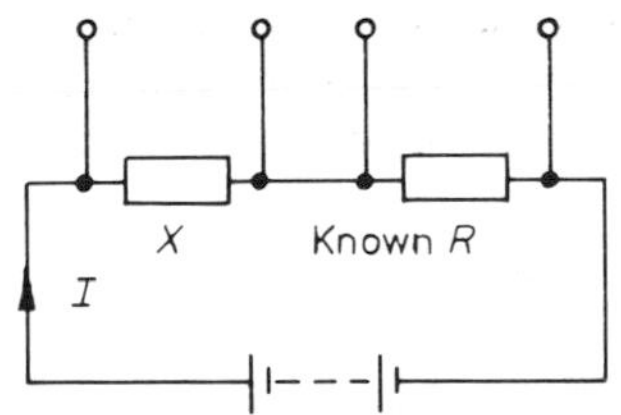

Figure 13.15

that matter), but it can be measured very precisely with a potentiometer. A known resistance of the same order of magnitude as the unknown is connected in series with the unknown (*Figure 13.15*), and a fairly large current is allowed to flow through the circuit. The p.d. across each resistor in turn is then measured on a potentiometer.

(14) Why is a fairly large current necessary in the circuit shown? If you had set up the potentiometer so that there were 2 V across the slide wire AB, what order of current would be required if you were to measure a resistor of value about 0.1 Ω?

Returning to the method of measurement, let the p.d. across $X = IX$ and the p.d. across the known resistor $R = IR$. Hence

$$\frac{\text{p.d. across } R}{\text{p.d. across } X} = \frac{IR}{IX} = \frac{R}{X}$$

$$\therefore \qquad X = R \times \frac{\text{p.d. across } X}{\text{p.d. across } R}$$

It is necessary for current I to remain constant throughout the period of measurement, and to ensure the power ratings of R and X are not exceeded.

(15) A d.c. potentiometer has a slide wire 1 m in length. With a standard cell of e.m.f. 1.0186 V in circuit, balance is obtained 38.15 cm from the 'A' end of the wire. What is the e.m.f. of a Leclanche cell which gives a balance point 57.1 cm from the same end?

ALTERNATING CURRENT MEASUREMENTS

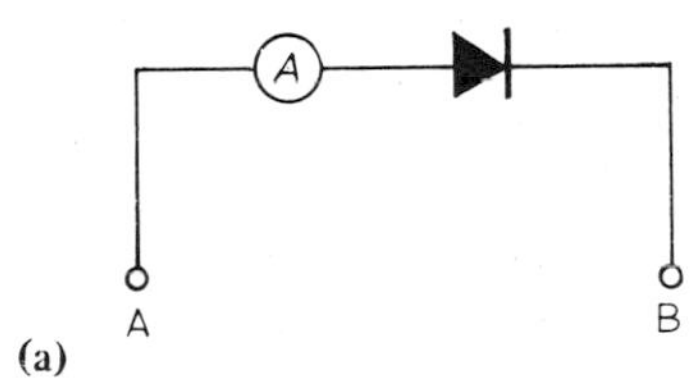

(a)

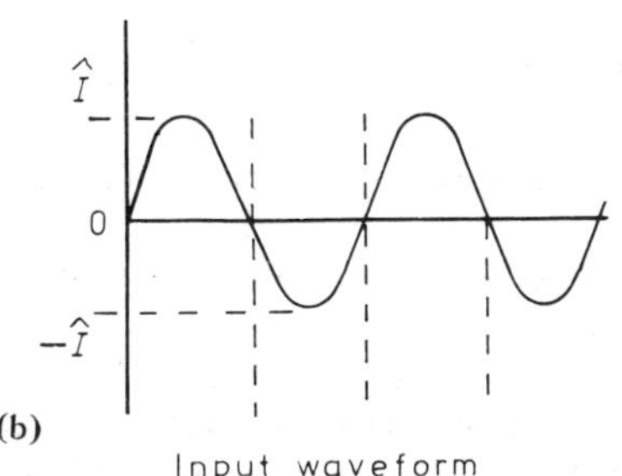

(b)

We have seen that the moving iron ammeter will give a direct indication of r.m.s. current when used in alternating current circuits. Since the torque produced is proportional to I^2, moving iron meters are accurate for both a.c. and d.c. inputs. This and their robustness, are two of the advantages of moving iron instruments, but set against these they have the disadvantages of relatively poor sensitivity and a much heavier power consumption than the moving coil meter. Moving irons are particularly suitable for measurement at 50 Hz mains frequency where the additional power requirements and poor sensitivity are not important factors, and such meters are usually found on power supply switchboards, battery charger units and car dashboards.

The sensitive and relatively fragile moving coil instrument, on the other hand, is a magnetically polarised device and the direction of pointer deflection depends upon the direction of current flow in its coil. It is essentially a direct current meter on this account. If it is connected to an alternating source, the pointer remains at zero, the suspension being unable to follow the rapid reversals of current in the coil. The meter, in fact, indicates the average value of a sinusoidal wave, which is zero.

When alternating quantities have to be measured, therefore, a direct current proportional to them has to be produced. As we noted in Unit Section 12, the device which can do this for us is the rectifier.

RECTIFIER INSTRUMENTS

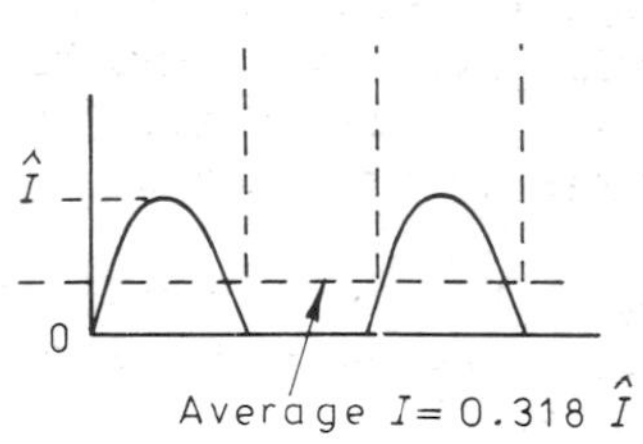

(c)

Figure 13.16

For most general purposes of a.c. measurement the moving coil meter is used in conjunction with a rectifier system. Multiplier resistances are then used to extend the range of the basic instrument and provide multirange a.c. and d.c. voltmeters.

The simplest arrangement would seem to be a single rectifier unit wired in series with the moving coil as shown in *Figure 13.16 (a)*. As the circuit is sketched, the rectifier will switch off when terminal A is negative with respect to terminal B, and switch on when these polarities reverse. The input current waveform shown in *Figure 13.16 (b)* will therefore be reduced to the half-wave pulses shown in (c), each pulse representing current flowing in only one direction. These unidirectional pulses flow through the meter coil, and as there is never any reversal of direction, a definite deflection will be indicated by the pointer.

Now the deflection of the moving coil is proportional to the average torque acting on the coil, hence is proportional to the average current flowing in the coil, since torque is proportional to current. You will recall that the average height of a sine wave is $2/\pi$ of the peak value or $0.637\hat{I}$. Since every alternate half-cycle is missing in the rectified wave, however, the average falls by a further one-half, hence the meter reading becomes

$$\frac{1}{2} \times \frac{2}{\pi} \times \hat{I} = \frac{\hat{I}}{\pi} = 0.318\hat{I}$$

The meter is normally scaled to indicate direct current, and when used on alternating supplies we should expect it to provide us with the r.m.s. value of the input waveform. Now the average value recorded is $0.318\hat{I}$ which, in proportion to the r.m.s. value $0.707\hat{I}$ is $0.707/0.318 = 2.22$. Hence the reading of a meter calibrated in terms of direct current has to be multiplied by a factor of 2.22 to indicate the r.m.s. value of the alternating current.

(16) A moving coil meter is correctly calibrated to indicate an f.s.d. of 10 mA d.c. It is used with a single series rectifier and connected into a circuit where an alternating current of peak value 8 mA flows. What will the meter indicate? If in another circuit the meter indicated 5 mA, what would be the r.m.s. value of the current flowing in that circuit?

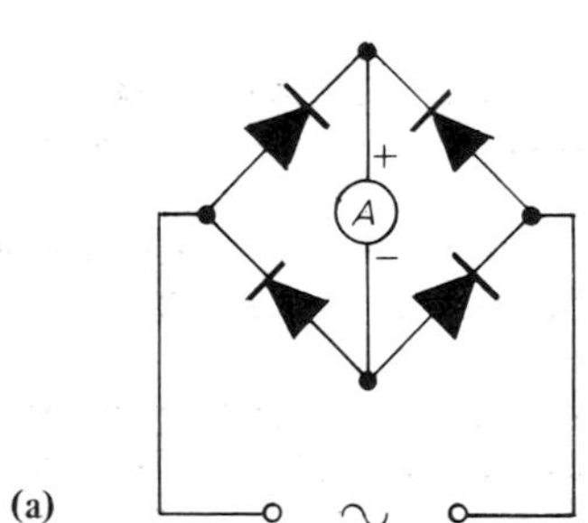

(a)

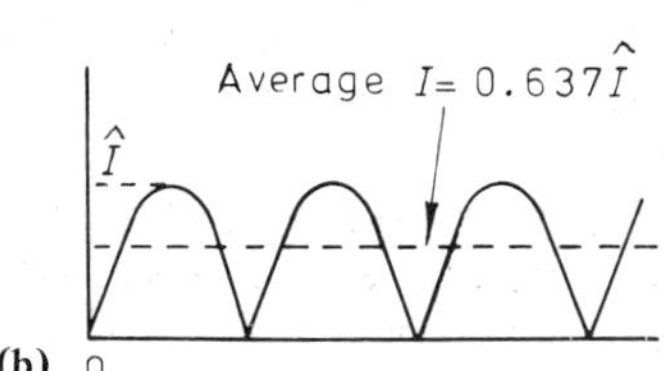

(b)

Figure 13.17

It is not customary to use a single series rectifier with a moving coil meter and the usual arrangement is shown in *Figure 13.17(a)*. Here four bridge-connected rectifiers are used and the output from these, you will recall. is a full-wave rectified current as shown in figure (b). The four diodes constituting the rectifier are generally made up as a small encapsulated unit with free output leads that can be neatly wired in close proximity to the meter itself.

The average value of a full-wave rectified current is $2/\pi$ of the peak value or $0.637\hat{I}$, hence the deflection obtained is twice that of the half-wave (single rectifier) instrument. Hence the reading of a meter calibrated on direct current has this time to be multiplied by the factor $0.707\hat{I}/0.637\hat{I} = 1.11$. This ratio is the *form factor* of a sinusoidal wave.

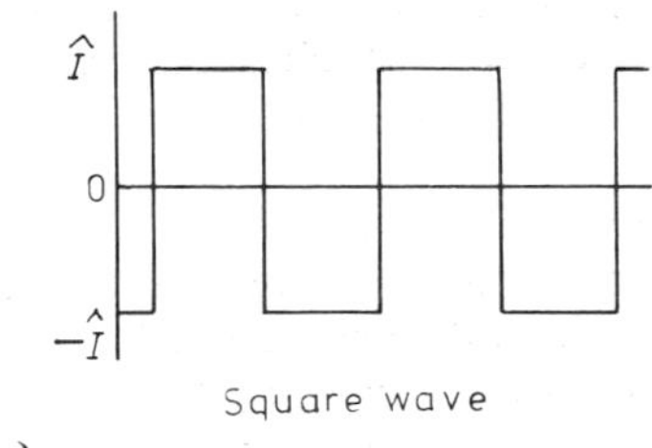

(a)

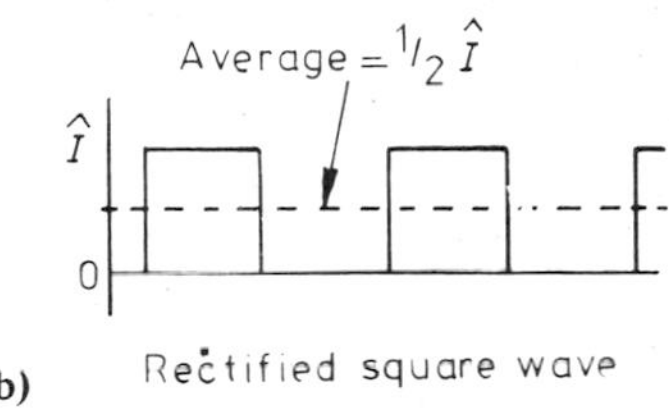

(b)

Figure 13.18

Example (17). When a meter employing a single rectifier unit is connected to a 50 Hz sinusoidal supply it reads 25 mA. This meter is now replaced by one employing a bridge rectifier without any of the other circuit conditions being affected. What does the second meter read? What would be the reading on each of these meters if the supply was a 50 Hz square wave instead of a sinusoidal wave?

The average value of the bridge rectifier output is twice that of the single rectifier. So if the single rectifier meter reads 25 mA, the bridge rectifier meter will read 50 mA.

If the supply is a square wave (see *Figure 13.18*) the single rectifier will ideally change it to the unidirectional form shown at (a). The average value of this is clearly half its peak value. This is what the meter would indicate. The bridge rectifier will convert the wave into a smooth direct current having a steady value equal to the amplitude of the square wave. This value is twice that indicated by the single rectifier instrument, so the reading on the second meter is again twice that shown on the first.

(18) Can you deduce, having regard to the previous example, that the r.m.s. value of a square wave is equal to its peak value?

(19) For a sinusoidal wave and for a square wave the second (bridge) meter reads twice the value indicated by the first (single) rectifier) meter. Will this always be true, irrespective of the waveform?

PROBLEMS FOR SECTION 13

Group 1

(20) A 0–5 mA meter of resistance 10 Ω is to be converted to an instrument reading 0–1.5 A and 0–3 A. Calculate the required value of the shunt resistor in each case.

(21) The basic meter of the previous problem is to be converted into an instrument reading 0–10 V and 0–2 V. Calculate the required series resistor in each case.

(22) Explain, with the appropriate calculations, how a meter with a f.s.d. of 120 μA having a resistance of 500 Ω can be converted to (a) a 0–1.2 mA, (b) a 0–3 V instrument.

(23) A voltmeter of range 0–10 V has a resistance of 1005 Ω. What will be its f.s.d. if a series resistor of value 29 145 Ω is added?

(24) A moving coil instrument has a resistance of 10 Ω and carries a current of 20 mA. Find (a) the p.d. across the meter, (b) the power dissipated in the coil.

(25) A moving coil instrument has a resistance of 54 Ω and with a shunt resistor in position the combined resistance is 5.4 Ω. Calculate (a) the resistance of the shunt, (b) the total f.s.d. with the shunt if the meter reads 0–50 mA without the shunt.

(26) A moving coil meter has a resistance of 20 Ω and gives a maximum deflection of 50 scale divisions for a coil current of 1 mA.

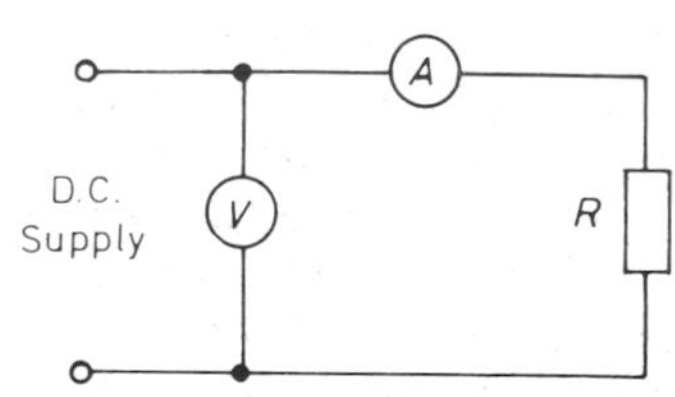

Figure 13.19

A resistor of value 99 980 Ω is connected in series with the meter so that it may be used as a voltmeter. Under this condition calculate the voltage represented by each scale division.

(27) The coil of a moving iron meter has 500 turns and f.s.d. is obtained when the coil current is 2 A. How many turns would be necessary if the meter was to give a f.s.d. for 10 A?

(28) An ammeter and a resistor are wired in series across a d.c. supply. The ammeter reads 10 mA and a voltmeter of resistance 30 000 Ω connected directly across the resistor reads 25 V. Calculate (a) the approximate value of the resistor, (b) the true value of the resistor.

(29) A resistor of about 30 Ω is to be measured by the method shown in *Figure 13.19*. V is a voltmeter having an f.s.d. of 100 V, and A is an ammeter having an f.s.d. of 5 A and resistance 1.2 Ω. Both meters have an accuracy of ±2% of f.s.d. V reads 90 V and A reads 3 A. Ignoring observational errors, find the limits between which the measurement of the resistor will lie.

Group 2

(30) Two resistors A and B are joined in series across a constant 50 V supply. A voltmeter of resistance 5000 Ω when connected across A reads 8.62 V and when connected across B reads 34.5 V. Find the values of the resistors A and B.

(31) A 35 V supply is connected across a resistance of 600 Ω in series with an unknown resistor R. A voltmeter having a resistance of 1200 Ω shows a reading of 5 V when connected across the 600 Ω. What is the value of R?

(32) A moving coil meter gives an f.s.d. with a current of 10 mA, and has a resistance of 5 Ω. The instrument is connected in series with a 490 Ω resistor and gives a deflection of half full scale when connected to the battery. Find (a) the battery p.d., (b) the deflection for a supply voltage of 4 V, (c) the power taken by the instrument for full scale deflection.

(33) A d.c. potentiometer is standardised to give a drop of 0.067 V per cm of the slide wire. A standard cell is replaced by an alkaline cell and zero galvanometer deflection is obtained for a length of 17.91 cm from the common end. What is the e.m.f. of the alkaline cell?

(34) Two moving coil meters differ only in that the moving coil of one has 750 turns and a resistance of 475 Ω and the other has 100 turns and a resistance of 15 Ω. Find the ratios of their deflections when: (a) each is connected in turn across a battery of 2 V e.m.f. and 25 Ω internal resistance, (b) the two meters are connected in series across this same battery.

(35) A half-wave rectifier is connected in series with a moving coil ammeter and a moving iron ammeter, to measure an alternating current. The moving iron ammeter indicates a current of 8 A. What does the other ammeter read?

(36) A sinusoidal current $i = 5.657 \sin t$ is (a) half-wave rectified, (b) full-wave rectified. What readings would you expect to obtain on a moving coil instrument and a moving iron instrument when each is used in turn to measure the rectified current?

(37) A sinusoidal alternating current has a peak value 5 A. If this current is full-wave rectified by a bridge circuit, what should be the readings on (a) a moving coil instrument, (b) a moving iron instrument, connected to measure the rectified current?

(38) A half-wave rectifier, a moving coil ammeter and a moving iron ammeter are connected in series across a 2 V supply. The rectifier has a forward resistance of 20 Ω and an infinite reverse resistance. When the 2 V supply is d.c. the ammeters give identical readings, but when the supply is 2 V r.m.s. at 50 Hz, the readings are different. Explain the reason for the difference and estimate the actual meter readings in all cases. What will the readings be if the a.c. supply is a square wave of peak value 2 V? (Ignore the meter resistances.)

(39) The current flowing in a circuit is made up of a direct current of 3 A with a superimposed alternating current of peak value 2 A. Wired into the circuit is a moving coil ammeter with a bridge rectifier, and a moving iron ammeter. What current reading will each of these meters indicate? Explain your answers.

14 Principles of control systems

Aims: At the end of this Unit section you should be able to:
Compare and differentiate between simple open-loop and closed-loop control systems.
Compare the advantages and disadvantages of such control systems.
Understand the characteristic behaviour of control systems using feedback.
Discuss the meaning of transient and steady-state conditions.
Understand the reasons for instability in control systems.

The study of automatic control and automatic control systems is a complicated one, and at this point in the course we introduce only the most basic principles.

Automatic control is a feature of everyday life; we find its applications in heating systems, water supplies, traffic control, medical treatment, lathe and machine tool operation, assembly of electronic circuits and their soldering, aircraft flight and landing, satellite guidance. In an ideal world all such control applications would be precise; whatever the system was 'asked to do', it would do it without hesitation or deviation. Real life controls are not so accommodating, there is always deviation and error along the chain of command. It is the job of the designer to make sure that these errant factors remain within critically specified and acceptable limits. Very precise control systems are, therefore, the most expensive ones.

In spite of the vast range and apparent diversity of control systems, a few of which have been mentioned above, basically they can all be analysed into a few similar component parts with similar underlying characteristics. They then fit into what are known as either closed-loop or open-loop control systems.

OPEN-LOOP AND CLOSED-LOOP SYSTEMS

An open-loop system is the most rudimentary form of control. Indeed, in many examples it is not in the strict sense of the word a control system at all. The principle is that we set up a system as precisely as we can, and then leave it to get on with things without any further attention. A very simple example of an open-loop device is a moving-coil ammeter. This may not raise any pictures of a control system at all, but we can categorise it under the heading of an open-loop system. The magnetic system is formed and stabilised, the moving coil is wound and pivoted within the magnetic field, restoring springs are fitted and connecting wires brought out to terminals. The ammeter is then calibrated and after that it is assumed that it will always correctly indicate to us the level of the current flowing through it. A footballer taking a shot at goal is another example; the ball is under open-loop conditions the moment it leaves the toe of his boot. If there has been an error on the part of the striker or if the wind suddenly decides to change direction while the ball is travelling, nothing can be done about making a correction.

To illustrate how we can work our way from an open-loop system to full automatic control, we take an example of such an open-loop system and modify it so that we go by way of an intermediate stage of manual control. This brings human intervention into the picture. Take an example of the heating of a room accomplished by the use of an electric heater and a switch. The switch, when operated, puts the heater ON or puts it OFF. There is no other possible setting. It is desired to maintain the room temperature at, say, 22°C. If left to itself unattended, the system would remain either switched ON or switched OFF; the room would then run to one temperature extreme or the other, cold or hot, and stay that way. *Figure 14.1* shows a block diagram of this open-loop system. In no way is there any possibility of keeping the room temperature steady at 22°C.

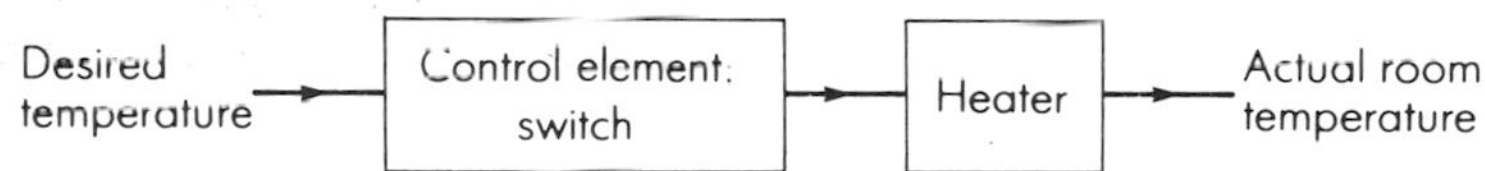

Figure 14.1

To get any sort of control at all somebody would have to be in the room to keep an eye on the temperature conditions. We would then have the manually controlled closed-loop system shown in *Figure 14.2*.

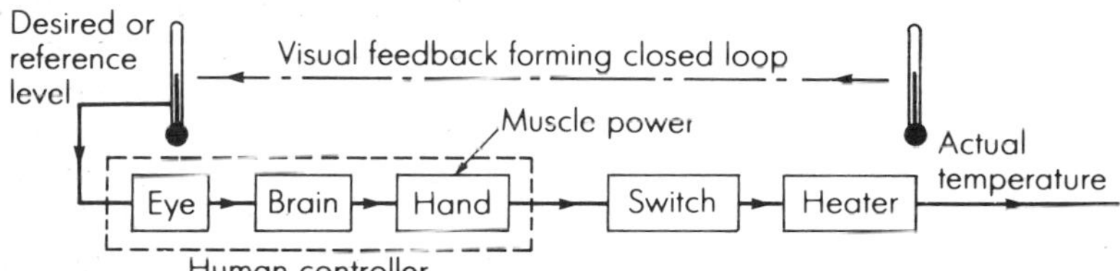

Figure 14.2

The occupant of the room becomes the controller. His - or her - eye would compare the actual reading of a thermometer with what his brain has been programmed to accept as the desired level, that is, 22°C. When a difference (or error) is detected by his eye between this desired temperature and the actual temperature, his brain operates his hand by way of his muscles to either close the switch if the error is negative (actual less than desired) or open the switch if the error is positive (actual greater than desired). Notice from the diagram that a completely closed loop is formed in the 'circuit', from output back to input, and that the feedback path here is a visual one. The *error signal* is the difference between the desired or reference level and the actual or measured level; this error signal actuates the hand muscles via the brain (a kind of power amplification for the error signal) and the hand operates the switch.

There are innumerable examples of such manually controlled closed-loop systems: adjusting the pressure on the accelerator pedal of a car to maintain (hopefully) a steady 70 miles per hour, say, on the motorway (as seen on the speedometer) is an obvious one. All such systems require human presence and intervention. If this could be avoided, a fully automatic system could be set up which almost certainly would be more reliable and consistent; automatic systems wouldn't daydream or fall asleep on the job!

Example (1). Sketch a block diagram for the car accelerator manual-control system mentioned above.

Starting off with the human controller (the driver), his or her brain will be the error detector which compares the actual reading of the speedometer with the mental reference of what it should be, that is, 70 miles per hour. The brain will then cause the foot pressure on the throttle pedal to adjust the engine revolutions so that the speed of the car coincides with the desired speed. As soon as the speed deviates from 70 miles per hour, up or down, a change in the foot pressure will restore it to the desired level. *Figure 14.3* shows a suitable block diagram. Notice again that the muscular power provides an amplification to the error signal detected by the eye. The brain *itself* cannot adjust the pressure on the pedal.

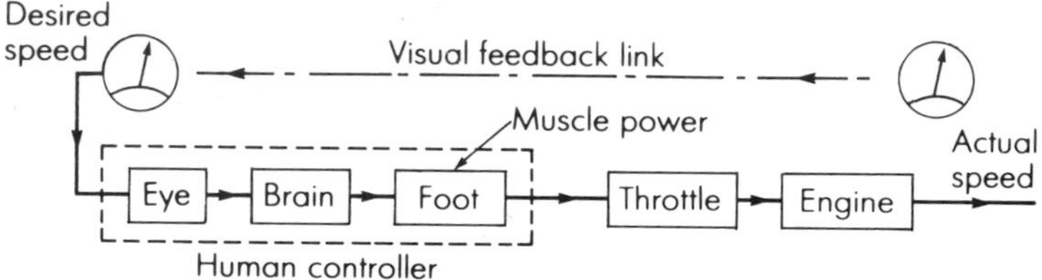

Figure 14.3

(2) Find two more examples of a manually-controlled closed-loop system and sketch block diagrams of the systems after the manner of *Figure 14.3* above.

CHARACTERISTICS OF CONTROL SYSTEMS

A control system may be designed to maintain a speed, a voltage level, a water level, and so on, constant within specified limits. Such a system is known as a *regulator*, and in it the reference is constant, though it may be capable of adjustment. In regulator controls, an error is *always* present when the system is working normally.

Position controllers or *followers* differ from regulators in that no error exists under operating conditions. Here the variation at the output duplicates the variation at the input. If the output is a translational or angular displacement, the position controller is called a *servomechanism*.

Control systems also exhibit a reaction (or response) time, as do human beings. This is the time interval which occurs between the error being detected and the system output making an appropriate adjustment. In sober humans, reaction time is normally only a fraction of a second; in some control systems, particularly mechanical systems, response times can extend to several minutes or longer. Electronic systems have times which are extremely short.

(3) Is a system which controls the angular position of an aerial array a regulator or a follower system?

(4) Identify from the diagram of *Figure 14.3* the following parameters: (a) the reference input, (b) the feedback signal, (c) the the feedback elements, (d) the output.

AUTOMATIC CONTROL

True closed-loop control does away with human intervention; the human operator is replaced by some mechanical or electrical system (often a combination of the two) which senses the difference between the reference level and the actual output level and utilises this difference to bring the output level as close as possible to the reference level - and keep it there.

We can illustrate this in a diagram such as *Figure 14.4*. This is essentially the basic block diagram of all automatic control systems.

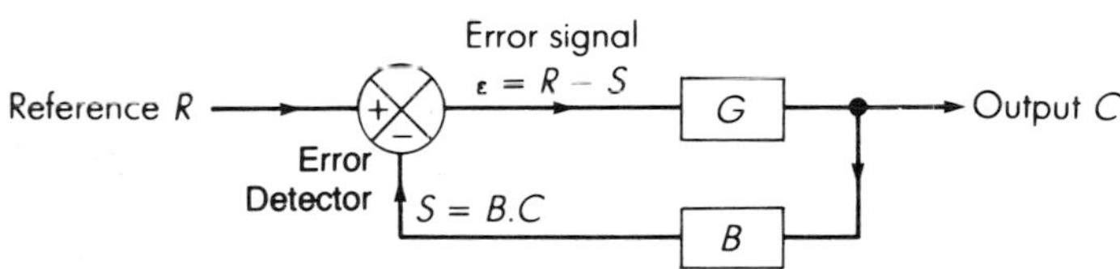

Figure 14.4

The controlled quantity C is connected back to the input through some feedback element B and the signal $S = B.C$ is compared with the reference R. In most practical systems, B is a fractional device which ensures that S is smaller than C. The ratio of the feedback signal S to error signal $\epsilon = (R - S)$ is the open-loop transfer function $B.G$. Make a note of the way the error detector symbol is drawn; the arithmetic signs indicate that the feedback signal S is subtracted from the reference R. We can treat this system as a loop in which a certain 'gain' or amplification is obtained in the G compartment, where muscular energy in the examples above gives the error signal the power to operate the switch or the foot pedal. In other systems, the G box could be an electronic amplifier, or some mechanical arrangement of levers or gears which would provide an amplification in power.

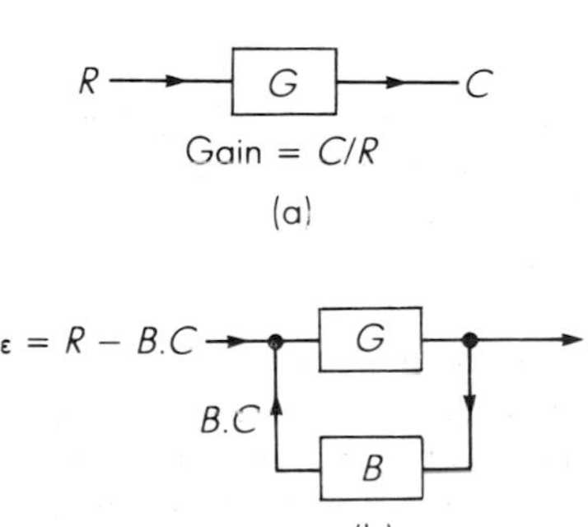

Figure 14.5

Without a feedback connection, the unit G has an input R and an output C, i.e. open-loop conditions. The gain of this unit is therefore output divided by input or C/R; *Figure 14.5(a)*. Now with the feedback applied (*Figure 14.5(b)*), the input to unit G is the error signal $\epsilon = (R - S)$ or $(R - BC)$. Let the new *overall* gain with the feedback be G'. Then

$$G' = \frac{C}{R - BC} = \frac{C/R}{1 - (BC/R)}$$

But C/R is the gain without feedback, hence

$$G' = \frac{G}{1 - BG}$$

This is the feedback equation and you will be meeting it again in your later electronics course. It tells us the way the gain of a system is modified by the application of feedback from output to input in terms of the *amount* of feedback and the gain *without* feedback. For true closed-loop control, the feedback signal, which is part or all of the output value to be controlled, is subtracted from the reference value; this is known as *negative feedback*, or sometimes 'degenerative feedback'. We will return to this equation and its implications later on.

Example (5). Write down and classify the three essential component parts of a closed-loop control with negative feedback.

The components parts are as follows:

(a) a controller which acts as error detector and amplifier;

(b) an actuator, operated by the output from the controller which corrects for any deviations in the output (measured) quantity;

(c) a feedback unit which provides a signal proportional to the output quantity for comparison with the reference.

TEMPERATURE CONTROL

Control systems of any sort are clearly designed to deal with changing conditions or disturbances. In evaluating a system we are interested in its dynamic characteristics, the way it behaves when there is a sudden change in the output conditions, for example, or a disturbance whose variability is completely random. In theory we want a correction to be applied instantly to any such variations, followed by an instant response, but such exact control is unattainable.

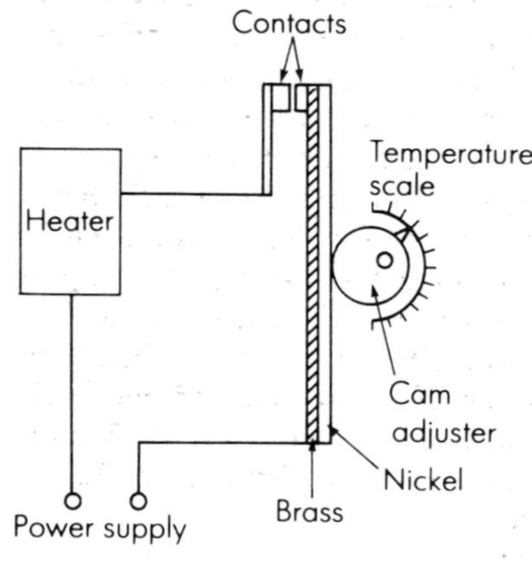

Figure 14.6

We can examine some of the possible problems by going back to *14.2* and making the temperature control in the room a fully automatic one. We can do this by replacing the human operator by a familiar piece of equipment, a thermostat. As its name implies, a thermostat is designed to maintain temperature constant; a basic form of the device is shown in *Figure 14.6*. Here a bi-metal strip, usually of nickel and brass, forms part of the electrical circuit in series with a pair of contacts and the heater. The separation of the contacts is adjustable by a control knob marked in degrees of temperature. This knob sets the reference level. Assume that the contacts are closed so that current passes from the mains supply through the heater element which then heats the surround ings. As the temperature rises, the greater expansion of the brass relative to the nickel produces a curvature in the strip and causes the contacts to open, switching off the supply. As the temperature falls, the strip straightens and contact is re-established. The cycle then repeats. In actual thermostats, the strip is spring-loaded so that the make and break changeovers take place rapidly in a snap action.

A block diagram is shown in *Figure 14.7*. Study this carefully and notice that the input quantity is a force, as is the feedback. Whenever the actual temperature is less than the desired, the heater is ON; otherwise it is OFF. So we have a means of controlling temperature using a relatively inexpensive error detector and controller. One point might be added here: the thermostat example is a case of a *discontinuous* closed-loop system. The correction is made in a series of discrete ON–OFF steps, changing from one state to the other as the error signal changes from

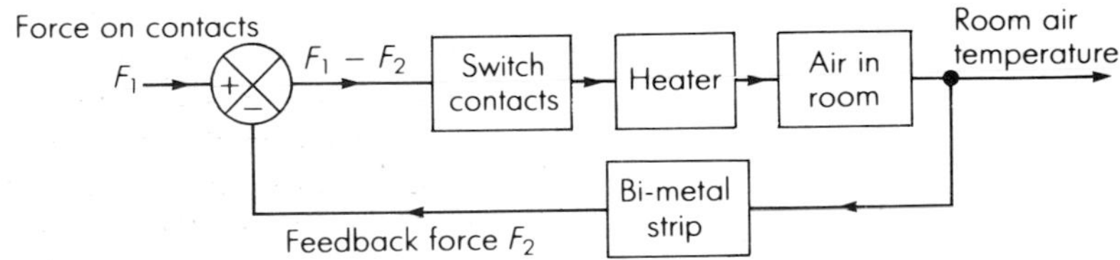

Figure 14.7

positive to negative. A continuous control system applies correction all the time, smoothly and without steps.

There are, however, inherent 'faults' in this system which are characteristic of control systems in general.

(6) Is the car speed control system of *Figure 14.3* a continuous or discontinuous system?

TRANSIENT AND STEADY-STATE BEHAVIOUR

So far we have assumed that the conditions in which our control systems have worked have been ideal. This happy state of affairs never happens in real life. Variations and disturbances are occurring all the time. The doors of the temperature-controlled room may be opened suddenly to let in cold air. The thermostat will respond to build up the temperature again but before the desired reference level is reached the door may be opened again. Movements within the room will also cause local variations in temperature. Then again, the thermostat itself is far from being an ideal device. There is always a 'dead zone' in which the temperature difference is insufficient to activate the thermostat, that is, the thermostat never switches itself off and on again at precisely the same temperature level. There is always a small range over which there is no response to a change. This may be only a fraction of a degree in a well designed thermostat, but could be as much as five degrees in a poor one. There is also a time lag between a change in the output of the heater and the response of the thermostat; heat takes time to distribute itself over the whole volume of the room. If the thermostat is mounted on the side of the room opposite to the heater, for instance, the heated side is likely to go well past the desired temperature level before the thermostat across the room is activated.

When the heater is first switched on in a cold room, the room gradually warms up until it reaches the desired level. This is known as the *transient* period. The thermostat then switches the heater off but the production of heat continues for some little while before the heater cools, and over this period the temperature continues to rise. Similarly, when the temperature of the room falls the heater switches on, but takes a short while before it produces its full output. So all the time the system is working the room temperature fluctuates about a mean (the desired) level. This is known as the *steady-state* condition. *Figure 14.8* shows a typical variation. This has been exaggerated in scale for clarity.

The extent of the range of temperature variation depends upon the design of the thermostat and how sensitive it is to temperature variation. Whatever the conditions, however, there has to be a deviation between desired and actual temperature.

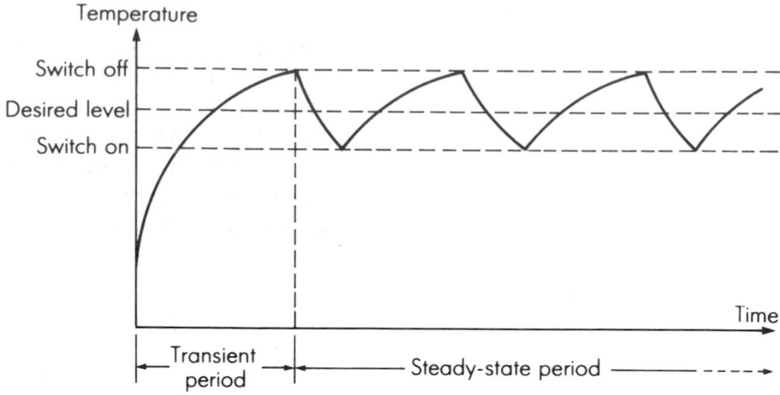

Figure 14.8

In any system the transient period occurs immediately after switching on, though the period itself may last for anything from a few microseconds to many minutes. During this period the output changes in some manner which is a characteristic of the system. Once steady-state conditions are established, the output adopts essentially the same form as the input.

(7) A pan of boiling water is taken from a stove and stood to one side in a room where the air temperature is 20°C. Sketch the transfer characteristics of this open-loop system.

(8) Does the extent of the range of variation between switch-off and switch-on shown in the graph of *Figure 14.8* depend upon whereabouts the thermostat is situated in the room?

HYSTERESIS

We have studied magnetic hysteresis in an earlier part of this book. Hysteresis also occurs in control systems and, as in the case of the magnetic example, it is a measure of the variation in the output value of a system for a given input value depending upon whether that input is increasing or decreasing. There is hysteresis in the heater control system discussed above in that the thermostat may switch off at some temperature T°C but, as the temperature falls, it may not switch on until a level lower than T°C is reached. A graph of input (temperature) against output (the switch operation) for the thermostat is shown in *Figure 14.9*. When the temperature is rising, the contacts may break at 23°C, say, and when the temperature is falling they may close at 21°C, say. This illustrates what we earlier referred to as the 'dead zone', the thermostat failing to respond to any temperature level between (in this case) 21° and 23°C.

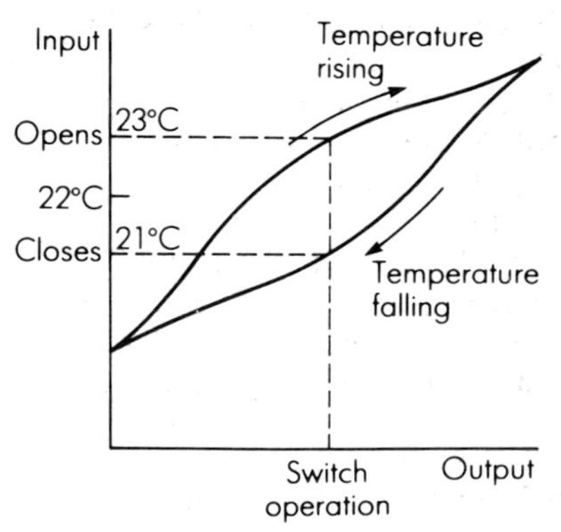

Figure 14.9

In mechanical systems, hysteresis usually results from the effects of friction and the slight 'looseness' found between the engaging teeth of a gear train.

POSITION CONTROL

So far we have looked at mechanical control systems; here is an electrical example which illustrates the principles of position control.

Example (9). A simple servomechanism system is illustrated in *Figure 14.10*. This system is used to control the angular position, or bearing, of an aerial which forms the loading on the electric motor M. The movement of the aerial is controlled by a reference potentiometer R_{ref}. Describe the way the output potentiometer R_{out}, and hence the aerial, is caused to follow the movements of the reference potentiometer.

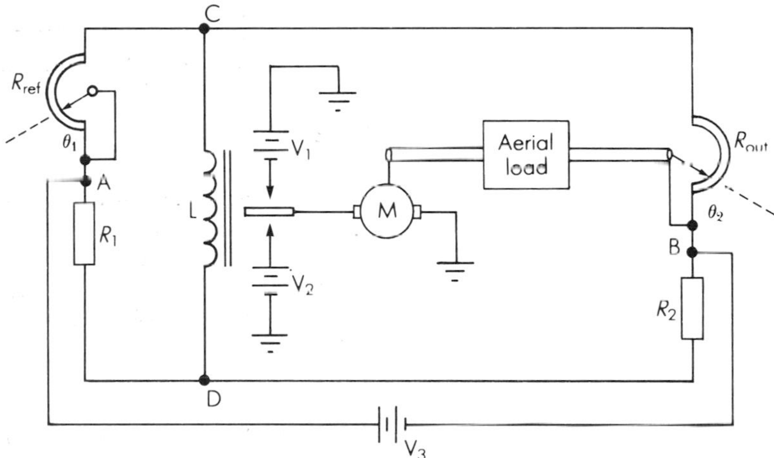

Figure 14.10

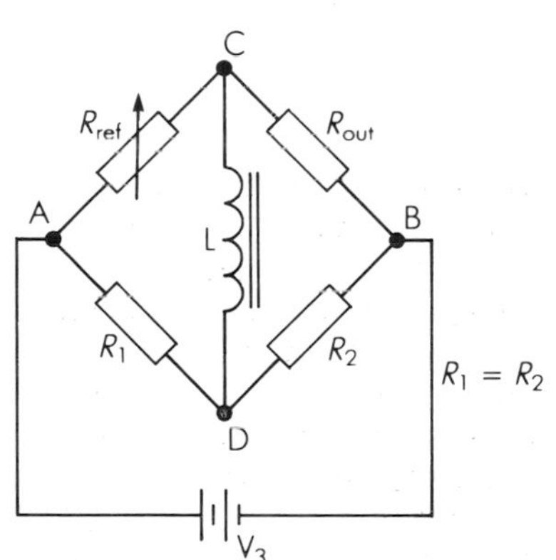

Figure 14.11

The first thing to do is to study the diagram and deduce the principle on which the system works. We notice that the four resistances R_{ref}, R_1, R_2 and R_{out} form a Wheatstone connected bridge as shown in *Figure 14.11*, with the power supply V_3 connected across points A-B and the centre-stable relay L across points C-D. When the bridge is balanced, that is, when R_{ref} is set to be equal to R_{out}, no current flows in the centre arm C-D (since $R_1 = R_2$) and so the relay is unenergised and neither of its contacts closed. Motor M is then inoperative.

Suppose now that the setting of R_{ref} is altered; angle θ_1 changes and the bridge is unbalanced. A current now flows between points C and D and the relay is energised, and the motor rotates. The direction of rotation depends upon the polarity of the power input to the motor, that is, which of the batteries V_1 or V_2 is connected by the relay contacts. This in turn depends upon the direction of current flow between points C and D, which is determined by the direction that potentiometer R_{ref} takes relative to the setting of R_{out}.

The system is set up so that the motor turns the output potentiometer in a direction which follows the reference. When the position of R_{out} coincides with the new position of R_{ref} the bridge is rebalanced, current flow between C and D ceases, and the motor switches off. Angles θ_1 and θ_2 are again equal, and the aerial has been moved in angular setting. The actual angle through which the aerial has moved is determined by the gearing in the drive. This provides any angular ratio between that set on the reference potentiometer and the actual aerial movement. Take particular note that there is no residual error in this system once the control has stabilised.

(10) If the aerial in the previous example was found to change only in one direction, make a list of the possible faults which might cause this condition.

(11) What would happen if the connections of the two battery supplies V_1 and V_2 were inadvertently reversed?

(12) Looking back at the examples of control illustrated in *Figures 14.2* and *14.3*, what are the most likely 'disturbances' that the systems would have to correct for? Whereabouts on the block diagrams would you indicate these disturbances?

STABILITY

The stability of a system is a measure of the ability of that system to restore itself to an initial state or condition after that state or condition has been disturbed. Unless it can do this, the system is unstable. A simple analogy of stable and unstable states is shown in *Figure 14.12*. Here a ball is placed first in a bowl, then on an inverted bowl and then on a level surface.

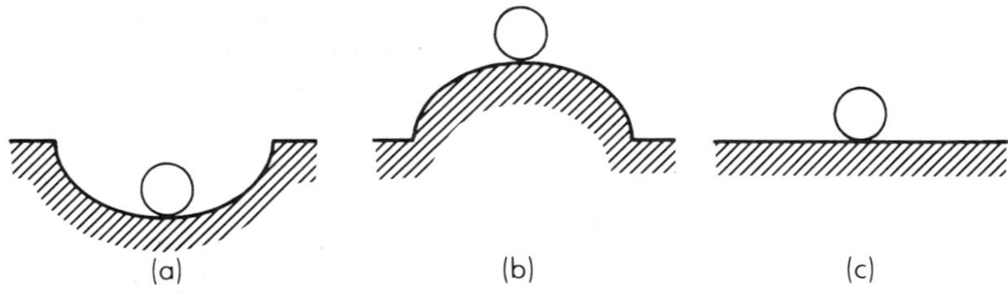

Figure 14.12

The ball in the bowl, diagram *(a)*, is stable, since it will always return to its initial position at the bottom of the bowl after any displacement. The ball on the inverted bowl, diagram *(b)*, is unstable; the slightest disturbance will cause it to roll uncontrollably off the bowl with no possibility of its returning to its initial position unaided. The ball on the level surface, diagram *(c)*, may appear to be stable, but if it is disturbed it will move away from its initial position and take up another; it will not restore itself without intervention. This is known as a *conditionally* stable state. When the word 'instability' is applied to control systems, mechanical or electronic, conditions *(b)* and *(c)* are both undesirable.

The designer of an automatic control system uses mathematical techniques which are beyond the scope of our work here, but if we look again at the feedback equation discussed earlier, we should be able to understand *why* a control system may not work in the manner a diagram might suggest it should. Recalling, we have

$$G' = \frac{G}{1 - BG}$$

which we might express as

$$\text{gain with feedback } G' = \frac{\text{gain without feedback}}{1 - (\text{feedback amount})\,(\text{gain without feedback})}$$

If there is no feedback ($B = 0$), the system will exhibit a gain $G = G'$. This is the open-loop condition. If there is feedback ($B \neq 0$) and the denominator of the equation is *greater* than unity, then G' will be less than G. This condition implies that B must be negative, and the term 'negative feedback' is derived from this fact. If the entire output is fed back to the input under negative feedback conditions, then $B = -1$ and

$$G' = \frac{G}{1 + G}$$

which makes G' just less than unity.

Positive feedback occurs whenever the denominator of the equation is less than unity, that is, when the product $B.G$ lies *between* the values 0 and +1. The gain with feedback is then always greater than the gain without feedback. This might seem a desirable state of affairs, but it is not so. Remember, we are dealing with a closed loop. If the gain around the loop is greater than unity, what is there to stop an increasing output feeding back an increasing input, which in turn increases the output still further, and hence the input still further?

The extreme case arises, if, under any condition, the denominator becomes zero. For this to happen, the product $B.G$ must equal +1. The gain G' then becomes infinite, which implies that the output is independent of the input and the system is completely uncontrollable. This situation has to be avoided as, in most circumstances, has positive feedback altogether.

How can this be interpreted in terms of the proper working of a typical automatic system? There are two points to consider. First of all, a control system is made up of a number of blocks, reaching from the reference input right through to the output. A further block, or blocks, feeds back all or part of this output to the input. Instability due to positive feedback can arise because:

(a) the signal takes time to make its way from input to output;
(b) the signal may be amplified in some way between input and output.

We make a note that time delays introduced by the blocks individually throughout the system are *added*, while the gains introduced by the blocks individually are *multiplied*. It might appear from the results of our simple mathematical analysis of the feedback equation that all we have to do to do to make sure that positive feedback cannot occur is to see that the total product of the individual gains around the system is always less than one.

Unfortunately, this isn't the whole story. What we must not overlook is the time delay. The time lag, which may be considerable in mechanical systems because of inertia, for example, in moving parts, may cause the *phase* of the feedback signal to be opposite to what we want. For negative feedback we want the feedback signal to be subtracted from the reference; this can only happen if it is acting in the opposite sense to the input at all times. We have already studied phase shift in *Section 8* earlier.

Suppose that the input to a system is subject to sudden disturbances, *Figure 14.13*. In a system where there was no time delay, the output would respond immediately to this change and the feedback signal, of opposite polarity, would be sent back to kill the original disturbance at once. With a delay, however, the output, and hence the feedback,

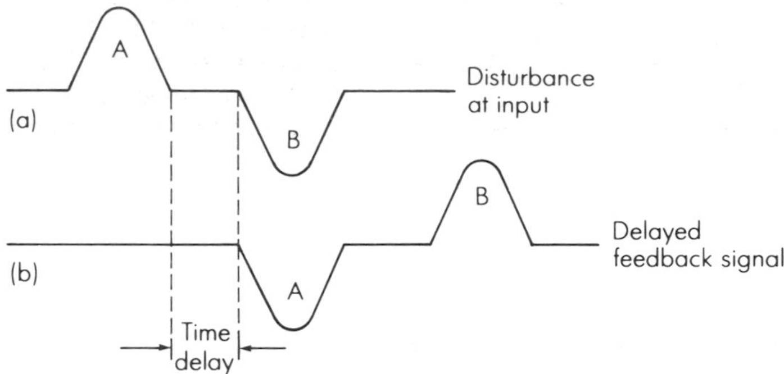

Figure 14.13

would lag behind the input and under certain circumstances would appear, via the feedback, at the input as an *assistance* to the existing disturbance instead of counteracting it. If at the same time there was amplification around the loop, control would be lost or, at best, seriously disturbed for a considerable period. Under the condition of a time delay which effectively puts the feedback signal in phase with the input, and a loop gain greater than unity, instability is inevitable.

Example (13). In the simple aerial position servomechanism of *Figure 14.10*, suggest a possible cause of instability.

We have here a position controller or follower system which might not at first appear to be subject to the feedback problems of a regulator system or to the possibility of instability. However, a delay in response in the motor and the aerial loading can lead to difficulties. This loading has inertia; it takes time to begin to move the aerial and it takes time to come to rest. While such changes are taking place, energy is stored in the system. Suppose the input potentiometer R_{ref} is suddenly moved to a new position, so that θ_1 changes. The relay contacts will close and the motor will switch on. There will be a very slight time delay in the switching of the relay but this can be ignored in relation to what happens in the motor. The drive shaft to the aerial system (and potentiometer R_{out}) will accelerate from rest and the load will store energy. When the position of R_{out}, and consequently θ_2, coincides with that of R_{ref}, and consequently with the new value of θ_1, the bridge will momentarily re-balance itself and the motor will switch off. But, because of inertia, the motor will cause the slider of R_{out} to overshoot the balance point, with the result that the bridge will unbalance in the opposite sense and the motor will be switched on again, this time in reverse. Energy will then be drawn from the load until the drive shaft comes to rest at some point *beyond* the proper balance setting. The stationary aerial system will now be caused to retrace its steps, but will again and for the same reason

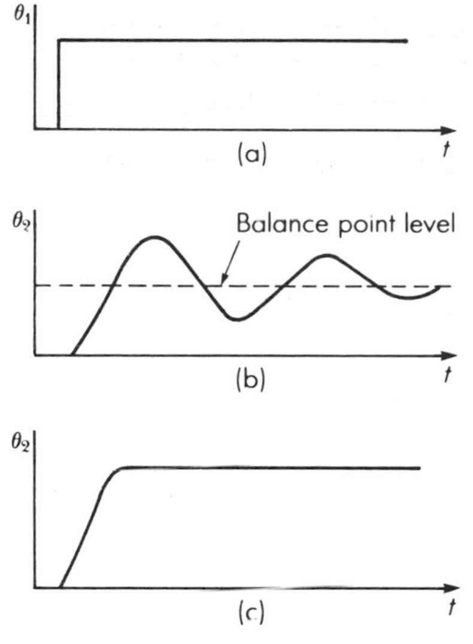

Figure 14.14

pass through the balance point before it is brought to rest. This to-and-fro movement of the aerial about the required position can, in a system with very low friction, go on for a long while and is a form of instability known as 'hunting'. *Figure 14.14 (a)* and *(b)* illustrate respectively the sudden change in angle θ_1 and the resulting change in θ_2. What we should really have is shown in diagram *(c)*, where θ_2 is approached quickly and maintained with negligible overshoot. This can be accomplished by the right degree of friction (braking) in the aerial drive shaft. *Figure 14.14 (c)* illustrates what is known as *critical damping*.

PROBLEMS FOR SECTION 14

(14) Give two examples, with block diagrams, of open-loop control systems.

(15) State the limitations of open-loop control systems.

(16) What is meant by a closed-loop control system? How does it differ from an open-loop system?

(17) How does a continuous control system differ from a discontinuous system? Draw a block diagram and give an account of the operation of a discontinuous (on–off) control system.

(18) What are the three essential features of a closed-loop control system?

(19) Explain the meaning of the following terms, as used in control system engineering:

(a) reference signal
(b) error signal
(c) power amplification
(d) a servomechanism.

(20) Explain the meaning of the term 'hysteresis. as used in control engineering. A gear chain exhibits a form of hysteresis; what do you understand by this statement?

(21) What is the cause of instability in a closed-loop system? Make a sketch graph demonstrating that negative feedback with 180° phase shift around the open loop is the same as a system with positive feedback and zero phase-shift.

(22) Explain the difference between positive and negative feedback. Why is positive feedback undesirable in a control system?

(23) *Figure 14.15* shows a simple automatic system for controlling the maximum and minimum levels of water in a tank. Two metal probes of different lengths sense the presence of water; when *neither* probe is contacting the water, i.e. when the water level is at its minimum, the amplifier switches on the motor which opens the valve and allows water into the tank. As soon as *both* probes contact water, i.e. when the water level is at its maximum,

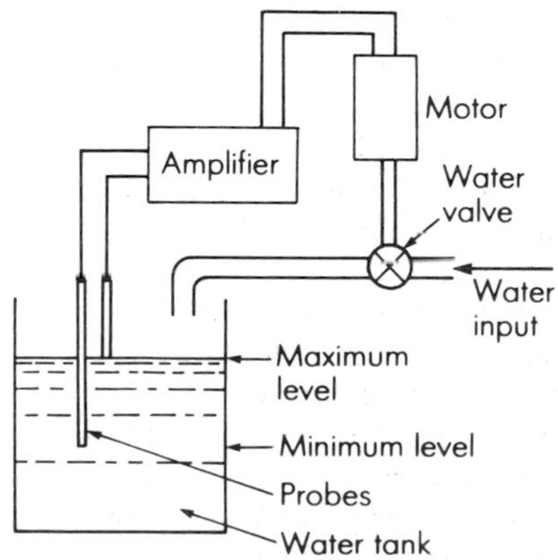

Figure 14.15

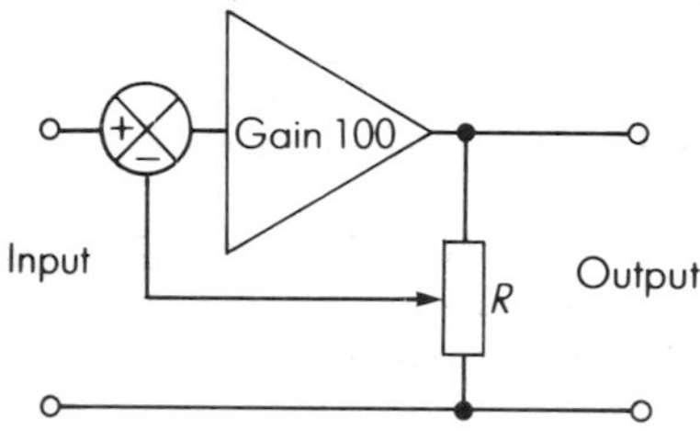

Figure 14.16

the motor switches off and the valve is closed.

(a) Deduce and sketch a block diagram of this system.

(b) How could the reference be altered?

(c) Is there a likelihood of instability in this system?

(d) What would a corresponding open-loop system consist of?

(24) A car has an automatic cruise control system. In this system, the desired speed is manually set on an electronic device which can compare it with the actual speed fed back from the speedometer. The electrical output of this comparator is fed to an amplifier whose power output operates the engine throttle by way of a magnetic solenoid.

(a) Draw a block diagram of this control system.

(b) Is this a continuous or discontinuous control system?

(c) Identify the reference input, the error detector, the feedback element and the controlled output.

(d) What, if anything, could cause instability in this system?

(25) *Figure 14.16* shows an electronic amplifier which has a gain of 100 and a phase shift of 180°. Part of the output is fed back to the input by way of a potential divider **R**. If one-tenth of the output is fed back in this way, what is the overall gain of the system with the feedback?

15 Elements of data transmission

Aims: At the end of this Unit section you should be able to:
Understand the distinction between analogue and digital quantities.
Appraise the systems and media available for the transmission of information in analogue form.
Explain the relationship between sound waves and analogue signals.
Understand how digital signals may be sent over the public switched telephone network.
Describe serial and parallel data format for digital transmissions, and how serial format may be synchronous or asynchronous.
Understand the problems of interfacing lines and peripherals to computer systems.

In this Unit section we shall cover only the most basic of the principles of data transmission involving the use of facilities provided by the existing telegraph and telephone networks. You will not be expected to know anything about the computer and peripherals which are connected together in this way.

ANALOGUE AND DIGITAL QUANTITIES

Analogue quantities can have any value. Natural physical quantities like temperature, pressure and time are analogue; in fact, we live in an analogue world. Sound waves generated in air by speech or music are an analogue form of information transmission; the air pressure is *continually* changing. A moving-coil meter such as an Avometer is an analogue instrument, since the pointer can indicate any one of an infinite number of positions within the scale length. The movement of the pointer is continuous in that there is no part of the scale it does not indicate in moving between any two positions.

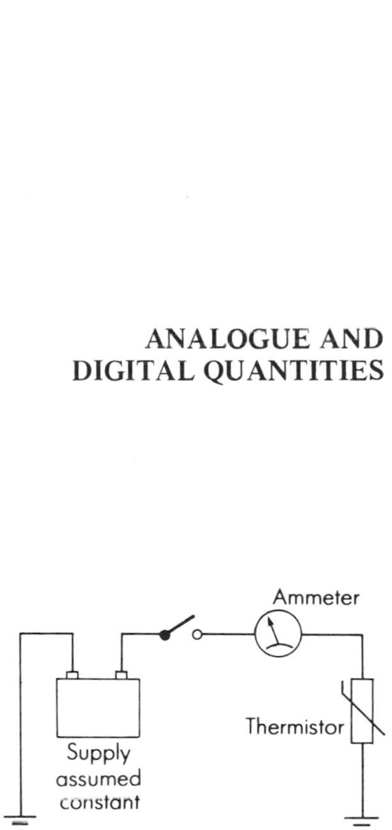

To represent an analogous condition in an electrical system, some property of electricity, such as voltage or current, has to be controlled so that it represents a precise 'copy' or an in-step following of the original data. An example of an analogue information system can be found in the water temperature indicator of a car, shown in a much simplified form in *Figure 15.1*. Here a thermistor, the resistance of which varies as the temperature is varied, is mounted in contact with part of the water-cooling system where the temperature needs to be measured. This is usually in the main engine block. The resistance of the thermistor element is then a function of the water temperature; when the temperature is low, the resistance is high; when the temperature is high, the resistance is low. Because the thermistor is connected to the car battery, a current will flow round the circuit when the ignition switch is closed, and the current meter (an ammeter) will indicate a current level dictated by the resistance of the thermistor. So if the minimum resistance of the thermistor at 120°C was 100 Ω and its

Figure 15.1

maximum at 20°C was 1000 Ω, the range of current, assuming a 12 V battery, would be 120 mA to 12 mA. At the instrument panel, the pointer of the meter would be scaled to indicate the temperature range 20°C to 120°C as it moved between the two extremes of measured current.

The point of importance is that the current is never off but flows in one direction all the time the ignition is switched on. The pointer in the meter 'copies' the change in temperature, and the current therefore conveys the information from one place to another in analogue form as a changing d.c. signal. A graph of the relationship would be of the form illustrated in *Figure 15.2*. This graph is a smooth continuous curve. The term *linear analogue system* is often used to describe such circuits, although the graph itself may not be a straight line.

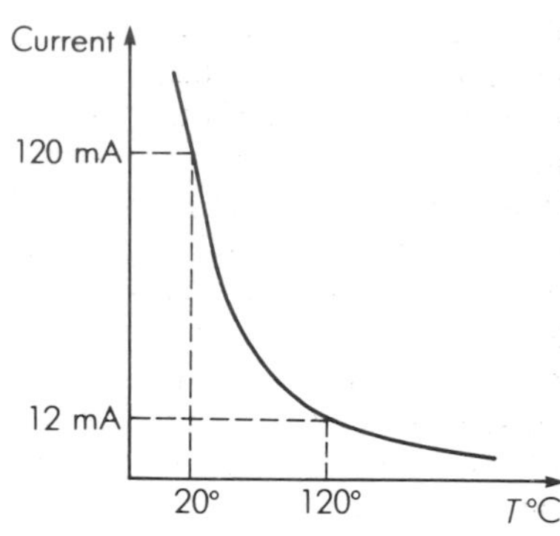

Figure 15.2

In contrast to analogue quantities, a digital signal can have only certain fixed values. In an electrical system it has to be either at one voltage or current level or at some other voltage or current level. It cannot take up intermediate positions between the two permitted states. It is, therefore, essentially a *discontinuous* system. *Figure 15.3* shows a digital signal made up of pulses varying in level between the limits 0 and 5 V. The parts of the signal are known as *bits*, and the bits represent (usually) the binary numbers 0 and 1.

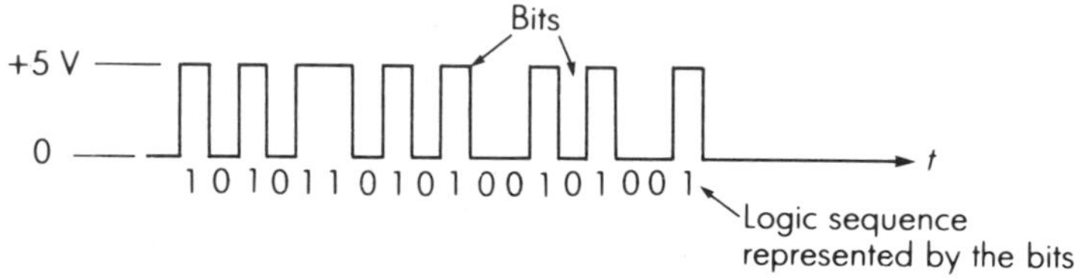

Figure 15.3

A digital meter is a now familiar example of a device which indicates an analogue voltage input in a digital form of display. Although inherently more accurately readable than an analogue meter, it nevertheless cannot indicate *every* voltage level within its range which an analogue meter (theoretically in so far as the ability to read its scale goes) can. A digital meter, for instance, cannot indicate a voltage level *between*, say, 1.254 V and 1.255 V, unless we introduce more digits to the display, which only shifts the same argument to the next decimal place. But of course, we could not expect to be able to read an analogue meter to that kind of discrimination, anyway.

It is possible to 'disguise' analogue signals so that they seem to be digital. For example, the sound output from a metronome is a succession of 'clicks' spaced by silences. The progression of discrete clicks may be interpreted as a digital (on-off) signal; on the other hand, each click is (while it lasts) an analogue of air pressure. Keep this idea in mind; it will give us a clue as to how we might be able to transmit a digital signal over an analogue system.

DATA TRANSMISSION

The term 'information transmission' covers systems for the distribution of information from one point to some other point, or from some point to a number of other points. Data networks which provide access over a large geographical area, nation-wide or world wide, are known as *wide area networks*. At the other extreme, networking over a small area comes under the heading of *local area networks*. Transmissions over such networks can take place in a great variety of ways: smoke signals (very local), the heliograph, jungle drums, the telegraph, the telephone, radio and radar, to name just a few. The first two of these possibilities depend upon light waves as the transmission medium, the third on sound waves and the remainder on electrical signals. All of them can be made to work with digital signals, although many of them were designed as purely analogue systems. Smoke signals, in fact, are inherently digital in form, which perhaps shows that there is nothing new under the sun. The telegraph, too, is a digital communicator, being concerned as it is with the transmission of coded signals such as Morse. In fact, the telegraph was carrying out digital transmissions long before the requirements of present-day computers and processor-based equipment were dreamed of. It certainly was not invented for that purpose.

Since then, of course, things have become rather more sophisticated. As equipment (particularly computers) has become more complex, faster and more expensive, the problems associated with interconnection over long distances have multiplied. Like the growth of the telephone network, the necessity of such linkages became inevitable. It is not practicable or economic for large business users, for example, to have their own on-the-spot computers, especially if full-time utilisation is not possible; besides, contact is necessary between the various parts of a business which may be nationally or internationally distributed. Individual banks, for instance, would not house on the premises a mainframe computer containing details of the customers accounts and other business for that particular branch. Contact is needed throughout the entire network of banks, not only necessarily among its own branches but with other bank networks and financial institutions as well. The solution is to have a large central computer to which all branches of that bank are connected; any branch can then call up the particulars it requires relating to any account. Again, cash card dispensers are connected to a central processor which records the transaction after verification by the code entered at the cashpoint, and debits the account accordingly. They can also supply the customer with a statement of his account or accept his request for, say, a new chequebook. So the communication link has normally to be a two-way affair.

As another familiar example of information transmission, more and more television receivers are being adapted to receive teletext services such as Ceefax and Oracle. These are computerised systems that broadcast digitally coded information in unused portions of the normal television signal. This information is decoded at the receiver and appears on the screen as pages of information about such things as the weather, sports reports or the latest news.

Links for the propagation of either analogue or digital data are available in a number of forms, many for a great number of years. The telegraph and telephone networks, radio channels, coaxial cables and optical fibres are the most important. As a preminary, we will examine systems involving the telegraph, telephone and radio links.

First, try these self-assessment problems.

(1) Is a slide rule (not much seen these days) an analogue or a digital device?

(2) An analogue system represents information as (a) a voltage, (b) a current, (c) a collection of discrete parts, (d) a continuous copy using some property of electricity. State which.

(3) A digital system represents information purely as (a) a voltage at a constant level, (b) a current at a constant level, (c) a voltage or current having only fixed levels, (d) a square wave. State which.

(4) What do you understand by a linear analogue system?

TRANSMISSION METHODS

Although we shall study the analogue transmission systems mentioned in this and later sections in much greater detail later in the course, they are introduced here to illustrate the basic techniques available and to point out their relative advantages and disadvantages.

The telegraph

The analogue transmission of temperature variation over a system as illustrated in *Figure 15.1* used only the simple electrical characteristics of voltage, current and resistance, and this is true of most *directly wired* transmission circuits. What we are doing is to vary the level of a unidirectional (one-way) current to convey the information. The same applies to a simple telegraph system. *Figure 15.4(a)* shows a very basic signalling circuit; when the key is operated, the lamp at the receiving end of the line lights up. Such an arrangement would not be very successful over a long length of line (unless a very high voltage were used) because of the resistance of the wires. An improvement would consist of replacing the lamp by a sensitive relay as shown in *Figure 15.4(b)*. The advantage would be that a smaller line current could be tolerated to operate the relay compared with that needed to light the lamp directly, and with a smaller current the system could be used over a greater distance.

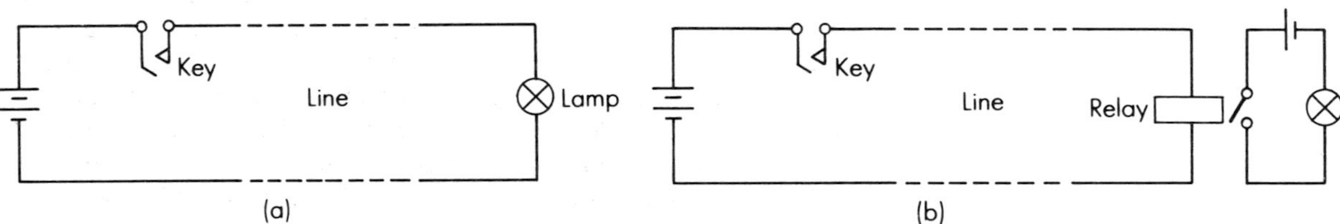

Figure 15.4

Practical telegraph circuits were designed to transmit and receive hand-keyed information generated by teleprinters. Telegraphic data (for example, that between a Telex exchange and a subscriber's teleprinter connected to the exchange) is made up of 0's and 1's which are sent along the telegraph link using signalling levels of +80 V for a space element (0) and –80 V for a mark element (1). If the line is to be used to connect computer systems together, it is only necessary to use interfacing equipment to provide compatibility between the ±80 V levels of the telegraph circuits and the typical 0 and 5 V levels of the computer; see *Figure 15.5*. The rate at which data can be sent is between 50 and 200 bits per second. This is perfectly adequate for the original design purpose but is too low for most modern computer communications. However, the system is still used where low data-rate transmission can be tolerated.

The problems which arise in high-speed signalling over directly connected terminals are not confined to the plain electrical resistance of

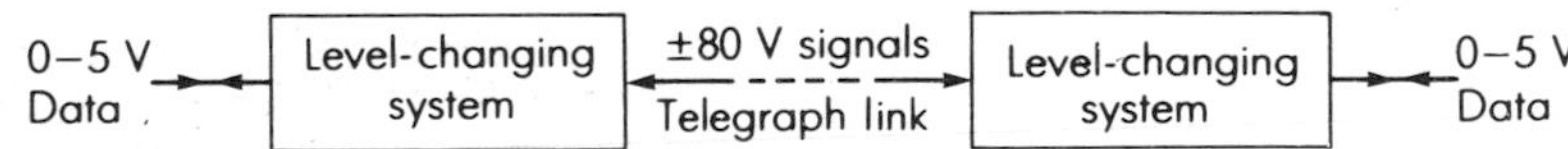

Figure 15.5

the wires, nor merely to the telegraphic network. Long lengths of line exhibit not only resistance but inductance bridged by capacitance, as shown in *Figure 15.6*. The significance of this is that the inductance of both the line and the receiving teleprinter prevent the current in the line from increasing quickly when the operating key is closed (or whatever method of sending is employed). When the key is operated, current begins immediately to flow and to increase in value; this rising current,

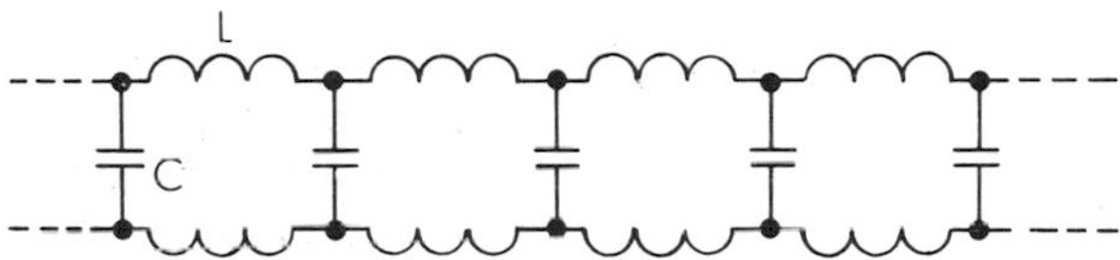

Figure 15.6

however, generates a back e.m.f. in the line which, according to Lenz's law (as we saw earlier) opposes the change producing it. The result is that the current build-up, which we should like to be immediate, is instead gradual and there is a delay before the signal reaches the receiver. So not only is the shape of the signal distorted but the speed of signalling is reduced. This effect worsens as current changes increase in rapidity, which is the same thing as trying to send a greater number of bits per second.

The presence of capacitance between the lines, or between a line and earth, also contributes to the problem. When the key is operated, a large initial current flow enters the line which simply goes to progressively charge up the distributed capacitance. At the receiving end the growth of current is delayed, this time by the effect of capacitance. Such direct-current signalling methods are therefore basically unsuitable for the transmission of high speed on-off digital data. Only low bit rates are permissible. It is a characteristic of such transmission lines that zero frequency (the d.c. component of the signal) is passed, which is not true for the telephone system.

The telephone

The public switched telephone network (PSTN) is shown in schematic form in *Figure 15.7*. Each subscriber is connected to the local exchange by a twin-wire circuit, and all local calls are made over this part of the network. For calls to more distant subscribers, the local exchanges are linked by four-wire trunk circuits (in practice these are coaxial cables) by way of group switching centres. These links require repeater amplifiers because of the greater distances involved.

When digital links were required, the use of the established telephone system seemed a logical and inexpensive choice since everything was already in place and working. The telephone network, however, was designed for voice frequency transmission, an analogue system.

A very basic telephone system is shown in *Figure 15.8*. This illustrates a one-way (simplex working) arrangement, although by simply duplicating the parts, the system would become two-way

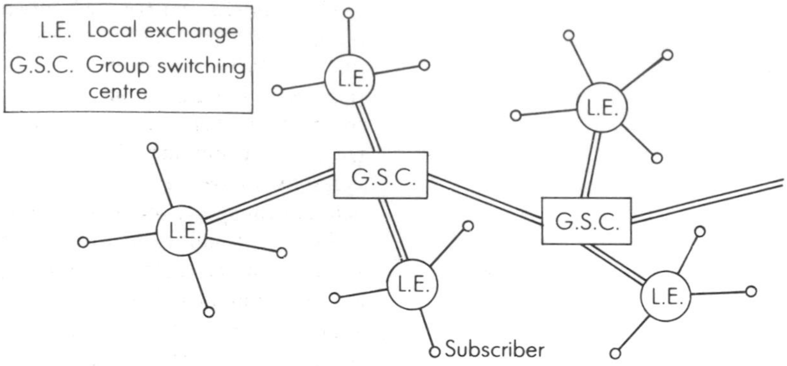

Figure 15.7

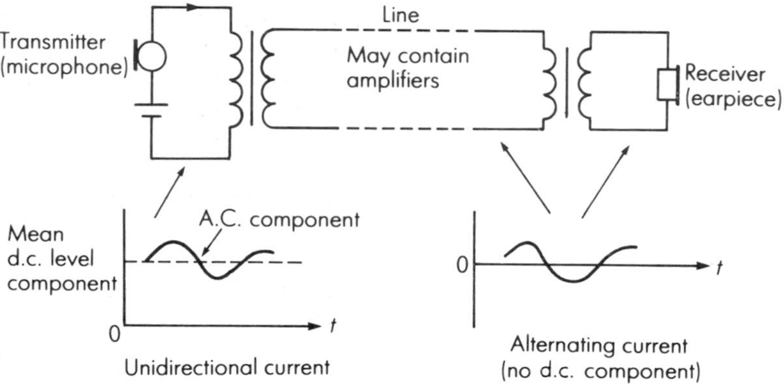

Figure 15.8

(duplex working). Current flows from the transmitter element (the microphone) to the receiving element (the earpiece) but not wholly in the form of a unidirectional current. Like the water temperature gauge described earlier, the amount of current flowing in the microphone circuit loop is a function of the resistance in the circuit. The resistance variation takes place in the microphone.

Sound waves consist of alternate compressions and rarefactions in the air. When someone speaks and the sound waves reach the microphone, a thin flexible diaphragm vibrates under the stimulus of the varying air pressure and the frequency and amplitude components of the wave are converted into vibrations of the diaphragm which correspond to the air pressure changes. This movement of the diaphragm backwards and forwards changes the pressure on a small chamber of carbon granules mounted behind the diaphragm and so changes the resistance of the conducting path presented by the granules. The current which passes from the battery through the granules then varies at a rate corresponding to the frequency of the impressed air waves and has a magnitude variation proportional to the amplitude (loudness) of the wave. Nevertheless, the current flowing remains unidirectional; it rises and falls about a mean value but never changes direction. It is the analogue representation of the original sound waves. The variation is superimposed on a direct-current component.

The transformer (or transmission bridge) which connects the microphone to the line does not pass on the direct-current component of the signal; only the variation which is effectively an alternating current is transmitted along the line. At the earpiece, a diaphragm mounted in front of an electromagnetic assembly is caused to vibrate in sympathy with the current variations, so setting up air pressure variations. These pressure changes reconstruct the original sound waves and the ear of the listener interprets them accordingly.

Now although it might seem that the telephone network would be suitable for the transmission of digital signals, there is a limit to the amount which can actually be sent. The fact that the telephone is an analogue instrument does not tell us the whole story of such a limitation. We have seen that computer information is made up of bit patterns, and a transmission medium such as wire may represent these bits as combinations of only two analogue voltages, typically +5 V representing logic level 1 and 0 V representing logic level 0. So whenever a digital signal is sent along a wire connection, be it telephone or any other such system, it is being sent as an analogue quantity. In theory, then, there should be no problem since the telephone system is an analogue system.

The telephone network, however, caters only for what is known as 'commercial' speech. This means that the frequency response is limited to a band of relatively low values. The upper operating frequency on standard lines is 3400 Hz, and the lower limit is about 300 Hz. We have already noted that the d.c. component (zero frequency) is removed altogether. We say the system has a bandwidth of (3400 - 300) Hz = 3100 Hz. This is greater than the bandwidth of the telegraph system, which is nominally 120 Hz. As we shall see, the greater the bandwidth, the higher the rate of transmission possible.

However, data transmission over the PSTN is not completely cut and dried because signal frequencies in the range 0 to 300 Hz are severely attenuated or cut off altogether. For particular bit-sequences applied directly to a line, difficulties arise, as shown in *Figure 15.9*. In this diagram, imagine the data sequence to change from a run of 0's to a sequence of 1's. The sequence of 1's is equivalent to a constant voltage level, that is, it is a zero frequency signal. Since the network does not transmit a zero frequency signal, the output dies away and the rest of the sequence is either of indeterminate level or represented incorrectly as 0's. So some modification is necessary before digital data can be transmitted by this means. Since we cannot modify the system itself, we must interpret the digital data into a form which will not suffer in

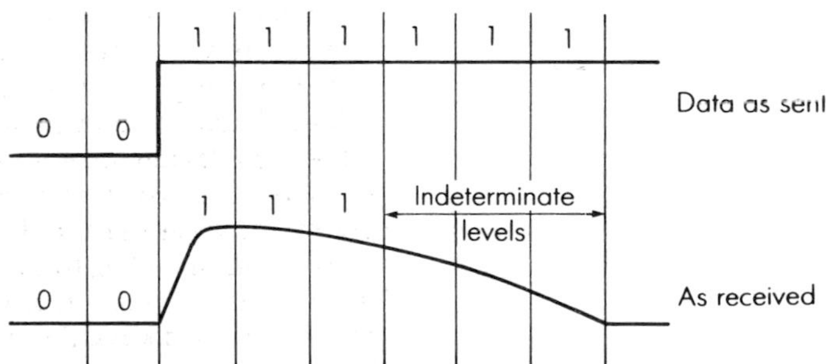

Figure 15.9

the way *Figure 15.9* shows. We have to get rid of its d.c. component. For this we have already had a clue in the note made about a metronome a few pages earlier.

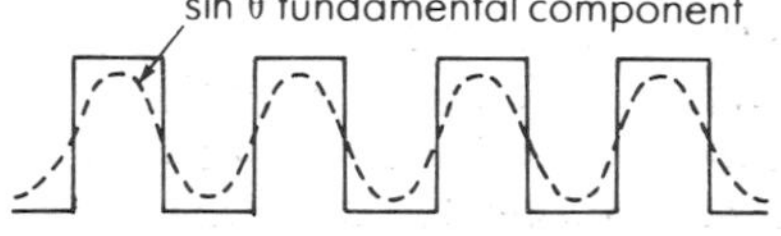

Figure 15.10

Example (5). A digital signal represented by the logical sequence 010101 . . . can be considered to be a square wave as shown in *Figure 15.10.* Why cannot this signal be transmitted directly over the telephone network?

We have already discussed the effects of line capacity and inductance together with the effects of removing the d.c. component of a signal of this sort. We can also look at the problem in a more technical sense. A pulsed wave-form of the kind shown in *Figure 15.10* can be analysed into a series of sine and cosine waves, all combining in such a way that their individual amplitudes and phase relationships make up the rectangular pulses. You may study this later in more advanced mathematics under the name of Fourier analysis. A true square wave, for example, can be shown to be made up of a d.c. compoenent plus the sum of an infinite number of sine waves where every odd harmonic frequency appears:

$$C + \sin\theta + \frac{1}{3}\sin 3\theta + \frac{1}{5}\sin 5\theta + \frac{1}{7}\sin 7\theta + \ldots$$

This forbidding expression tells us that a square wave contains a d.c. component represented by the constant C, a fundamental frequency component represented by $\sin\theta$, and all the odd harmonic frequency components up to infinity. Hence, if the wave shape is not to suffer distortion, the transmission link must be capable of passing all frequencies up to infinity, starting at zero frequency. Of course, this argument is hypothetical in so far as there is no transmission link which has an infinite bandwidth, any more than we can generate perfectly rectangular pulses in the first place. However, we can make approximations; it can be proved that if the first six terms (or more) of the above series are within the frequency band coverage of the link, then a very good approximation to a square wave will get through the network. This is because, as you can see, the successive terms are diminishing in magnitude. Beyond about the sixth term, their values become so small that their omission contributes a negligible amount to the distortion of the wave already established. In fact, we should get something like that shown in *Figure 15.11(a)* which is compared with a perfect square wave at *(b)*, if we include all the terms up to the sixth.

The telephone network not only removes the constant term C from the series but does not pass frequency components above about 3400 Hz. Hence, unless the fundamental frequency $\sin\theta$ is very low, only the first two or three terms are, at best, likely to get transmitted. The result is a badly distorted signal.

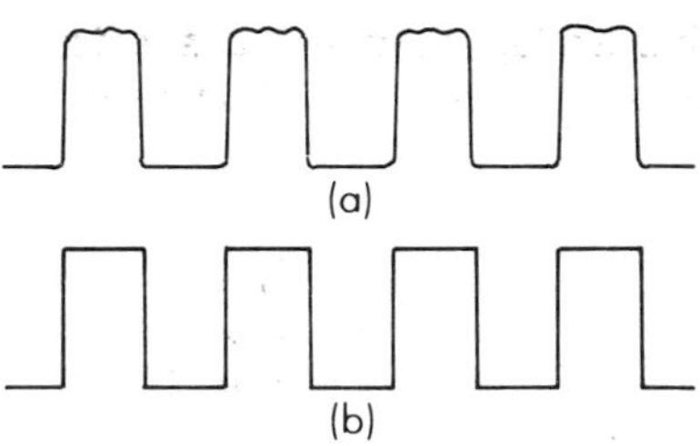

Figure 15.11

The PSTN network is essentially a 'stop-gap' communications complex, nationwide though it is, since it allows only poor data signalling rates and its reliability is sometimes criticised. Other data networks exist designed specifically for digital communications, though permitting low quality speech transmission. These come under the title of Packet Switched Stream (PSS) networks and have been operational since about 1982, mostly in private systems. Here the data information is put together in a continuous stream of bits called a packet; included in this packet are bits representing the address of the destination. The packet is entered into the network, each stage of which contains electronic equipment which samples the destination bit information and routes the packet to the next stage. This is repeated until the packet arrives at its destination. Unlike the telegraph and telephone network, the linkage from sender to receiver does *not* have to be established before information can be transmitted.

Since 1985 some new digital communications suitable for both speech and data have been introduced into the UK public section having signalling rates up to 64 000 bits per second. Looking to the future, the PSTN will be eventually based on pure digital techniques, all networks being integrated into what is provisionally known as the Integrated Services Digital Network (ISDN).

(6) What factor(s) restrict(s) the transmission of high frequencies over the public telephone network?

(7) What prevents the d.c. component of a signal from being transmitted over the public telephone network?

(8) What do you understand by the bandwidth of a transmission link?

(9) The fundamental frequency of a square wave is 1 kHz. It is transmitted over a communications channel which has a bandwidth extending from zero to 12 kHz. Would this square wave be adequately transmitted over this channel?

Radio links

A link between a transmitter and a receiver does not have to be by a direct wire connection. In radio links the connection is made through the medium of electro-magnetic waves. This is again a subject which you will investigate fully later in the course; it is introduced here as a way of illustrating how digital signals may be successfully transmitted over the telephone network.

There are a number of ways of sending analogue signals over a radio link. One of these is illustrated in *Figure 15.12*. This method is known

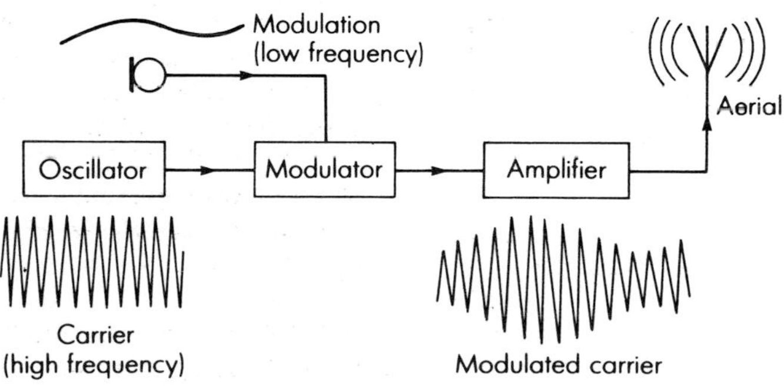

Figure 15.12

as *amplitude modulation* or A.M. Here the wires of the telephone system are 'replaced' by a *carrier* radio wave having a very high frequency, anything from 100 kHz upwards to hundreds of megahertz. This wave is then varied (or modulated) by the relatively low-frequency speech or music waves which cover the frequency band of some 20 Hz up to about 15 kHz for high quality transmissions. Like the analogue speech waves in the telephone wires which vary the flow of a unidirectional current, the low-frequency speech waves vary the *amplitude* of the high-frequency carrier. Look again at *Figure 15.12.* Here a high-frequency oscillator generates a signal of *constant* amplitude and frequency. This signal is fed to a special circuit known as the modulator, as is also the output from, say, a microphone, usually after some preliminary amplification. The microphone, as in the case of the telephone system, converts air pressure waves into a varying voltage or current wave. In the modulator the two waves are combined in such a way that the amplitude (or height) of the carrier is made to follow the variations of the low-frequency signal; the resulting combinational wave is then like that shown on the right of the diagram. This carrier wave with its low-frequency information content is then propagated from the transmitting aerial.

At the receiver a process of *demodulation* (or detection) takes place. In this process the high-frequency wave is discarded (now having served its purpose of carrying the intelligence), only the low-frequency wave representing the required speech or music being amplified to operate a loud-speaker or a pair of headphones.

An alternative to amplitude modulation is *frequency-shift modulation* or F.M. Here the amplitude of the carrier is kept constant and the frequency is varied in accordance with the impressed intelligence. Frequency modulation is used for high-fidelity radio transmission (VHF) and for television sound (UHF), as well as for police, shipping and aircraft communications.

Figure 15.13 shows the basic arrangement for F.M. The high-frequency carrier wave (usually above some 30 MHz) is generated by an

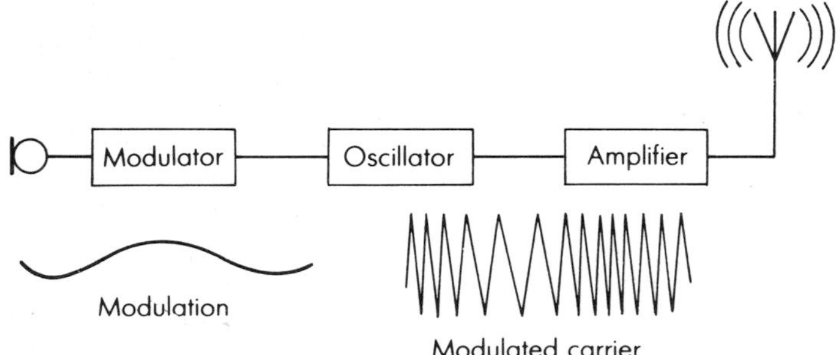

Figure 15.13

oscillator as before and the low-frequency signal from, say, the microphone, is fed by way of a modulator into the oscillator. This time the effect of the low-frequency input is to change or 'wobble' the carrier frequency by a certain amount alternately above and below its mean (no modulation) value. The extent of this frequency *deviation* is proportional to the *amplitude* of the signal and the rate of deviation is equal to the frequency of the signal. At the receiver the required signal is extracted from the carrier and separately amplified.

bandwidth of a system is somehow related to the signalling rate or, as it is known, the *capacity* of a communications link.

A formula which relates the capacity of a channel to the bandwidth W Hz and the signal-to-noise ratio S/N is

$$C = 3.32W \log \left(1 + \frac{S}{N}\right) \text{ bits per second.}$$

The signal-to-noise ratio (which is again a subject you will study in detail later on) is simply the ratio of the wanted signal strength to any unwanted 'noise' on the line. Noise here is made up of background sounds introduced by the various electronic devices themselves (transistors, connecting wires and so on), and by extraneous interference from electrical machines, atmospheric disturbances and the like.

Example (11). A certain communications channel has a bandwidth of 3 kHz and a signal-to-noise ratio of 50. What is the channel capacity?

Here $W = 3000$ Hz, $S/N = 50$

Then
$$\begin{aligned} C &= 3.32 \times 3000 \times \log 51 \\ &= 3.2 \times 3000 \times 1.707 \\ &= 17\,000 \text{ bits/sec} \end{aligned}$$

This is about the sort of capacity we get from the standard PSTN lines.

The rate at which bits are transmitted over a link is called the *baud rate*, sometimes the modulation rate. Baud rate is expressed as 1/(time for 1 bit); if, for example, the bit time is 6.66 ms, the baud rate is 1/6.66 = 600 baud. Common rates are 110, 150, 300, 600, 1200, 2400 and 9600 baud.

The number of bits received per second is known as the *data signalling rate*. If, for example, the bit is received every 6.66 ms, then the signalling rate is 600 bits/sec.

It might appear that the baud rate and the signalling rate are always going to be identical, but this is true only for signals which are in the form of the basic two-level code, that is, for signals which have the form shown earlier in *Figure 15.3* and reproduced for convenience in *Figure 15.16(a)*. A four-level code may be used instead. Here the data bits are sequentially paired off into the following combinations: 00, 01,

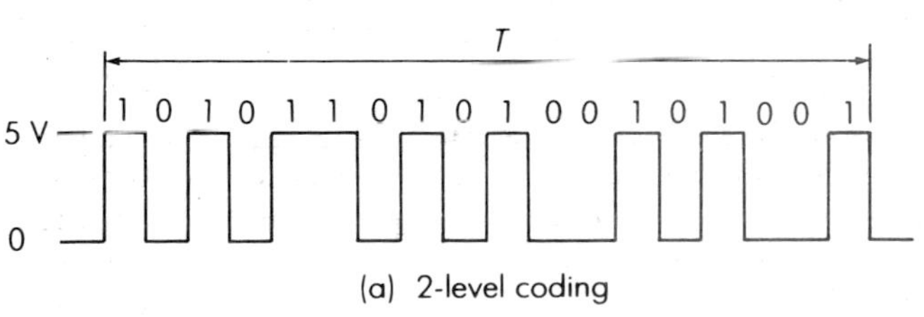

(a) 2-level coding

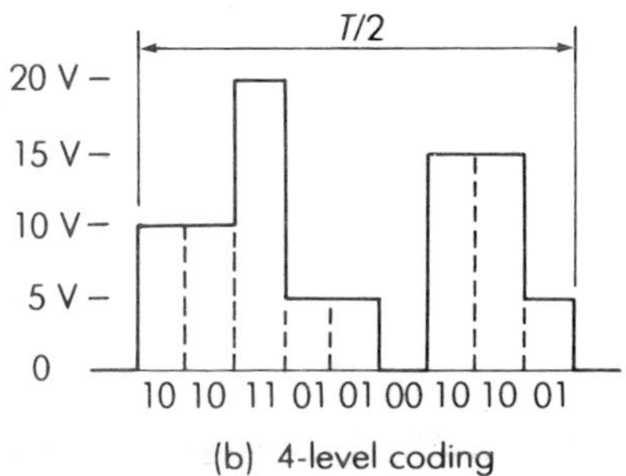

(b) 4-level coding

Figure 15.16

10 and 11. These pairings are known as *dibits*. In terms of amplitude modulation, to provide an example, each dibit is assigned one of four voltage levels as shown in *Figure 15.16(b)*. This now permits *two* bits of data to be sent per signalling element; since the time is halved, the data signalling rate has been doubled. So although the baud rate is the same as it was for the two-level coding, the data signalling rate is twice that of its two-level value.

This procedure may be further extended. An eight-level code may be used, each of eight different voltage levels being assigned to the dibits 000, 001, 010, 011, 100, 101, 110 and 111.

(12) Sketch, after the manner of *Figure 15.6(b)* the analogue line signal for an eight-level representation of *Figure 15.16(a)*. Let the voltage levels range from 0 to 35 V in 5 V steps.

(13) In a communications link using an eight-level code, the value of the baud rate is three times the value of the data signalling rate. True or false?

SERIAL AND PARALLEL TRANSMISSION

Suppose that an item of information is made up of C characters (or words) and that N bits are needed for each character. The total number of bits to be transmitted is $N \times C$. The way in which this information can be sent is either in serial or in parallel form. Suppose as illustration that one character is represented by the logic sequence 10101101.

If the pulses follow one another in sequence on one signal path, they are being routed in *serial* mode; *Figure 15.17(a)*. If the time of each bit is t seconds, then the transfer of the complete character would take Nt seconds. If there are eight signal paths, one for each of the bits in the character as shown in *Figure 15.17(b)*, then the pulses are being routed in *parallel* mode. Parallel routing is faster than serial because all of the bits are operated on at the same time, but clearly this calls for more

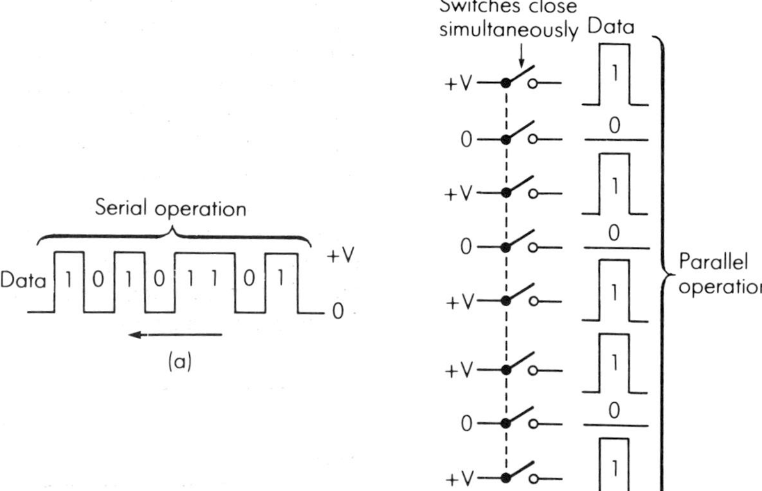

Figure 15.17

complicated and hence expensive circuitry compared with the serial mode.

Modern computers transfer data in parallel mode, but, to reduce the number of connecting links required to transmit digital information over long distances, the data is sent in serial mode. Over the telephone network, serial transmission is always used. This means that a serial-to-parallel interface is needed between the line and the terminal. Such an interface is known as a UART or universal asynchronous receiver-transmitter.

Characters may be sent serially in either *synchronous* or *asynchronous* format. In asynchronous format, the *bits* of a character are sent at a constant rate but the *characters* can come at any rate or arrive at irregular intervals, without any particular timing or synchronising signals between transmitter and receiver. Data typed from keyboard units such as teleprinters come into this asynchronous category.

The asynchronous character format is generalised in *Figure 15.18*. When no character is being sent, the line is kept high (logical 1) or *marking*. The beginning of a character is indicated by logic 0, known as

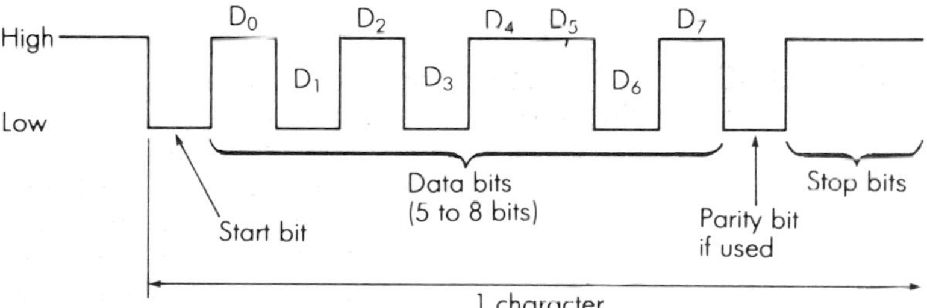

Figure 15.18

the start bit. This is necessary because if the first bit of the character itself was used, a start on logical 1 would not be distinguished from the marking condition and hence would be ignored by the receiver. After the start bit, the data bits are sent out in serial order with the least significant bit (the 'lowest' indicated as D_0) first. Different systems use 5, 6, 7 or 8 bits. A parity bit often follows the data bits; this is included for the purpose of error detection and is not our present concern. Finally, the end of the character is indicated by one or more always-high *stop* bits. Different systems use 1, $1\frac{1}{2}$ or 2 stop bits. Both stop and start bits are wasteful in that they do not convey useful information; considering eight-bit characters with a start and two stop bits, nearly 30% of the signal time is wasted.

In synchronous serial transmission this problem is overcome by sending the information in long strings. The basic format is shown in *Figure 15.19*. There are a number of such formats in use, each with its own set

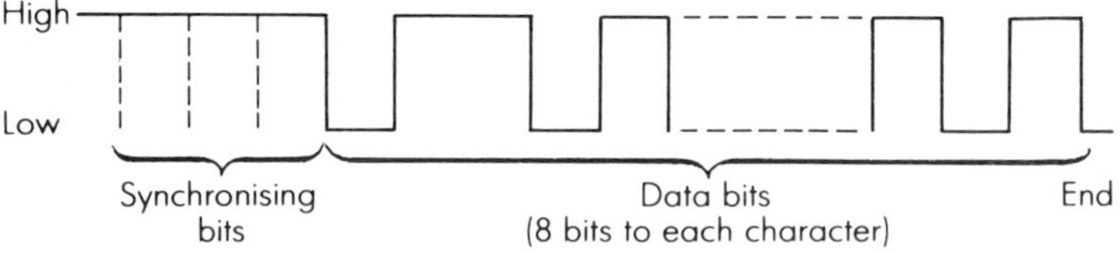

Figure 15.19

of rules, known as a *protocol*. The general procedure is that the transmitter and receiver are started simultaneously and are thereafter kept in step or synchronism by using a common clock signal. How this is done does not concern us at this stage but clearly such synchronisation obviates the need for start and stop bits. It also enables the receiver to know that every eight bits received is a data character.

If no data is being sent the line is continually high as it is for asynchronous working. To signal the start of a message, the transmitter sends two or more recognised synchronising characters. The receiver uses these to lock its clock into exact synchronism with that of the transmitter. After this start has been detected, the receiver groups the bit stream into characters. Although the synchronising signals, like start and stop bits, are wasteful of time, the length of the actual data run is such that the overall percentage of time lost is very much smaller than it is with asynchronous format.

RS232C INTERFACE

Equipment such as modems which are used to send serial data over considerable distances is referred to as data communication equipment, or DCE. The computers that are sending or receiving the serial data are known as data terminal equipment, or DTE. To ensure compatibility between equipment manufactured by a number of different makers, standards or protocols have been adopted for interfacing systems and one of the most common of these is the RS232C/V24. The RS232C standard is that of the American Electrical Industries Association (EIA), while the V24 recommendations are those of the European CCITT. These standards define the voltage levels of the signals and the necessary interconnections. There is another form of serial interface which is superseding the RS232C and this is the RS423, which is compatible with the RS232C.

The general arrangement is shown in *Figure 15.20*, and the pin functions in *Figure 15.21*. The standard is used at both the computer and the peripheral ends of the line. A typical connection between a large

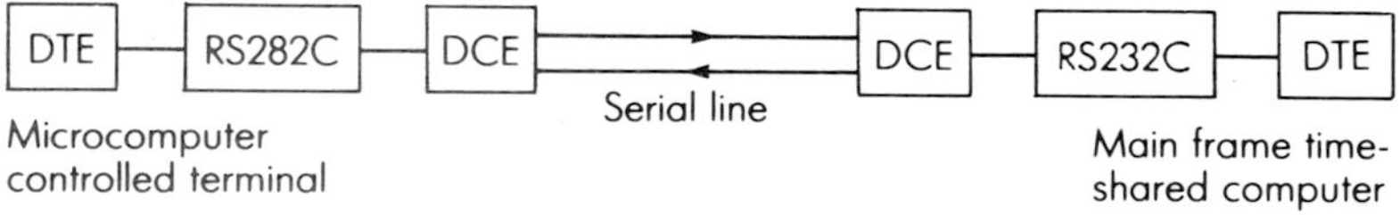

Figure 15.20

time-shared computer and a microcomputer at, say, a branch of a business, is shown in *Figure 15.22*. This is a simplified representation where only seven of the available output pins are used. The direction of signal flow is indicated by arrows. Because computers can send data at a rate beyond the capacity of printers to print it, the interface must include some means of control so that the flow of data is kept within the capabilities of the peripheral; also, the transmitter must know that the receiver is ready to accept the data and act on it. This is accomplished by the use of what are known as 'handshaking' signals. A simplified explanation of this process is that the DTE sends DTR to the modem: 'data terminal ready'. The modem responds with DSR (data set ready); this ensures that the terminal knows that the modem is ready. The modem at the other end of the line is then dialled. This second modem is in the answer mode of operation and responds with a

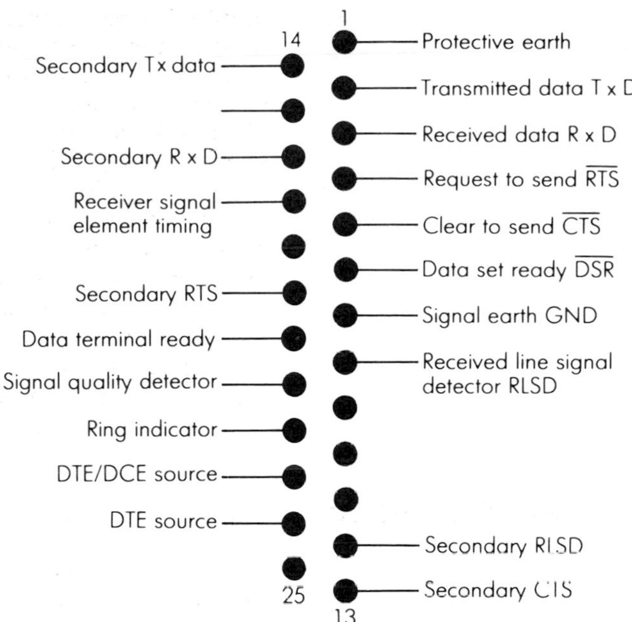

Figure 15.21

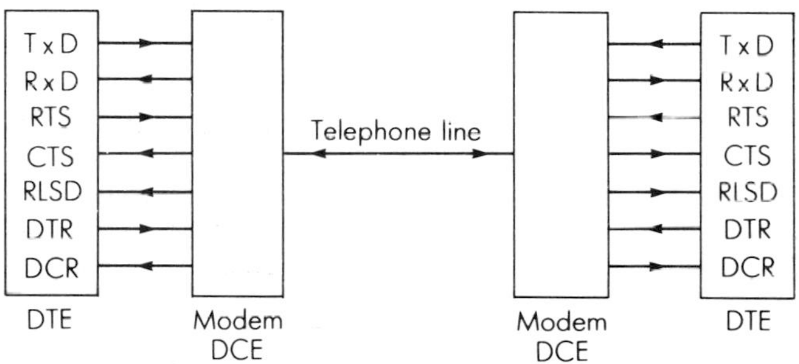

Figure 15.22

carrier signal tone lying within the passband of the telephone system. When the first modem receives this carrier, it relays CD (carrier detect) to the terminal. The terminal in turn then relays a RTS (request to send) signal to the modem. The modem responds with a CTS (clear to send) acknowledgement. The data from the terminal is then transmitted form the TxD output. The same handshake routine takes place for receiving data. Notice that when dealing with DTE it is the CTS line which provides the handshake output; the DTR (data terminal ready) is the connection which receives the data from a peripheral. For DCE equipment, these roles are reversed.

RS232C is specified for a maximum transmission distance of 15 m for a maximum baud rate of 20 000 bauds. This is usually outside the capability of standard telephone lines. If lower rates are tolerated, the length of line can be as much as 900 m. The RS423 protocol is an improvement on the RS232C in that longer transmission distances and higher baud rates are possible.

PROBLEMS FOR SECTION 15

(14) Is a stopwatch an analogue or a digital instrument?

(15) Distinguish between Local Area Networks and Wide Area Networks.

(16) What are the essential differences between direct-current signals and voice-frequency signals?

(17) A signalling code comprises elements (bits) and characters. Distinguish between the two.

(18) Explain fully what you understand by a modulation rate of 200 baud.

(19) What name is given to a method of modulation by which digital signals are conveyed by a constant frequency signal having two different amplitudes?

(20) What is the capacity of a channel with a frequency response of 200 Hz to 4200 Hz and a signal to noise ratio of 100?

(21) Frequency-shift keying is a method of transmitting digital information over analogue lines. True or false?

(22) A teleprinter operates at 20 characters per second using a 10 unit code. What is the modulation rate?

(23) Define the following terms:

(a) Data signalling rate (b) Dibits
(c) Modem (d) Modulation rate.

(24) Which of the diagrams of *Figure 15.23* represents a frequency modulated signal?

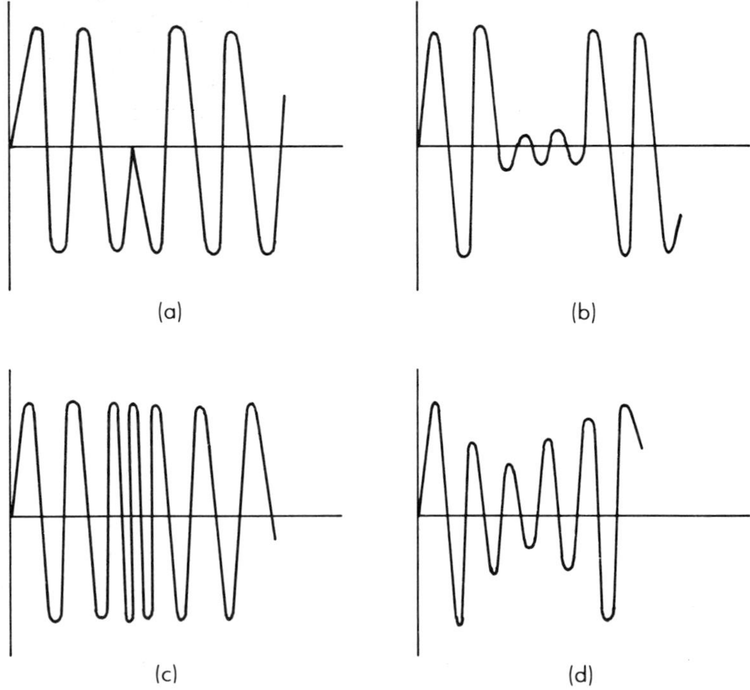

Figure 15.23

(25) A certain communications link has a receiver capable of differentiating between eight possible signal amplitude levels. The amount of information that can be extracted from each dibit is

(a) 1 bit (b) 3 bits (c) 4 bits (d) 8 bits.

(26) A telegraph signal is transmitted at a rate of 40 bauds. In the code used the average word plus one word space occupies 40 bauds. In the code used the average word plus one word space occupies 40 signalling elements. The rate of transmission of the message is

(a) 40 words/min (b) 60 words/min (c) 80 words/min.

(27) A modem is used for digital transmission of analogue information. True or false?

(28) The function of a carrier is to provide a means of

(a) increasing the amount of information carried;
(b) changing the frequency of signals;
(c) transferring information at high frequency;
(d) converting digital into analogue signals.

(29) Match the following types of modulation with signal variations (a)–(e):

Amplitude modulation	(a) Frequency and phase
Frequency-shift keying	(b) Frequency only
Phase modulation	(c) Amplitude and frequency
	(d) Amplitude only
	(e) Phase only

(30) Allocate the appropriate bandwidth (a)–(e) to the following types of signal:

High-fidelity radio	(a) 0–120 Hz
Commercial speech	(b) 0–3400 Hz
Television	(c) 300–3400 Hz
Telegraphy	(d) 50 Hz–15 kHz
	(e) 0–5.5 MHz

Solutions to problems

UNIT SECTION 1

(1) 500 N
(2) 4078 N
(3) 196.2 kN; 10.5 h.p.
(4) 4 W
(5) 15.9 N m
(6) 100 C
(7) 5 s
(8) 500 W (or 0.5 kW)
(9) 20π or 62.8 rad/s
(10) 191 rev
(11) (a) newton, (b) joule, (c) watt, (d) metres/s, (e) metres/s^2
(12) (a) ampere, (b) volt, (c) ohm, (d) volt, (e) coulomb
(13) 400 N
(14) 6.25 m/s^2
(15) 0.2 kg (or 200 g)
(16) 4 m/s^2
(17) 15 kg
(18) (a) 5.2 rad/s, (b) 95 rev/min
(19) 12 rad/s
(20) 3.12×10^{21} electrons
(21) 50 A
(22) 10 kJ (or 10 000 J)
(23) 875 kJ
(24) 98.1 kJ, 817.5 W
(25) 14.6 h.p.
(26) (a) 20π rad/s; (b) 9.45 m/s
(27) (a) 75 N m; (b) 84.82 kJ; (c) 1.414 kW

UNIT SECTION 2

(4) 6 A
(5) 666.7 Ω
(6) 8.25 V
(7) (a) 8 A; (b) 0.4 A
(9) 10 V across 5 Ω; 20 V across 10 Ω
(10) (a) 3 Ω; (b) 0.5 A; (c) 0.25 V across 0.5 Ω; 0.5 V across 1 Ω; 0.75 V across 1.5 Ω
(11) 1000 Ω (or 1 kΩ)
(12) 9.43 Ω
(15) 2.86 Ω
(16) 4 Ω
(17) Five are required. If *n* equal resistors are connected in parallel, the equivalent resistance is equal to $1/n$ th of the resistance of one of them.
(19) 3.33 A in 6 Ω; 1.66 A in 12 Ω; 0.833 A in 24 Ω. Total 5.83 A.
(20) 0.0256 Ω
(22) (a) 6 Ω, (b) 10 Ω, (c) 68 Ω
(23) 2.2 V: 0.1 Ω
(24) 14.74 V
(27) 0.2 A
(28) 1000 Ω (or 1 kΩ)

(29) 40 V
(30) (a) 24 Ω; (b) 2.55 Ω; (c) 0.35 Ω.
(31) 3.33 Ω
(32) 0.43 Ω
(33) 30 Ω
(34) 4.44 A; 88.9 W
(35) 25 kW; 33.5 h.p.
(36) 384 Ω; 10 lamps to nearest whole number
(37) 10.66 A, 8 A and 5.33 A respectively; 354.5 V
(38) 13 Ω; 10 V, 25 V and 65 V; 50 W, 125 W and 325 W
(39) 325 Ω
(40) 100 Ω, 40 Ω, 25 Ω and 8 Ω
(41) (a) 2.38 Ω; (b) 8.27 Ω
(42) 1.0375 V; 0.15 Ω
(43) 30 Ω. This value is called the characteristic resistance of the T-section.
(44) 32 Ω; 4.16 A, 6.25 A, 7.5 A
(45) 1.73 A
(46) (a) 1.18 Ω; (b) 0.06 Ω

UNIT SECTION 3

(2) Refer to *Figure A.1*.
(3) 0.263 A
(4) 5.0 A
(5) Current in 2 Ω = 0.871 A
Current in 3 Ω = 0.419 A
Current in 5 Ω = 0.452 A
(7) $I_1 = 40$ A, $I_2 = 80$ A, $I_3 = 90$ A, $I_4 = 150$ A
(9) $xR_1 - yR_2 + zR_3 = 0$
(10) $-xR_1 - zR_3 + yR_2 = -E$
(13) In these solutions you may not have used the same directions as those stated, but your equations for the various loops should be algebraically identical.

(a) Circuit AFCB: $24x + 4(x+y) = 20$
Circuit FCDE: $24x - 8y = 0$
Circuit AEDB: $8y + 4(x+y) = 20$

(b) Circuit AFCB: $3x = 10 - 4$
Circuit FCDE: $3x - 6y = -4$
Circuit AEDB: $6y = 10$

(c) Circuit ABEF: $4x + 10(x+y) = 4$
Circuit BEDC: $10(x+y) + 5y = -2$
Circuit AFDC: $-4x + 5y = -4-2$

(14) (a) 2.0 A; (b) 4.66 A; (c) 0.727 A in 4 Ω, 0.109 A in 10 Ω, 0.618 A in 5 Ω
(15) To the left
(17) 5.0 A
(18) 281 Ω
(20) (a) $I_1 = 70$ A, $I_2 = 50$ A, $I_3 = 50$ A, $I_4 = 140$ A, $I_5 = 150$ A, $I_6 = 110$ A;
(b) $I_1 = 10$ A, $I_2 = 20$ A, $I_3 = 5$ A, $I_4 = 35$ A

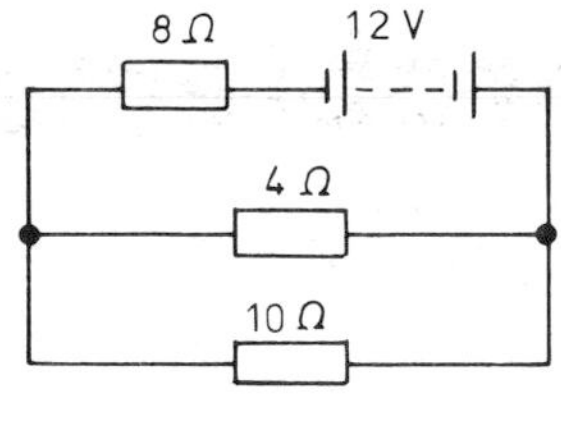

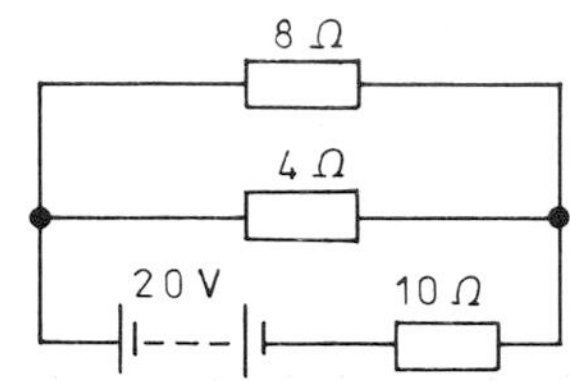

(a)

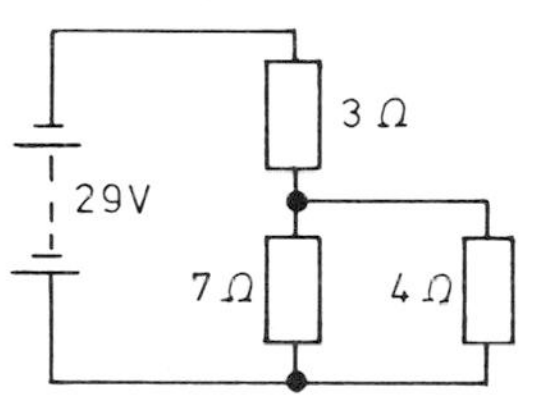

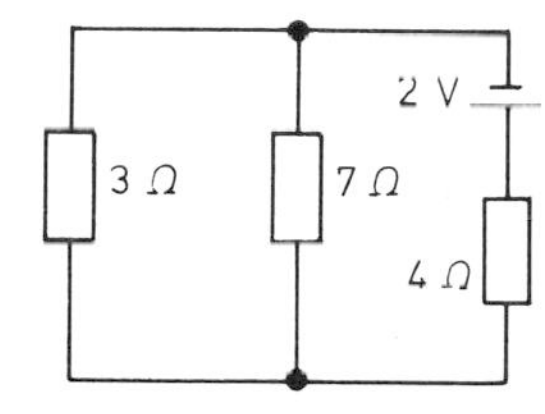

(b)

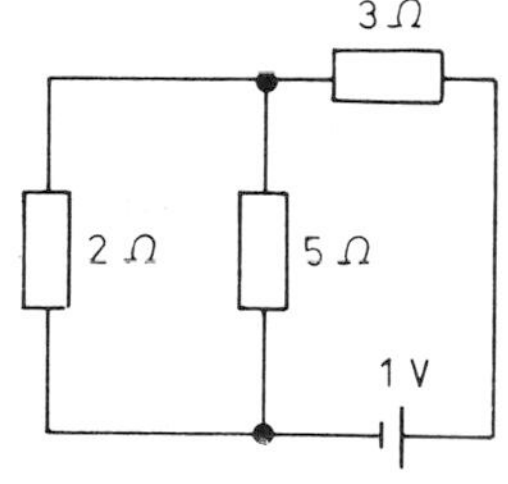

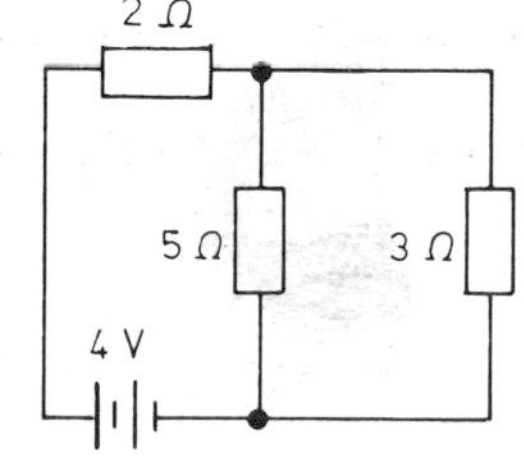

(c)

Figure A.1

(21) (i) 15.48 A, (ii) 25 mA, 0.6 V, (iii) each battery carries 2 A; current in the 4 Ω = 4 A, hence p.d. across the 4 Ω is 16 V.
(22) Battery A, current = 1.29 A. terminal p.d. = 3.42 V. Battery B, current = 0.95 A, terminal p.d. the same as battery A. Power in 10 Ω = 1.17 W.
(23) 1 A in 10 V battery, 1.5 A in 6.5 V battery, 2.5 A in the 2 Ω resistor.
(24) 6 Ω
(25) 0.618 A
(26) E_1 = 30 V, E_2 = 10 V

UNIT SECTION 4

(3) 63.6 μC/m²
(4) 0.8834 μC/m²
(5) (a) charge, (b) coulombs, (c) voltage gradient, (d) D/E; 8.85×10^{-12}, (e) $\epsilon_0 \epsilon_r$, (f) vacuum.
(6) 2000 μC (or 0.002 C)
(7) 1 μF
(9) 0.443 μF, 22.5V
(10) 0.0028 m²
(12) 1.6×10^{-19} C
(13) 66.7 μC/m²
(14) 6.24×10^{11} electrons
(15) 450 kV/m
(16) (a) 1.77 μC/m², (b) 4.78 μC/m². Field strength = 200 kV/m and is the same for both cases.
(17) 53.8 kV/m
(18) 4.61 μC
(19) 5000 μC (or 0.005 C)
(20) 0.6 μF
(21) (a) 200 μC/m²; (b) 10^7 V/m
(22) 16.7 pF; 83.5 pF
(23) 4.51 m²
(24) (a) 132 pF; (b) 0.0132 μC; (c) 100 kV/m
(25) 265 pF

UNIT SECTION 5

(3) 6 μF
(4) 2.73 μF; 273 μC; 54.54 V, 27.27 V, 18.18 V
(7) 15 μF connected in series with the 30 μF
(8) 50 μF; 1200 μC, 1800 μC, 3000 μC
(9) 1.6 μF, 10 μF, 28 μF; C_E = 39.6 μF
(10) C_E = 8 μF; voltage across 4.25 μF = 100 V; across 15 μF = 25 V; across 5 μF = 75 V
(11) V = 1 kV; 0.6 μF, 0.4 μF
(12) 0.25 J
(13) 1118 V
(14) 20 μF in series; 3.75 μF in parallel
(15) 15 μF
(16) 8 μF
(17) 10 μF
(18) 7.83 μF; 0.488 μF
(19) (a) 0.02 μF, (b) 100 μJ

(20) (a) 40 V, (b) 8000 μJ
(21) (a) 2.73 μF; (b) 109.2 V, 54.6 V, 36.4 V respectively; (c) 546 μC
(22) 86.4 mJ; 360 mJ
(23) (a) 66.6 V across 3 μF, 33.3 V across 6 μF; (b) 100 V
(24) (a) 100 V, (b) 100 μF
(25) 104.17 V. The charge on the 5 μF capacitor is distributed over 12 μF after parallelling. No *charge* is lost in the process.
(26) (a) 150 μC; (b) 44.12 μC, 88.24 μC and 17.65 μC respectively; (c) 22.06 V
(27) (a) 4.425 J; (b) 8.85μC/m^2; (c) 1000 kV/m
(28) (a) 0.015 μF; (b) 15 μC
(29) 0.5 μF
(30) 60 V and 40 V respectively; 0.006 J; 0.0058 J. The loss of *energy* is due to the heating of the connecting wires and the spark which is produced when the capacitors are connected together. There is no loss of *charge.*

UNIT SECTION 6

(3) 0.8 m
(4) 0.0125 T
(5) 2.51 T
(8) (a) tesla, (b) ampere, (c) m.m.f., (d) 4×10^{-7}, (e) silicon iron, (f) H; B, (g) At/m, (h) tesla
(10) 250
(11) 0.583 T
(12) 0.001 17 m^2 (or 11.7 cm^2)
(13) 8.3 N
(14) 126 A
(15) 5000 At/m
(16) 0.5 A
(17) 2330
(18) 119 370 At/m; 5970 At
(19) 0.67 T
(20) 3586 At
(21) 365; 100; 1770
(22) This question is deliberately premature. You may know enough to work it out for yourself, but if you are unacquainted with the method of finding the force on a conductor, knowing B and the current in the conductor, wait until you get to the appropriate point in the text (page 55).
(23) 47 N, 0, 47 N.

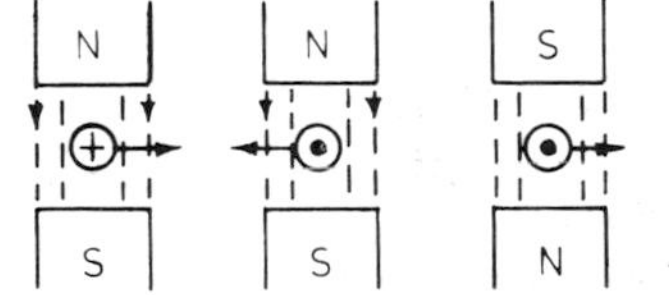

Figure A.2

UNIT SECTION 7

(3) 4.167 m/s
(4) 0.375 V; 0.28 V
(6) 46.3 A
(7) (a) Rate of change, (b) right-hand, (c) right-angles, (d) webers.
(8) See *Figure A.2.*

(11) (a) 66.7 V, (b) 200 V. The total current change when 100 A is reversed is 200 A occurring in 0.05 s, i.e. a rate of 4000 A/s.
(12) 0.05 s
(13) 0.002 H (or 2 mH)
(14) 840 V
(15) 50 V secondary voltage, 0.05 A secondary current; 0.25 A primary current
(17) 0.75 V
(18) 1.78 m
(19) Taken in order of the angle from 0° to 180°, the induced e.m.f.s are 0, 0.375, 0.53, 0.65, 0.75, 0.65, 0.53, 0.375 and 0 V. A graph of these voltages against angle will give you part of a *sinusoidal* wave.
(20) (a) 0.1 N, (b) 0.05 N, (c) zero
(21) 0.163 N
(22) 1.92 mH
(23) 0.0006 Wb (or 600 μWb)
(24) 120 V
(25) 0.006 s (or 6 ms)
(26) 25 μH
(27) 24 V
(28) (a) 44.4 mH, (b) 118.4 μWb, (c) 0.355 J
(29) This may have proved troublesome. Look at *Figure A.3* for a moment. When conductors are arranged in the form of a rectangular coil and this is rotated in a magnetic field, the cutting of flux is continuous, and an e.m.f. is generated as long as the rotation goes on. If the radius of the coil is R m and if it rotates at a speed of N rev/s, then *each side* conductor moves a distance $2\pi RN$ m/s. Hence the conductor velocity $v = 2\pi RN$ m/s. If the coil has T turns, it has $2T$ active conductors in the field, since both sides of the coil will be cutting flux.

Now using your $B\ell v$ formula with the appropriate substitutions, you should get an answer to the problem of 37.7 V.

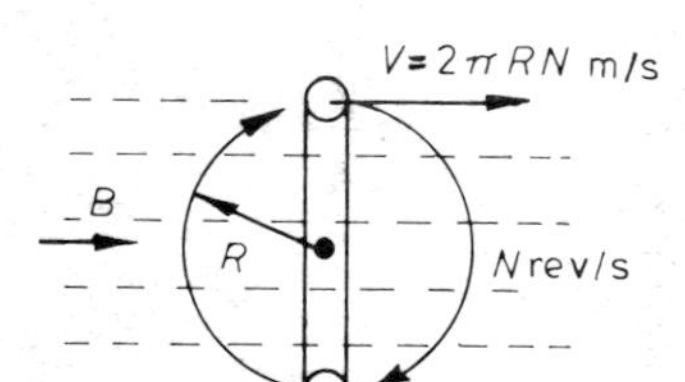

Figure A.3

(30) 0.1 H
(31) 250 V; 4.0 A
(32) 151.5 turns
(33) 0.417 A, 3.125 A

UNIT SECTION 8

(1) 0.02 s
(2) 500 kHz
(3) 6.37 A average; 7.07 r.m.s.
(4) 340 V
(6) 35.36 V; 500 Hz; 0.002 s
(7) $v = 340 \sin 314t$; 323 V
(10) $v_1 + v_2 = 50 \sin(\omega t - 0.64)$; phase angle is 53.1° or 0.93 rad
(11) (a) $21.8 \sin(500t - 0.64)$; (b) 80 Hz; (c) 15.4
(12) $v_1 - v_2 = 2.95 \sin(800t - 0.5)$
(13) $v_1 + v_2 = 364 \sin(314t - 0.28)$; $v_1 - v_2 = 180 \sin(314t + 0.58)$
(14) (a) 0.002 s, (b) 0.2 ms, (c) 0.01 ms, (d) 0.67 μs
(15) 283 peak, 127 average

(16) 14.14 mA, −14.14 mA
(17) 377 V r.m.s., 314 V average
(18) 14.14 mA; 1 kHz; 0.001 s (or 1 ms)
(19) 142 sin 251*t* V
(20) See *Figure A.4.*
(21) $v = 660\,(314t + \pi/3)$; −244 V
(22) (a) $142 \sin(\omega t + \pi/4)$; (b) $25 \sin(\omega t - 0.64)$; (c) 85 sin $(628t + 0.73)$
(23) $15.5 \sin(\omega t + 0.245)$
(24) 132.3 V

$V_1 = 500 \sin \omega t$

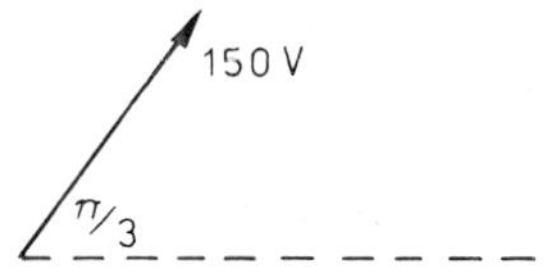

$V_2 = 150 \sin(\omega t + \pi/3)$

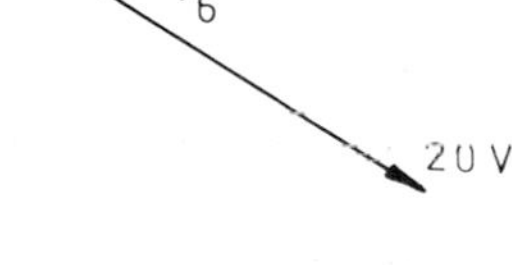

$V_3 = 20 \sin(\omega t - \pi/6)$

Figure A.4

UNIT SECTION 9

Note: where reference has been made to magnetisation curves, small discrepancies will occur between the given solutions and those you will have obtained.

(1) S = m.m.f./Φ, i.e. At/Wb. Hence units of S are At/Wb.
(4) 0.062 A
(5) (a) 1.512×10^6 At/Wb; (b) 453 turns
(7) 66 mA; 796 mA increase required
(8) 0.157 T
(9) 267; 796
(10) 300 At
(11) 0.6 A
(12) 1400
(13) 80 At
(14) 2285 At
(15) 575 turns
(16) 275 mA
(17) 1260 At
(18) (a) 0.5 T; (b) $\mu_r = 1000$
(19) (a) 1.0 T; (b) $\mu_r = 1590$; (c) $S = 3.34 \times 10^5$ At/Wb

UNIT SECTION 10

(2) 78.54 Ω
(3) About 200 mH
(4) Your completed table should look like this:

Frequency	*Reactance*
100	15
200	30
5 000	750
10 000	1500
1 000	150

(5) ϕ will be zero if the circuit is purely resistive; ϕ will be 90° if the circuit is purely inductive.
(8) 15.6 Ω
(9) Nearly 0.2 H
(10) $Z = 74.5\ \Omega$; $I = 0.67$ A; $\phi = 57.5°$ (or 1 rad)
(11) 86.6 V
(14) 318.3 Ω at 25 Hz; 79.6 Ω at 100 Hz
(15) 0.0834 μF
(16) 0.2 μF
(17) 63 mA

(18) ϕ will be zero if the circuit is purely resistive; ϕ will be $-90°$ if the circuit is purely capacitive.
(20) (a) 3.14 Ω; (b) 503 Ω; (c) 6283 Ω
(21) 0.5 H
(22) 600 Hz
(23) (a) 6366 Ω; (b) 398 Ω; (c) 159 Ω
(24) 88.4 μF
(25) 8 kHz
(26) 13 Ω
(27) 10 Ω
(28) 11.05 A; 46.3° (0.81 rad) lagging
(29) (a) 4 Ω, (b) 3 Ω, (c) 4.8 mH
(30) (a) 1.57 A, (b) 63 mA
(31) (a) 45.8 V, (b) 1.157 μF, (c) 66.5° (1.16 rad) leading
(32) 306 Hz
(33) 72 mH; 346 Ω
(34) (a) 250 Ω; (b) 1.215 H
(35) 23.1 Ω, 120 mH; 56.5° (0.986 rad) lagging
(36) (a) 500 Hz; (b) 5.656 A; (c) 5.44 mH and 47 Ω

UNIT SECTION 11

(1) 4 W
(2) 125 W. Only the resistor dissipates power, and it is wired directly across the supply.
(5) $Z = 219\ \Omega; I = 0.137$ A; $P = 2.82$ W
(6) $R = 16.3\ \Omega$, $L = 75$ mH
(8) 685 kHz
(9) 0.0127 μF
(11) 218 Hz
(13) The voltage across C at resonance will be about 2500 V. A 2000 V working capacitor would break down.
(14) 2 W
(15) 2.52 W; 63.5° (1.11 rad) leading
(16) 2.083 W
(17) (a) 48.18 Ω; (b) 0.519 A; (c) 8.08 W
(18) (a) 500 Ω; (b) 20 mA; (c) 37° (0.646 rad); (d) 160 mW
(19) $Z = 30\ \Omega; R = 18.75\ \Omega$
(20) 5.47 W
(21) $R = 30\ \Omega; L = 0.127$ H
(22) 63.2° (1.103 rad) lagging
(23) 1.186 mHz
(24) (a) 80 kHz; (b) 4 mA; (c) 40 V; (d) 0.8 mW
(25) (a) 318 Hz; (b) 20 mA; (c) 2mW
(26) 102 μF in parallel; 5 A
(27) 1256 V; a 1500 V capacitor would be suitable

UNIT SECTION 12

(1) The current and voltage change over *100 times* a second.
(3) The anode; you must connect this to the positive pole of the supply to make the diode conduct.
(5) 9.1 V; 100 V. When the diode is off, all the applied voltage must be developed across it as there is no voltage drop across R. The diode must be able to withstand this reverse voltage.

(6) Power in resistor = 8.41 W; in the diode = 0.84 W
(7) 300 mW; 1.248×10^{16} electrons per second
(8) (a) 76 mA; (b) 7.6 V; (c) −3.8 V
(9) (a) 70.7 V; (b) 1.67 A
(10) (a) the output voltage across R would be reduced to about one-half; (b) current would flow during the negative half-cycle through the parallel resistor, so the output would no longer be unidirectional.
(11) (a) Average $= 0.637 \dfrac{\hat{V}}{R + r}$; r.m.s. $= 0.71 \dfrac{\hat{V}}{R + r}$

(b) Average $= 0.637 \dfrac{\hat{V}}{R + 2r}$; r.m.s. $= 0.71 \dfrac{\hat{V}}{R + 2r}$

UNIT SECTION 13

(1) 2.7×10^{-6} N m
(3) (a) 5995 Ω in series; (b) 0.0125 Ω in parallel
(4) 6661.7 Ω
(5) For the 1.5 A meter, power in meter = 0.25 mW; power in shunt = 75 mW. For the 2 V meter, power in meter = 0.25 mW; power in series resistor = 9.75 mW. For the 100 V meter, power in meter = 0.25 mW; power in series resistor = 0.5 W
(6) Voltmeters V_2 and V_3 would read the same as they are in parallel.
(7) Zero; infinite
(8) 28.5 V and 32.5 V
(10) Diagram (a) is best for low values of R: the ammeter resistance does not affect the reading of the voltmeter, and as the voltmeter resistance is very high compared with R it does not appreciably shunt R. Diagram (b) is best for high values of R: the voltmeter resistance does not affect the ammeter reading, and the ammeter resistance is so small compared with R that its effect is negligible.
(11) $X = 134.6\ \Omega$; when $\ell_1 = 57.37$ cm
(12) $X = 154.3$ kΩ
(13) Reduce the 5 Ω by 1 Ω, i.e. make it 4 Ω. The bridge is then balanced, hence no current flows through the 3 Ω branch
(14) Because a small resistance will only develop an appreciable voltage across it if the current is relatively large. For the 0.1 Ω resistor you would need at least 1.1 V across it to be about the centre of the slide wire, hence about 10 A would be necessary. It is important not to heat up the resistance, though.
(15) 1.524 V
(16) 2.54 mA; 11 mA r.m.s.
(18) Think of the square wave being used to heat a filament. The heat generated would be the same as that of a direct current having a value equal to the peak of the square wave; remember, the rectification of the square wave 'fills in' the wave completely. Hence the heat-equivalent (r.m.s.) value of the square wave is equal to its equivalent d.c. value which is is peak value.
(20) 0.0334 Ω, 0.0167 Ω

(21) 1990 Ω, 390 Ω
(22) (a) 55.56 Ω in parallel; (b) 24 500 Ω in series
(23) 300 V
(24) (a) 0.2 V, (b) 4 mW
(25) (a) 6 Ω; (b) 0.5 A
(26) 2 V per division
(27) 100 turns
(28) (a) 2500 Ω; (b) 2727.3 Ω
(29) 27.187 Ω and 30.524 Ω
(30) $A = 1000\,\Omega, B = 4000\,\Omega$
(31) 2400 Ω
(32) (a) 2.475 V; (b) 8.08 mA; (c) 0.5 mW
(33) 1.2 V
(34) (a) Ratio 5:3, the 100-turn coil reads higher; (b) 7.5 :1, the 750-turns coil reads higher
(35) 5.09 A
(36) 1.8 A; 2.83 A; 3.6 A; 4 A
(37) (a) 3.185 A; (b) 3.563 A
(38) On d.c. both meters will read 100 mA. On a.c. the moving coil will read 45 mA, the moving iron will read 50 mA. On square wave, both readings will be identical at 50 mA.
(39) 3 A, 3.32 A

UNIT SECTION 14

(3) A follower system
(6) A continuous system
(7) The characteristic is shown in *Figure A.5*. The steady state period begins as soon as the water reaches room temperature.
(8) No; only upon the design of the thermostat.
(10) Faulty relay contacts on one side most likely. Could be that either of the supplies V_1 or V_2 was faulty.
(11) The aerial would run to one end or other of its possible travel and stay there.
(18) Negative feedback, error actuation, no human intervention.
(23) See *Figure A.6* for part (a). (b) Reference can be altered by adjusting lengths and positions of the probes; (c) May be slight overfilling due to the inertia of the motor; (d) The open loop system would have a tap in place of the valve, set to let water flow into the tank at an average rate based on the usage expected. The tank will, at times, be overflowing and at other times empty, depending upon the demand being different from the 'average'.
(24) (a) See *Figure A.7*. (b) Continuous
(25) 9.09

UNIT SECTION 15

(1) Analogue: we are comparing lengths.
(2) (d)
(3) (c)
(7) Transformers (transmission bridges); a.c. coupled repeater

amplifiers on the line. There are others.
(9) Yes, the Fourier series could go to the sixth or seventh term.
(13) False
(14) Analogue
(18) 200 bits are transmitted per second
(19) Amplitude modulation
(20) About 26 560 bits/sec
(21) True
(22) 200 baud
(24) (c)
(25) (d)
(26) (a)
(27) False
(28) (c)
(29) (d), (b), (c)
(30) (d), (c), (e), (a)

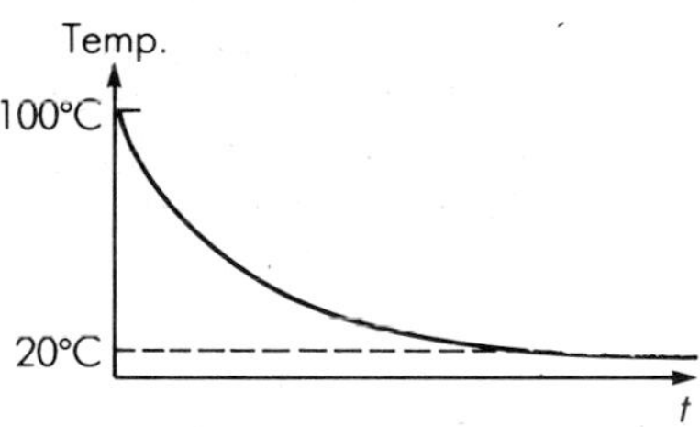

Figure A.5

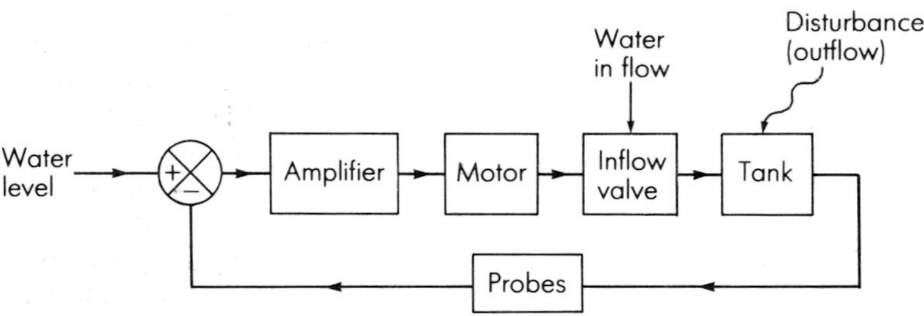

Figure A.6

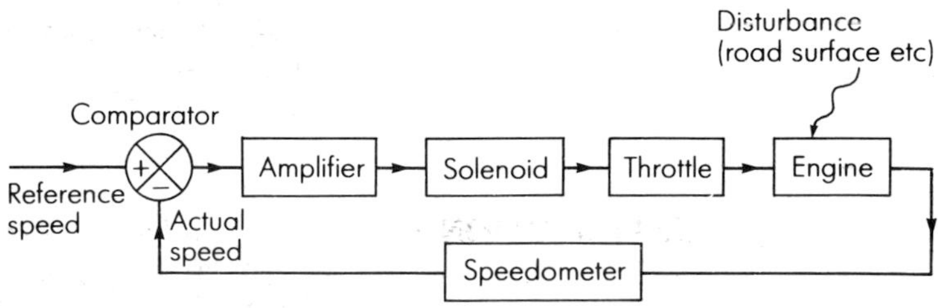

Figure A.7

Index

[illegible]